CONNECTED  MATHEMATICS®3

Teacher Resources Grade 7

Glenda Lappan
Elizabeth Difanis Phillips
James T. Fey
Susan N. Friel

PEARSON

Boston, Massachusetts • Chandler, Arizona • Glenview, Illinois • Upper Saddle River, New Jersey

Connected Mathematics™ was developed at Michigan State University with financial support from the Michigan State University Office of the Provost, Computing and Technology, and the College of Natural Science.

This material is based upon work supported by the National Science Foundation under Grant No. MDR 9150217 and Grant No. ESI 9986372. Opinions expressed are those of the authors and not necessarily those of the Foundation.

As with prior editions of this work, the authors and administration of Michigan State University preserve a tradition of devoting royalties from this publication to support activities sponsored by the MSU Mathematics Education Enrichment Fund.

13-digit ISBN 978-0-13-327426-4
10-digit ISBN 0-13-327426-8
4 5 6 7 8 9 10 V001 17 16 15

PEARSON

Authors

A Team of Experts

Glenda Lappan is a University Distinguished Professor in the Program in Mathematics Education (PRIME) and the Department of Mathematics at Michigan State University. Her research and development interests are in the connected areas of students' learning of mathematics and mathematics teachers' professional growth and change related to the development and enactment of K–12 curriculum materials.

Elizabeth Difanis Phillips is a Senior Academic Specialist in the Program in Mathematics Education (PRIME) and the Department of Mathematics at Michigan State University. She is interested in teaching and learning mathematics for both teachers and students. These interests have led to curriculum and professional development projects at the middle school and high school levels, as well as projects related to the teaching and learning of algebra across the grades.

James T. Fey is a Professor Emeritus at the University of Maryland. His consistent professional interest has been development and research focused on curriculum materials that engage middle and high school students in problem-based collaborative investigations of mathematical ideas and their applications.

Susan N. Friel is a Professor of Mathematics Education in the School of Education at the University of North Carolina at Chapel Hill. Her research interests focus on statistics education for middle-grade students and, more broadly, on teachers' professional development and growth in teaching mathematics K–8.

With... Yvonne Grant and Jacqueline Stewart
Yvonne Grant teaches mathematics at Portland Middle School in Portland, Michigan. Jacqueline Stewart is a recently retired high school teacher of mathematics at Okemos High School in Okemos, Michigan. Both Yvonne and Jacqueline have worked on all aspects of the development, implementation, and professional development of the CMP curriculum from its beginnings in 1991.

Development Team

CMP3 Authors

Glenda Lappan, University Distinguished Professor, Michigan State University

Elizabeth Difanis Phillips, Senior Academic Specialist, Michigan State University

James T. Fey, Professor Emeritus, University of Maryland

Susan N. Friel, Professor, University of North Carolina – Chapel Hill

With...

Yvonne Grant, Portland Middle School, Michigan

Jacqueline Stewart, Mathematics Consultant, Mason, Michigan

In Memory of... **William M. Fitzgerald,** Professor (Deceased), Michigan State University, who made substantial contributions to conceptualizing and creating CMP1.

Administrative Assistant

Michigan State University
Judith Martus Miller

Support Staff

Michigan State University
Undergraduate Assistants:
Bradley Robert Corlett, Carly Fleming,
Erin Lucian, Scooter Nowak

Development Assistants

Michigan State University
Graduate Research Assistants:
Richard "Abe" Edwards, Nic Gilbertson,
Funda Gonulates, Aladar Horvath,
Eun Mi Kim, Kevin Lawrence, Jennifer Nimtz,
Joanne Philhower, Sasha Wang

Assessment Team

Maine
Falmouth Public Schools
Falmouth Middle School: Shawn Towle

Michigan
Ann Arbor Public Schools
Tappan Middle School:
Anne Marie Nicoll-Turner

Portland Public Schools
Portland Middle School:
Holly DeRosia, Yvonne Grant

Traverse City Area Public Schools
Traverse City East Middle School:
Jane Porath, Mary Beth Schmitt

Traverse City West Middle School:
Jennifer Rundio, Karrie Tufts

Ohio
Clark-Shawnee Local Schools
Rockway Middle School: Jim Mamer

Content Consultants

Michigan State University
Peter Lappan, Professor Emeritus,
Department of Mathematics

Normandale Community College
Christopher Danielson, Instructor,
Department of Mathematics & Statistics

University of North Carolina – Wilmington
Dargan Frierson, Jr., Professor,
Department of Mathematics & Statistics

Student Activities
Michigan State University
Brin Keller, Associate Professor,
Department of Mathematics

Consultants

Indiana
Purdue University
Mary Bouck, Mathematics Consultant

Michigan
Oakland Schools
Valerie Mills, Mathematics Education Supervisor

Mathematics Education Consultants:
Geraldine Devine, Dana Gosen

Ellen Bacon, Independent Mathematics Consultant

New York
University of Rochester
Jeffrey Choppin, Associate Professor

Ohio
University of Toledo
Debra Johanning, Associate Professor

Pennsylvania
University of Pittsburgh
Margaret Smith, Professor

Texas
University of Texas at Austin
Emma Trevino, Supervisor of
Mathematics Programs, The Dana Center

Mathematics for All Consulting
Carmen Whitman, Mathematics Consultant

Reviewers

Michigan
Ionia Public Schools
Kathy Dole, Director of Curriculum
and Instruction

Grand Valley State University
Lisa Kasmer, Assistant Professor

Portland Public Schools
Teri Keusch, Classroom Teacher

Minnesota
Hopkins School District 270
Michele Luke, Mathematics Coordinator

Field Test Sites for CMP3

Michigan
Ann Arbor Public Schools
Tappan Middle School: Anne Marie Nicoll-Turner*

Portland Public Schools
Portland Middle School: Mark Braun,
Angela Buckland, Holly DeRosia, Holly Feldpausch,
Angela Foote, Yvonne Grant*, Kristin Roberts,
Angie Stump, Tammi Wardwell

Traverse City Area Public Schools
Traverse City East Middle School
Ivanka Baic Berkshire, Brenda Dunscombe,
Tracie Herzberg, Deb Larimer, Jan Palkowski,
Rebecca Perreault, Jane Porath*, Robert Sagan,
Mary Beth Schmitt*

Traverse City West Middle School
Pamela Alfieri, Jennifer Rundio,
Maria Taplin, Karrie Tufts*

Maine
Falmouth Public Schools
Falmouth Middle School: Sally Bennett,
Chris Driscoll, Sara Jones, Shawn Towle*

Minnesota
Minneapolis Public Schools
Jefferson Community School:
Leif Carlson*,
Katrina Hayek Munsisoumang*

Ohio
Clark-Shawnee Local Schools
Reid School: Joanne Gilley
Rockway Middle School: Jim Mamer*
Possum School: Tami Thomas

*Indicates a Field Test Site Coordinator

Teacher Resources

For Grade 7

Dear Family,

The first Unit in your child's mathematics class this year is **Shapes and Designs: Two-Dimensional Geometry.** Students will recognize, analyze, measure, and reason about the shapes and visual patterns that are important features of our world. Students analyze the properties that make certain shapes special and useful.

Unit Goals

The goal of *Shapes and Designs* is to have students discover and analyze many of the key properties of polygonal shapes that make them useful and attractive.

This Unit focuses on polygons and develops two basic sub-themes:

- *How do the measures of angles in a polygon determine its possible shapes and uses?*
- *How do the lengths of edges in a polygon determine its possible shapes and uses?*

While some attention is given to naming familiar figures, each Investigation focuses on particular key properties of figures and the importance of those properties in applications. For example, students are asked to examine what properties of triangles make them useful in construction and design, and why triangles are preferred over quadrilaterals. Students also examine and evaluate angle properties of polygons that make some able to tile a surface whereas others cannot. We frequently ask students to find and describe places where they see polygons of particular types and to puzzle over why those particular shapes are used.

Homework and Having Conversations About The Mathematics

In your child's notebook, you can find worked-out examples, notes on the mathematics of the Unit, and descriptions of the vocabulary words.

You can help your child with homework and encourage sound mathematical habits during this Unit by asking questions such as:

- What kinds of shapes/polygons will cover a flat surface?
- What do these shapes have in common?
- How do simple polygons work together to make more complex shapes?
- How can angle measures be estimated?
- How can angles be measured with more accuracy?

You can help your child with his or her work for this Unit in several ways:

- Point out different shapes you see, and ask your child to find other shapes.
- Whenever you notice an interesting shape in a newspaper or a magazine, discuss with your child whether it is one of the polygons mentioned in the Unit, and suggest that it might be cut out and saved for the *Shapes and Designs* Unit Project.

Common Core State Standards

While all of the Standards of Mathematical Practice are developed and used by students throughout the curriculum, particular attention is paid to constructing viable arguments and critiquing the reasoning of others as students make conjectures about the construction of geometric shapes (angles and side lengths) and justify their responses to others. *Shapes and Designs* focuses largely on the Geometry domain.

A few important mathematical ideas that your child will learn in *Shapes and Designs* are on the next page. As always, if you have any questions or concerns about this Unit or your child's progress in class, please feel free to call.

Sincerely,

Important Concepts	Examples

Polygon

A shape formed by line segments so that each of the segments meets exactly two other segments, and all of the points where the segments meet are end points of the segments.

Examples of Polygons	Non-Examples

Polygon Names

Triangle: 3 sides and 3 angles

Quadrilateral: 4 sides and 4 angles

Pentagon: 5 sides and 5 angles

Hexagon: 6 sides and 6 angles

Heptagon: 7 sides and 7 angles

Octagon: 8 sides and 8 angles

Nonagon: 9 sides and 9 angles

Decagon: 10 sides and 10 angles

Dodecagon: 12 sides and 12 angles

Regular polygon: Polygons whose side lengths are equal and interior angle measures are equal.

Irregular polygon: A polygon which either has two sides with different lengths or two angles with different measures.

Line (or mirror) Symmetry

If the polygon is folded over the line of symmetry, the two halves of the shape will match exactly.

Rotational (or turn) Symmetry

A polygon with turn symmetry can be turned around its center point less than a full turn and still look the same at certain angles of rotation.

Angles

Angles are figures formed by two rays or line segments that have a common vertex. The **vertex** of an angle is the point where the two rays meet or intersect. Angles are measured in degrees.

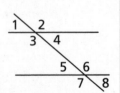

Angle Measures

Work is done to relate angles to right angles, to develop students' estimation skills. Combinations and partitions of 90° are used. 30°, 45°, 60°, 90°, 120°, 180°, 270°, and 360° are used as benchmarks to estimate angle size.

The need for more precision requires techniques for measuring angles. Students use an **angle ruler** or **protractor** to measure angles.

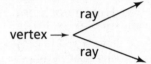

Angles and Parallel Lines

Students explore the angles created when two parallel lines are cut by a line. The line that cuts (intersects) the parallel lines is called a **transversal**. Angles 1 and 5, angles 2 and 6, angles 3 and 7, and angles 4 and 8 are called **corresponding angles**. Angles 4 and 5 and angles 3 and 6 are called **alternate interior angles**. Parallel lines cut by a transversal create equal corresponding angles and equal alternate interior angles.

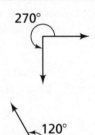

Parallel lines and transversals help explain some special features of parallelograms such as the opposite angles have equal measures or that the sum of the measures of two adjacent angles is 180°.

Polygons that Tile a Plane

For regular polygons to tile a plane, the angle measure of an interior angle must be a factor of 360°.

Only three regular polygons can tile a plane: an equilateral triangle (60° angles), a square (90° angles) and a regular hexagon (120° angles). There are also combinations of regular polygons that will tile, such as 2 octagons and a square.

Triangle Inequality Theorem

The sum of two side lengths of a triangle must be greater than the 3rd side length.

If the side lengths are a, b, and c, then the sum of any two sides is greater than the third: $a + b > c$, $b + c > a$, $c + a > b$

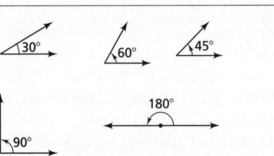

Estimada familia:

La primera Unidad de la clase de Matemáticas de su hijo(a) este año es **Figuras y diseños: Geometría bidimensional**. Los estudiantes reconocerán, analizarán, medirán y razonarán acerca de las figuras y los patrones visuales que son características muy importantes en la vida cotidiana. Los estudiantes analizarán las propiedades que hacen especiales y útiles a ciertas figuras.

▷ Objetivos de la unidad

El objetivo de *Figuras y diseños* es que los estudiantes descubran y analicen muchas de las propiedades clave de las figuras poligonales que las hacen útiles y atractivas.

La Unidad se concentra en los polígonos y desarrolla dos subtemas básicos:

- *¿Cómo las medidas de los ángulos de un polígono determinan sus formas y usos posibles?*
- *¿Cómo las longitudes de las aristas de un polígono determinan sus formas y usos posibles?*

Mientras que se pone algo de atención a identificar figuras conocidas, cada Investigación se enfoca en propiedades clave particulares de las figuras y la importancia de esas propiedades en algunas aplicaciones. Por ejemplo, se pide a los estudiantes examinar qué propiedades de los triángulos los hacen útiles en la construcción y el diseño, y por qué se prefieren los triángulos a los cuadriláteros. Los estudiantes también examinan y evalúan propiedades de los ángulos de polígonos que hacen a algunos de ellos apropiados para cubrir como mosaico una superficie. Con frecuencia pedimos a los estudiantes que encuentren y describan lugares donde hayan visto polígonos de tipos particulares y que se cuestionen por qué se usan esas figuras en particular.

▷ Tareas y conversaciones acerca de las Matemáticas

Usted puede ayudar a su hijo(a) con la tarea y alentar hábitos matemáticos sólidos durante esta unidad haciendo preguntas como las siguientes:

- ¿Qué tipos de figuras/polígonos pueden cubrir una superficie plana?
- ¿Qué tienen esas formas en común?
- ¿Cómo se pueden usar los polígonos en conjunto para formar figuras más complejas?
- ¿Cómo se pueden estimar medidas de ángulos?
- ¿Cómo se pueden medir ángulos de manera más precisa?

Usted puede ayudar a su hijo(a) con la tarea para esta Unidad de varias maneras:

- Señale las diferentes figuras que vea y pídale a su hijo(a) que halle otras figuras.
- Cada vez que encuentre una figura interesante en un periódico o revista, comente con su hijo(a) si es uno de los polígonos mencionados en esta Unidad y sugiérale que lo recorte y guarde para el proyecto de la Unidad de *Figuras y diseños*.

En el cuaderno de su hijo(a) puede encontrar ejemplos resueltos, notas sobre las matemáticas de la Unidad y descripciones de vocabulario.

▷ Estándares estatales comunes

Mientras que los estudiantes desarrollan y usan todos los Estándares de prácticas matemáticas a través del currículum, se presta especial atención a elaborar argumentos viables y analizar el razonamiento de los demás mientras desarrollan conjeturas sobre la construcción de figuras geométricas (ángulos y longitudes de los lados) y justifican sus respuestas ante los demás. *Figuras y diseños* se enfoca sobre todo en los dominios de *Geometría*.

Algunas ideas importantes de matemáticas que su hijo(a) aprenderá en *Figuras y diseño* se presentan en la página siguiente. Si usted tiene cualquier pregunta o preocupación acerca de esta Unidad, o con respecto al progreso de su hijo(a), por favor no dude en llamar.

Sinceramente,

Conceptos importantes	Ejemplos
Polígono Una figura formada por segmentos de recta de manera que cada uno de ellos coincide exactamente con los otros dos, y todos los puntos donde los segmentos se unen son extremos de los segmentos. 	Nombres de polígonos **Triángulo:** 3 lados y 3 ángulos **Cuadrilátero:** 4 lados y 4 ángulos **Pentágono:** 5 lados y 5 ángulos **Hexágono:** 6 lados y 6 ángulos **Heptágono:** 7 lados y 7 ángulos **Octágono:** 8 lados y 8 ángulos **Nonágono:** 9 lados y 9 ángulos **Decágono:** 10 lados y 10 ángulos **Dodecágono:** 12 lados y 12 ángulos
Polígono regular: Polígonos cuyos lados son iguales y cuyos ángulos interiores tienen la misma medida.	**Polígono irregular:** Tiene dos lados de distintas longitudes o dos ángulos de distintas medidas.
Simetría axial (o de reflexión) Si el polígono se dobla por el eje de simetría, las dos mitades de la figura coinciden exactamente. 	**Simetría rotacional:** Un polígono con simetría rotacional se puede girar sobre su punto central menos de una vuelta completa y aún tener la misma apariencia en ciertos ángulos de la rotación.

Ángulos
Los ángulos son figuras formadas por dos semirrectas o segmentos de recta que tienen un vértice común. El **vértice** de un ángulo es el punto donde se encuentran o intersecan dos semirrectas. Los ángulos se miden en grados.

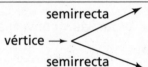

Medidas de ángulos
Se trabaja para relacionar ángulos con ángulos rectos, para desarrollar las destrezas de estimación de los estudiantes. Se emplean combinaciones y divisiones de 90°. Se emplean 30°, 45°, 60°, 90°, 120°, 180°, 270° y 360° como puntos de referencia para estimar medidas de ángulos.

La necesidad de mayor precisión requiere de técnicas para medir ángulos. Los estudiantes usan la **regla de ángulo** o el **transportador** para medir ángulos.

Ángulos y rectas paralelas
Los estudiantes exploran los ángulos que se crean cuando dos rectas paralelas son cortadas por otra recta. La recta que corta (interseca) a las paralelas se llama **transversal**. Los ángulos 1 y 5, 2 y 6, 3 y 7, y 4 y 8 se conocen como **ángulos correspondientes**. Los ángulos 4 y 5 y 3 y 6 se conocen como **ángulos interiores alternos**. Las rectas paralelas cortadas por una transversal generan ángulos iguales correspondientes y ángulos interiores alternos iguales.

Las rectas paralelas y transversales explican algunas características de los paralelogramos, como que los ángulos opuestos tengan iguales medidas o que la suma de las medidas de dos ángulos adyacentes sea de 180°.

Polígonos que cubren un plano Para que polígonos regulares puedan cubrir como mosaico un plano, la medida de un ángulo interior debe ser un factor de 360°.	Sólo tres polígonos regulares pueden cubrir como mosaico un plano: un triángulo equilátero (cuyos ángulos miden 60°), un cuadrado (ángulos de 90°) y un hexágono regular (ángulos de 120°). También hay combinaciones de polígonos regulares que se ajustan en mosaico, como dos octágonos y un cuadrado.
Teorema de desigualdad del triángulo La suma de las longitudes de dos lados de un triángulo debe ser mayor que la longitud del tercero.	Si las *longitudes* de los lados son *a*, *b* y *c*, entonces la suma de dos lados es mayor que la longitud del tercero: $a + b > c, b + c > a, c + a > b$ 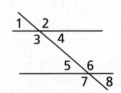

6

Labsheet 1.2   Four in a Row

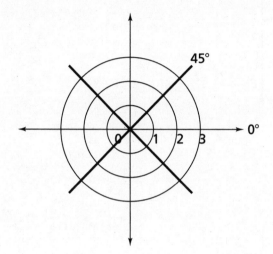

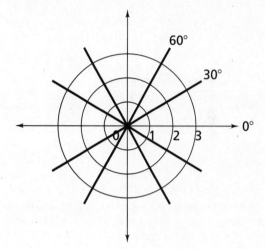

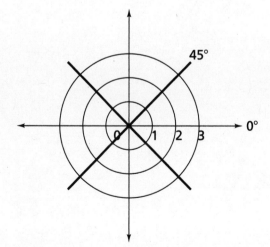

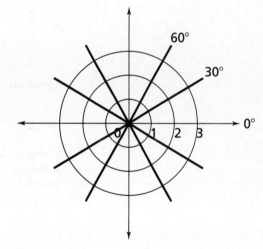

Labsheet 1.3   Question A Angles

Estimate the measure of each angle in degrees. Name each angle with the ∠ symbol.

1.

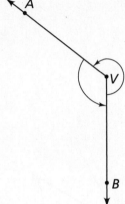

2.

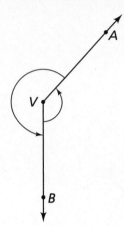

3.

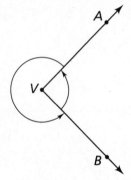

4.

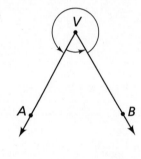

Labsheet 1.4   Question E Angles

Find the measures of the angles. Use an angle ruler or a protractor.

1.

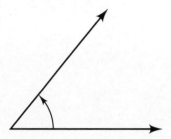

2.

3.

4.

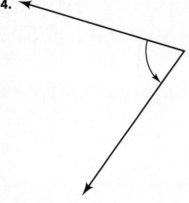

Labsheet 1ACE Exercise 1

1. Tell whether each figure is a polygon. Explain how you know.

a.
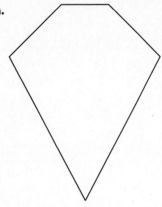

b.
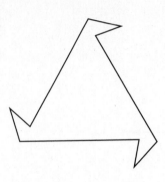

c.

d.
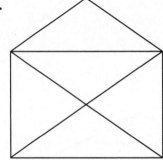

e.
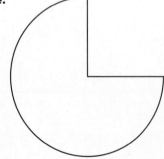

f.
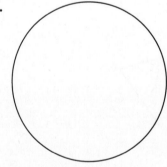

Labsheet 1ACE   Exercise 2

Common Polygons

Number of Sides and Angles	Polygon Name	Examples in the Shapes Set
3	triangle	
4	quadrilateral	
5	pentagon	
6	hexagon	
7	heptagon	
8	octagon	
9	nonagon	
10	decagon	
12	dodecagon	

Labsheet 1ACE Exercise 29

29. Without measuring, decide whether the angles in each pair have the same measure. If they do not, tell which angle has the greater measure. Then find the measure of the angles with an angle ruler or protractor to check your work.

a.

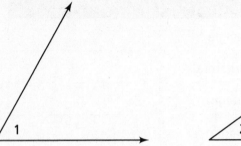

b.

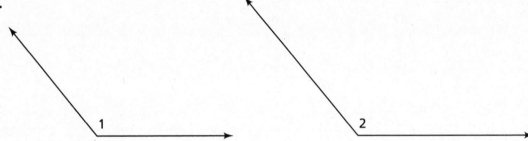

c.

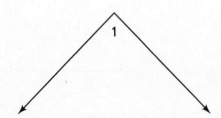
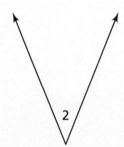

Labsheet 1ACE   Exercise 30

30. For each polygon below, measure the angles with an angle ruler.

a.

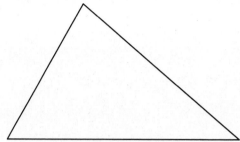

b.

Labsheet 1ACE   Exercise 31

31. Estimate the measure of each angle, then check your answers with an angle ruler or a protractor.

a.

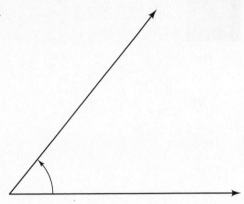

b.

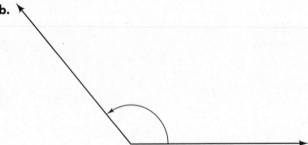

c.

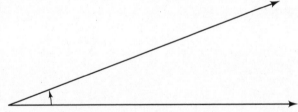

d.

e.

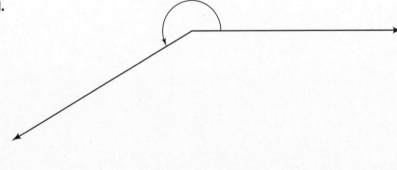

Labsheet 1ACE Exercise 64

Common Quadrilaterals

Sides and Angles	Name	Examples in the Shapes Set
All sides are the same length.	rhombus	
All sides are the same length and all angles are right angles.	square	
All angles are right angles.	rectangle	
Opposite sides are parallel.	parallelogram	
Only one pair of opposite sides are parallel.	trapezoid	

Labsheet 1ACE   Exercise 69

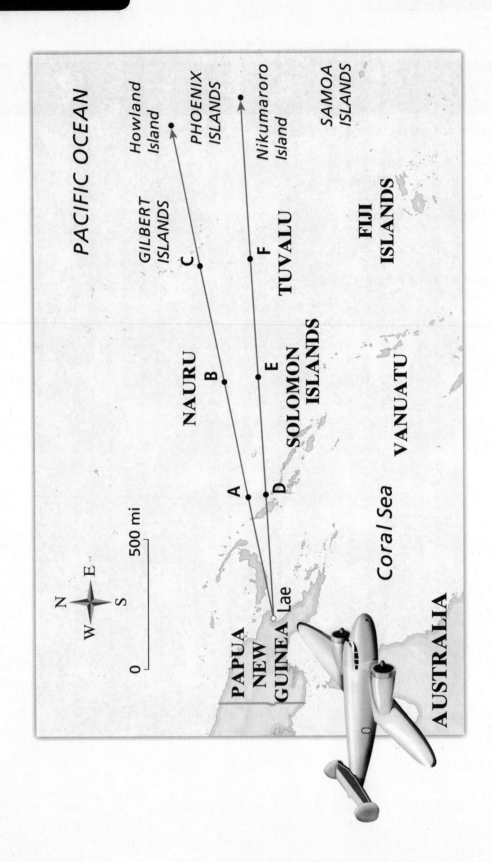

Labsheet 2.2   Trevor's and Casey's Methods

Trevor's Method

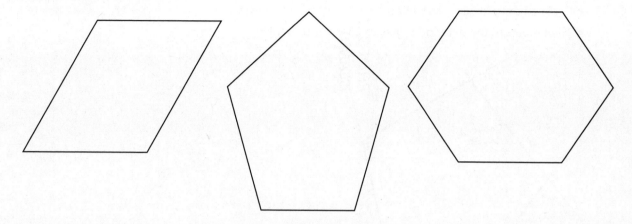

Casey's Method

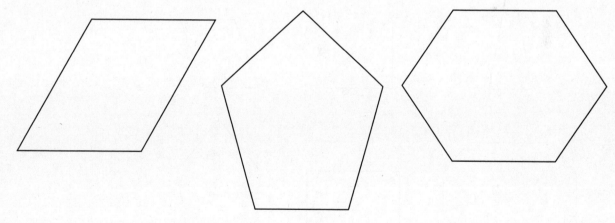

Labsheet 2.4A Question A

1. What is the sum of the left-turn exterior angles?
   - Explain how you can arrive at an answer without measuring.
   - Then measure the exterior angles to check your thinking.

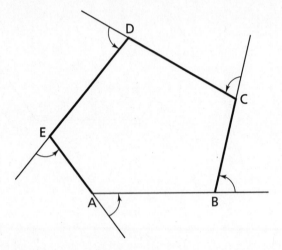

2. Find the sums of the left-turn exterior angles if you cycle around each figure and return to your start point and direction.

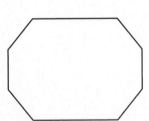

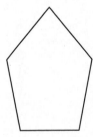

Labsheet 2.4B Question D

For each of the following triangles, write and solve an equation to find the value of *x*. Use the results to find the measure of each angle. Find the supplement of each interior angle.

1.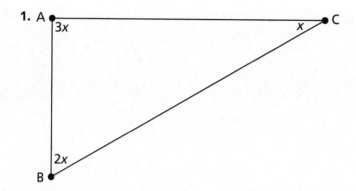

2.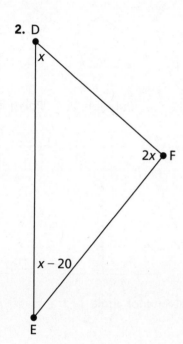

Labsheet 2ACE   Exercise 2

2. Below are sets of **regular polygons** of different sizes. Use these polygons to complete the table. You may need to measure the length of one side of each polygon and measure one angle of each polygon.

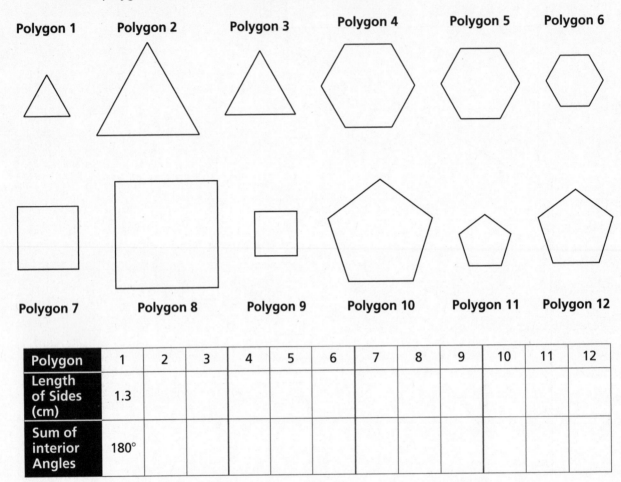

Polygon	1	2	3	4	5	6	7	8	9	10	11	12
Length of Sides (cm)	1.3											
Sum of interior Angles	180°											

Does the length of a side of a regular polygon affect the sum of the interior angle measures? Explain.

Labsheet 2ACE   Exercise 2

2. Below are sets of **regular polygons** of different sizes. Remember regular polygons are shapes that have all their sides and all their angles equal.

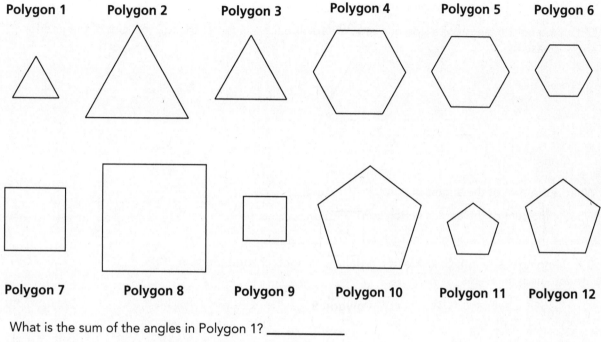

Polygon 1   **Polygon 2**   **Polygon 3**   **Polygon 4**   **Polygon 5**   **Polygon 6**

Polygon 7   **Polygon 8**   **Polygon 9**   **Polygon 10**   **Polygon 11**   **Polygon 12**

What is the sum of the angles in Polygon 1? _____

What is the sum of the angles in Polygon 2? _____

What is the sum of the angles in Polygon 3? _____

Did changing the length of a side of a regular triangle change the sum of the interior angle measures?

What is the sum of the angles in Polygon 4? _____

What is the sum of the angles in Polygon 5? _____

What is the sum of the angles in Polygon 6? _____

Did changing the length of a side of a regular hexagon change the sum of the interior angle measures?

Shapes and Designs   **21**   Investigation 2

Labsheet 2ACE   Exercise 2

What is the sum of the angles in Polygon 7? _____

What is the sum of the angles in Polygon 8? _____

What is the sum of the angles in Polygon 9? _____

Did changing the length of a side of a regular retangle (i.e. a square) change the sum of the interior angle measures?

What is the sum of the angles in Polygon 10? _____

What is the sum of the angles in Polygon 11? _____

What is the sum of the angles in Polygon 12? _____

Did changing the length of a side of a regular pentagon change the sum of the interior angle measures?

Does the length of a regular polygon affect the sum of the interior angles? Explain.

Labsheet 3.1   Building Triangles

Side 1	Side 2	Side 3	Triangle? (yes or no)	Sketch	Different Shape? (yes or no)

Labsheet 3.2 Question B

B. Write the shortest possible message to tell how to draw each triangle below.

1.

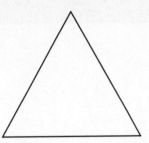

2.

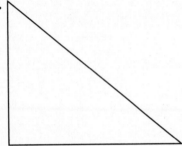

3.

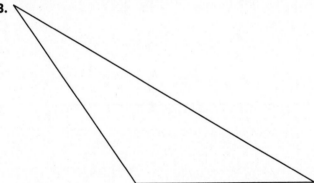

4.

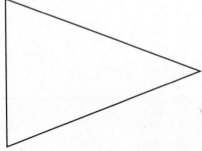

Labsheet 3.3   Building Quadrilaterals

Side 1	Side 2	Side 3	Side 4	Quadrilateral? (yes or no)	Sketch

Labsheet 3.4A   Parallelograms

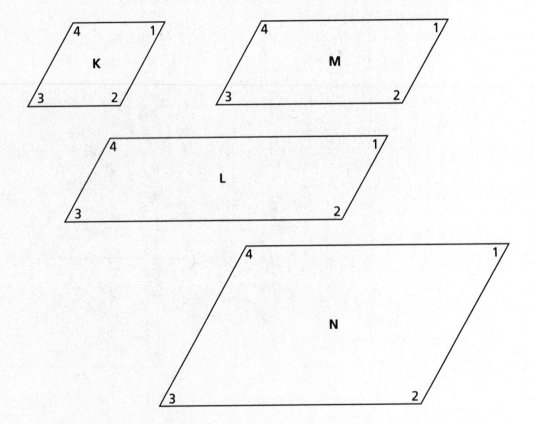

Labsheet 3.4B   Questions A–E

What are the measures of the angles in parallelograms *ABCD* and *JKLM* below?

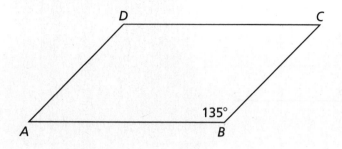

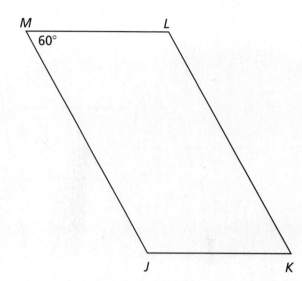

Find the measures of all labeled angles in this diagram. Be prepared to justify each answer.

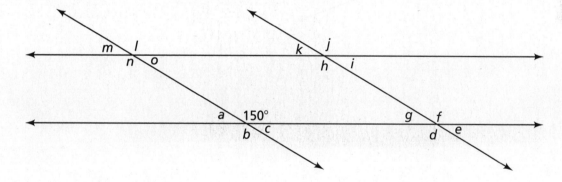

Labsheet 3.4B   Questions A–E

Suppose the measure of angle *e* is 80˚. What are the measures of the other labeled angles?

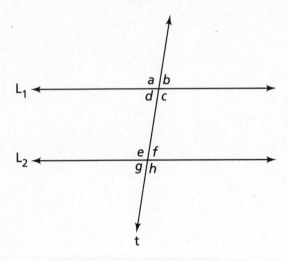

Find the value of *x* and the size of each angle in this figure.

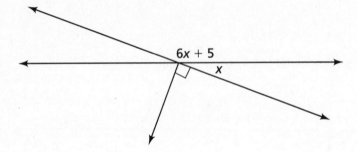

Labsheet 3.5   Quadrilateral Game Grid

Row 6	A quadrilateral that is a square	**Add 1 point to your score and skip your turn**	A rectangle that is not a square	A quadrilateral with two obtuse angles	A quadrilateral with exactly one pair of parallel sides	A quadrilateral with one pair of opposite side lengths equal
Row 5	**Subtract 2 points from your score and skip your turn**	A quadrilateral that is not a rectangle	A quadrilateral with two pairs of consecutive angles that are equal	A quadrilateral with all four angles the same size	A quadrilateral with four lines of symmetry	A quadrilateral that is a rectangle
Row 4	A quadrilateral with no reflection or rotation symmetry	A quadrilateral with four right angles	**Skip a turn**	A quadrilateral with exactly one pair of consecutive side lengths that are equal	A quadrilateral with exactly one right angle	A quadrilateral with two 45° angles
Row 3	A quadrilateral with no angles equal	A quadrilateral with one pair of equal opposite angles	A quadrilateral with exactly one pair of opposite angles that are equal	**Add 2 points to your score and skip your turn**	A quadrilateral with no sides parallel	A quadrilateral with exactly two right angles
Row 2	A quadrilateral with both pairs of adjacent side lengths equal	A quadrilateral with two pairs of equal opposite angles	A quadrilateral with a diagonal that divides it into two identical shapes	A quadrilateral that is a rhombus	A quadrilateral with 180° rotation symmetry	**Subtract 1 point from your score and skip your turn**
Row 1	A quadrilateral with one diagonal that is a line of symmetry	A quadrilateral with no side lengths equal	A quadrilateral with exactly one angle greater than 180°	A parallelogram that is not a rectangle	**Add 3 points to your score and skip your turn**	A quadrilateral with two pairs of opposite side lengths equal
	Column 1	**Column 2**	**Column 3**	**Column 4**	**Column 5**	**Column 6**

Labsheet 3ACE   Exercise 18

Which of these shapes have reflection symmetry? Which of these shapes have rotation symmetry?

Check Up *for use after Investigation 1*

1. Give the measure of angle 2 in each of the shapes below.

a.

```
1          2

      B

3          4
```

b.

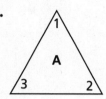

c.

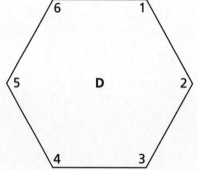

d.

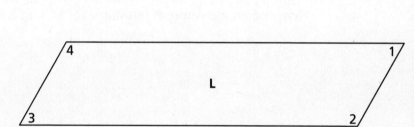

Check Up (continued)

2. Autumn places the following shapes into a group.

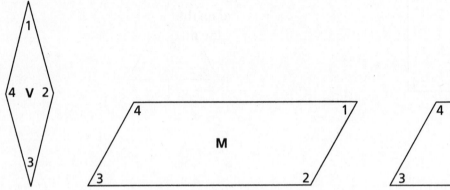

The shape below does not belong in the group.

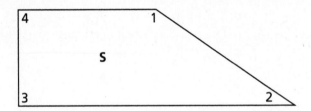

Give one reason Autumn put shapes V, M, and K in a group.

3. Draw and label the polygon with the following properties.

$\angle ABC = 90°$, $\angle BCA = 45°$, and side $BC = 1$ in.

Name .... Date .... Class ....

Shapes and Designs

Check Up (continued)

4. One common place we see angles is on the face of a clock. At the start of each hour, the minute hand points straight up to the twelve.

   a. Use the clock below. Sketch the minute hand on the clock at the start of an hour. Then sketch the angle formed by the minute hand after ten minutes have passed.

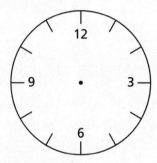

   b. Give the measure of the angle.

5. Use the figure below.

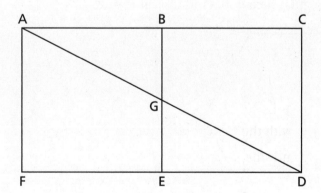

   a. Find one angle that is supplementary to ∠*BGA*.

   b. Find one angle that is complementary to ∠*BAG*.

Partner Quiz *for use after Investigation 2*

1. **a.** Can you use a square to tile a floor? Explain why or why not.

    b. Can you use a regular pentagon to tile a floor? Explain why or why not.

2. Is it possible for a triangle to have a 54° angle and a 126° angle? Explain why or why not.

3. The polygon below is a regular hexagon. Find the value of *x*.

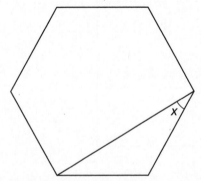

Partner Quiz (continued)

4. a. Use the quadrilateral below. Find the measures of angles 1, 2, 3, and 4.

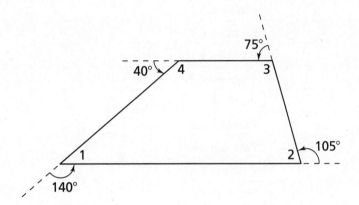

Measure of angle 1 _____   Measure of angle 2 _____

Measure of angle 3 _____   Measure of angle 4 _____

b. Explain how you know that the measures in part (a) are correct without using an angle ruler or protractor.

5. What is the angle sum of a 14-sided polygon? Show your work.

Unit Test Correlation

Unit Test Item	Problem
Item 1, part (a)	Problem 2.1
Item 1, part (b)	Problem 2.4
Item 2	Problem 3.1
Item 3	Problem 2.2
Item 4, parts (a)–(d)	Problem 1.3
Item 5	Problem 2.2
Item 6, parts (a)–(d)	Problem 3.4
Item 7, parts (a) and (b)	Problem 1.4
Item 8, parts (a) and (b)	Problem 1.4
Item 9	Problem 3.3
Item 10	Problem 3.2

Unit Test *for use after Investigation 3*

1. a. What is the *interior angle sum* of a regular octagon?
   Explain your reasoning.

   b. How many degrees are in *one exterior angle* of a regular octagon?

2. A triangle has sides of 4 and 6 units. The measurement of the longest side is missing.

   Ted says that one possibility for the unknown side length is 11.

   Do you agree with Ted? Why or why not?

3. Is a triangle with angle measures 46°, 35°, and 100° possible? Explain why or why not.

Name .... Date .... Class ....

Shapes and Designs

Unit Test (continued)

4. Estimate the measures of the angles below.

a.

b.

c.

d.

5. Use rectangle *ABCD* with diagonal *DB*. Find the measure of the angle marked *x*. Show your work.

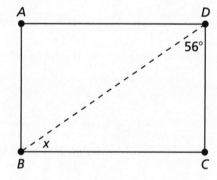

Name .... **Date** .... **Class** ....

Shapes and Designs

Unit Test *(continued)*

6. Use the figure below which shows parallel lines and a transversal. The measure of ∠2 is 45°. Find the measures of angles 1, 3, and 6. Explain how you found each measure.

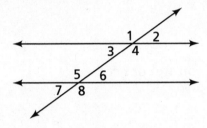

    a. measure of ∠1 = _____

    b. measure of ∠3 = _____

    c. measure of ∠6 = _____

7. a. Suppose the measure of an angle is 25°. What is the measure of its complementary angle?

    b. Draw the angles to show that you are correct.

Unit Test (continued)

8. a. Suppose two angles are supplementary and one of them measures 31°. What is the measure of the other angle?

b. Draw the angles to show that you are correct.

9. Draw a parallelogram with two sides of length 5 cm, two sides of length 3 cm, and angles of 50° and 130°.

10. Draw a triangle *ABC* with *AB* = 7 cm, *BC* = 5 cm, and ∠*ABC* = 65°.

Self Assessment

Mathematical Ideas

After studying the mathematics in this Unit:

1. a. I learned these things about mathematics:

b. Here are page numbers of notebook entries that give evidence of what I have learned, along with descriptions of what each entry shows:

2. a. These are the mathematical ideas that I am still struggling with:

b. This is why I think these ideas are difficult for me:

c. Here are page numbers of notebook entries that give evidence of what I am struggling with, and descriptions of what each entry shows:

Class Participation

I contributed to the classroom **discussion** and understanding of the mathematics in this Unit when I ... (Give examples.)

Self Assessment (continued)

Learning Environment

Rate each learning activity listed below using this scale:

1. I consistently struggled to understand the mathematics and I'm still not sure that I understand it.

2. I struggled somewhat but now I understand more than I did.

3. I had to work, but I feel confident that I understand now.

4. I understood everything pretty easily and I feel confident that I know the mathematics in these problems.

5. Everything came easily. I knew most of the mathematics before we did this.

Learning Activities

____ Problems from the Investigations

____ ACE Homework Assignments

____ Mathematical Reflections

____ Check Ups

____ Partner Quiz

____ Looking Back

____ Unit Test

Check any of the following that you feel are the most helpful in adding to the success of your learning.

☐ Working on my own in class

☐ Discussing a problem with a partner

☐ Working in a small group of 3 or 4 people

☐ Discussing a problem as a whole class

☐ Hearing how other people solved the problem

☐ Summarizing the mathematics as a class and taking notes

☐ Completing homework assignments

Notebook Checklist

Place a ✔ next to each item you have completed.

Notebook Organization

_____ Problems and Mathematical Reflections are labeled and dated.

_____ Work is neat and easy to find and follow.

Vocabulary

_____ All words are listed.   _____ All words are defined or described.

Assessments

_____ Check Up   _____ _____

_____ Partner Quiz   _____ _____

_____ Unit Test   _____ _____

Assignments

_____ _____   _____ _____

_____ _____   _____ _____

_____ _____   _____ _____

_____ _____   _____ _____

_____ _____   _____ _____

_____ _____   _____ _____

_____ _____   _____ _____

_____ _____   _____ _____

_____ _____   _____ _____

_____ _____   _____ _____

Assessment Answers

Check Up

1. **a.** 90°
    b. 60°
    c. 120°
    d. 120°

2. **a.** Answers will vary. Students may say that opposite angles are equal, or that each shape has two angles equal. Other answers may occur.

3. Students should draw a right, isosceles triangle, with side lengths of 1, 1, and $\sqrt{2}$; and angle measurements of 45°, 45°, and 90°.

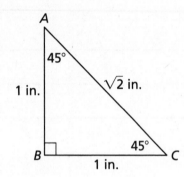

4. **a.**

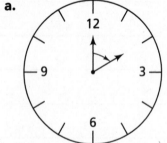

    b. 60°

5. **a.** ∠BGD
    b. ∠GAF

Partner Quiz

1. **a.** Yes; squares can be used to tile since all angles are 90°, and $4 \times 90° = 360°$, which is the degree measure in a full turn.

    b. No; regular pentagons cannot be used alone to tile a floor. Since the angle sum of a regular pentagon is 540°, each interior angle is $540° \div 5 = 108°$, which is not a factor of 360. Thus, copies of a 108° angle will not fit around a point.

2. No; the sum of the angles of a triangle are 180°, and the two given angles already equal 180°.

3. 30°

4. **a.** $m\angle 1 = 40°$, $m\angle 2 = 75°$, $m\angle 3 = 105°$, $m\angle 4 = 140°$.

    b. Possible answer: The interior angle is equal to (180° − exterior angle).

5. 2160°; possible answer: $(14 - 2) \times 180°$

Unit Test

1. **a.** The angle sum is $(8 - 2) \times 180° = 1080°$. To find the angle sum you can pick a vertex of the polygon and draw triangles. If you do this with an octagon, you will get 6 triangles, each of which has 180°, so the answer is $6 \times 180° = 1080°$.

    b. There are $360° \div 8 = 45°$ in each exterior angle. To find the number of degrees in the exterior angle of a regular polygon you divide 360° by the number sides (or number of angles).

Assessment Answers (continued)

2. Ted's estimate is too large. The third side must have a length less than $4 + 6 = 10$.

3. No; the sum of the angles is $46° + 35° + 100° = 181°$. A triangle has an angle sum of exactly $180°$.

4. $90°$, $120°$, $60°$, $30°$ (estimation should be within $10°$)

5. $x = 34°$. Since $ABCD$ is a rectangle, it must have four right angles; therefore $m\angle BCD$ must be $90°$. A triangle has $180°$, so subtract $90°$ and $56°$ from $180°$ to get the value of x, which is $34°$.

6. a. $m\angle 1 = 135°$, because $\angle 1$ and $\angle 2$ are supplementary and they are a linear pair.

   b. $m\angle 3 = 45°$, because $\angle 2$ and $\angle 3$ are vertical angles, so they must be congruent.

   c. $m\angle 6 = 45°$, because $\angle 2$ and $\angle 6$ are corresponding angles, so they must be congruent.

7. a. $65°$, because if two angles are complementary, then their sum is $90°$; so $90° - 25° = 65°$.

   b.
   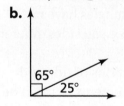

8. a. $149°$, because if two angles are supplementary, then their sum is $180°$; so $180° - 31° = 147°$.

   b.
   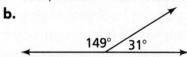

9. Possible answers:

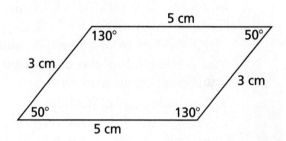

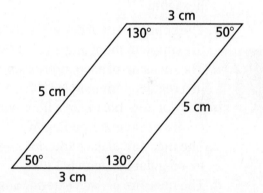

10.

Looking Back Answers

1. **a.** Labeled angle F appears to be a right angle. Angles C, D, and H appear to be acute angles. Angles B, E, I, and J appear to be obtuse angles. Angle G appears to be a straight angle and angle A is greater than a straight angle (sometimes referred to as a reflex angle).

   b. $\angle C = \angle D \approx 30°$, $\angle H \approx 45°$, $\angle F \approx 90°$, $\angle B = \angle E \approx 120°$, $\angle I = \angle J \approx 145°$, $\angle G = 180°$, and $\angle A \approx 240°$. Students might have different but close measures.

   c. The building plan includes a triangle, quadrilaterals (rectangles and trapezoids), a pentagon, and a hexagon.

   d. The supplement of angle J is 35° and the supplement of angle H is 135°.

2. **a.** The measure of each interior angle in a regular pentagon is 108°.

   b. It is not possible to tile a floor with copies of a regular pentagon.

   c. The measure of each interior angle in a regular hexagon is 120°.

   d. The measure of each exterior angle in a regular hexagon is 60°.

   e. It is possible to tile a floor with copies of a regular hexagon.

   f. Regular pentagons have 5 line reflection symmetries (through each vertex and perpendicular to the opposite side) and 4 non-trivial rotation symmetries (multiples of 72°). Regular hexagons have 6 line reflection symmetries (through pairs of opposite vertices and perpendicular bisectors of opposite sides) and 5 non-trivial rotation symmetries (multiples of 60°).

   g. Regular hexagons have parallel opposite sides.

3. **a.** A triangle with side lengths of 4 cm, 6 cm, and 9 cm is possible, but only one.

   b. A triangle with side lengths of 4 cm, 7 cm, and 2 cm is not possible.

   c. A rectangle with a pair of opposite sides whose lengths are 8 cm is possible, but there are many, depending on the length of the other pair of opposite sides.

   d. A parallelogram with side lengths of 8 cm, 8 cm, 6 cm, and 6 cm is possible, but the sides must be in order 8, 6, 8, 6. There are many such parallelograms with that sequence of side lengths.

4. **a.** Triangles are useful in building structures because they are rigid figures that hold their shape even when stressed.

   b. A triangle that has both rotation and reflection symmetries must be equilateral.

   c. A triangle that has only one line of symmetry must be isosceles.

   d. All scalene triangles have no symmetries (i.e., all sides different lengths).

   e. The combinations of side and angle measurements that can be used to decide if two given triangles are congruent include SSS, SAS, and ASA.

Parent Letters

Labsheets

Assessments

Dear Family,

The next Unit in your child's mathematics class this year is ***Accentuate the Negative: Positive and Negative Numbers.*** Students have experienced positive and negative numbers informally in their everyday world—in temperatures, in sports scores, and in game contexts. Students have intuitively used operations on integers to make sense of these situations; now they will develop formal ways to compute with these numbers.

▶ Unit Goals

In this Unit, the focus is on understanding and developing systematic ways to add, subtract, multiply, and divide positive and negative numbers. While working on this Unit, students will use positive and negative numbers to represent problem situations. Students will develop algorithms for computation and will use the Order of Operations, the Commutative Property, and the Distributive Property to solve problems.

▶ Helping With Homework and Conversations About the Mathematics

In your child's notebook, you can find worked-out examples, notes on the mathematics of the Unit, and descriptions of the vocabulary words. You can help with homework by asking questions such as the following:

- How do negative and positive numbers help in describing the situation?

- What will addition, subtraction, multiplication, or division of positive and negative numbers tell about the problem?

- What model(s) for positive and negative numbers would help in displaying the relationships in the problem situation?

You can help your child with his or her work for this Unit in several ways:

- Ask your child to describe some real-world situations in which integers are used.

- Ask your child to tell you about a problem that he or she has enjoyed solving.

- Read some of the explanations that your child has written in his or her notebook and, if they aren't clear, talk with your child about why you think the explanations may need to be reviewed.

▶ Common Core State Standards

Students develop and use all of the Standards for Mathematical Practice throughout the curriculum. In *Accentuate the Negative*, particular attention is paid to looking for and making sense of structure as students develop algorithms for operating with positive and negative numbers. *Accentuate the Negative* focuses largely on the Number System domain in the Common Core State Standards. As students explore rational numbers, parts of the Expressions and Equations domain are also addressed.

A few important mathematical ideas that your child will learn in *Accentuate the Negative* are given on the next page. As always, if you have any questions or concerns about this Unit or your child's progress in class, please feel free to call.

Sincerely,

Important Concepts	Examples
Negative Numbers Some subsets of the positive and negative numbers have special names.	The set of the whole numbers and their opposites is called **integers.** Examples include: $-4, -3, -2, -1, 0, 1, 2, 3, 4$ The positive and negative integers and fractions are **rational numbers.** Examples include: $-2, -1.5, -1\frac{2}{3}, -1, -\frac{3}{4}, -\frac{1}{2}, 0, \frac{1}{2}, \frac{3}{4}, 1, 2, 2.5, 2\frac{3}{4}$
Addition and Subtraction Students model and symbolize problems to develop meaning and skill in addition and subtraction before developing algorithms. The **colored chip model** requires an understanding of opposites. The **number line model** helps make the connection to rational numbers as quantities. Sometimes it is helpful to restate an addition problem as a subtraction or a subtraction problem as an addition.	One color chip (black) represents positive numbers and another color (red) represents negative numbers. *Tate owes his sister, Julia, $6 for helping him cut the lawn. He earns $4 delivering papers. Is Tate "in the red" or "in the black"?* Black and red chips on a board represent income and expenses. The result is that he is "in the red" 2 dollars or has $^-2$ dollars. This problem may be represented with the number sentence $^-6 + 4 = {}^-2$. The number line below models a temperature change from $^-4°F$ to $^+45°F$. The sign of the change shows the direction of the change. $^-4° + n° = {}^+45°$ or $^-4° + {}^+49° = {}^+45°$ **Julia's Chip Board** When calculating $^+12 + {}^-8$, the result is the same as if you subtracted $^+8$ in the problem $^+12 - {}^+8$. When calculating $^+5 - {}^-7$, the result is the same as if you added $^+7$ in the problem $^+5 + {}^+7$.
Multiplication Multiplication can be explored by counting occurrences of fixed-size movement along the number line.	*If a runner passes the 0 point running to the left at 6 meters per second, where will he be 8 seconds later?* This can be represented as 8 jumps of $^-6$ on the number line. $^-6 + {}^-6 + {}^-6 + {}^-6 + {}^-6 + {}^-6 + {}^-6 + {}^-6 = {}^-48$ or $8 \times {}^-6 = {}^-48$
Division A multiplication fact can be used to write two related division facts.	You know that $5 \times {}^-2 = {}^-10$. You can write related division sentences: $^-10 \div {}^-2 = 5$ and $^-10 \div 5 = {}^-2$. By developing division based on its relationship to multiplication, students can determine the sign (positive or negative) of the answer to a division problem.
Order of Operations Mathematicians have established rules for the order in which operations $(+, -, \times, \div)$ should be carried out.	1. Compute any expressions within parentheses. 2. Compute any exponents. 3. Do all multiplication and division in order from left to right. 4. Do all addition and subtraction in order from left to right. $3 + 4 \times \underline{(6 \div 2)} \times 5 - 7^2 + 6 \div 3 =$ $3 + 4 \times 3 \times 5 - \underline{7^2} + 6 \div 3 =$ $3 + \underline{4 \times 3 \times 5} - 49 + \underline{6 \div 3} =$ $\underline{3 + 60} - 49 + 2 =$ $\underline{63 - 49} + 2 =$ $\underline{14 + 2} = 16$
Commutative Property This property does not hold for subtraction or division.	The order of addends does not matter. $5 + 4 = 4 + 5$ $\quad -2 + 3 = 3 + (-2)$ The order of factors does not matter. $5 \times 4 = 4 \times 5$ $\quad -2 \times 3 = 3 \times (-2)$ Order does matter in subtraction. $5 - 4 \neq 4 - 5$ $\quad -2 - 3 \neq 3 - (-2)$ Order does matter in division. $5 \div 4 \neq 4 \div 5$ $\quad -2 \div 3 \neq 3 \div (-2)$
Distributive Property This property is introduced and modeled through finding areas of rectangles.	This property shows that multiplication *distributes* over addition. $6 \times (12 + 8) = (6 \times 12) + (6 \times 8)$

Estimada familia:

La siguiente Unidad de la clase de Matemáticas de su hijo(a) de este año es **Resaltar lo negativo: Enteros y números racionales**. Los estudiantes tienen experiencia con números positivos y negativos de manera informal en la vida diaria: en temperaturas, puntajes deportivos y en el contexto de algunos juegos. Los estudiantes ya han usado intuitivamente operaciones con enteros para entender estas situaciones; ahora desarrollarán maneras formales de hacer cálculos con esos números.

▷ Objetivos de la unidad

En esta Unidad, su hijo(a) se concentrará en entender y desarrollar maneras sistemáticas de sumar, restar, multiplicar y dividir números positivos y negativos. Al trabajar en esta unidad, los estudiantes usarán números positivos y negativos para representar situaciones relacionadas con problemas. Los estudiantes desarrollarán algoritmos de cálculo y usarán el orden de las operaciones, la propiedad conmutativa y la propiedad distributiva para resolver problemas.

▷ Tareas y conversaciones acerca de las matemáticas

Usted puede ayudar a su hijo(a) con la tarea haciéndole preguntas como las siguientes:

- ¿Cómo ayudan los números negativos y positivos a describir la situación?
- ¿Qué indican acerca de la situación del problema la suma, resta, multiplicación y división de números positivos y negativos?
- ¿Qué modelo o modelos de números positivos y negativos ayudarían a mostrar las relaciones en la situación del problema?

Usted puede ayudar a su hijo(a) con su tarea para esta Unidad de varias maneras:

- Pida a su hijo(a) que describa algunas situaciones de la vida diaria en las que se usen los números enteros.
- Pida a su hijo(a) que le comente acerca de un problema que le haya gustado resolver.
- Lea algunas de las explicaciones que su hijo(a) haya escrito en su cuaderno y, si no son claras, comente por qué es necesario que las mejore.

▷ Estándares estatales comunes

Los estudiantes desarrollan y usan todos los Estándares de prácticas matemáticas a través del currículum. En *Resaltar lo negativo*, se pone especial atención en observar y encontrar el sentido de la estructura, a medida que los estudiantes desarrollan algoritmos para hacer operaciones con números positivos y negativos. *Resaltar lo negativo* se concentra sobre todo en el dominio del Sistema numérico de los Estándares estatales comunes. A medida que los estudiantes exploran los números racionales, también trabajan en temas del dominio Expresiones y ecuaciones.

Algunas ideas importantes de matemáticas que su hijo(a) aprenderá en *Resaltar lo negativo* se presentan en la página siguiente. Si usted tiene cualquier pregunta o preocupación acerca de esta Unidad, o con respecto al progreso de su hijo(a), por favor no dude en llamar.

Sinceramente,

Conceptos importantes	Ejemplos
Números negativos Algunos subconjuntos de los números positivos y negativos tienen nombres especiales.	El conjunto de los números enteros y sus opuestos se conoce como los **enteros**. Entre los ejemplos se incluyen: $-4, -3, -2, -1, 0, 1, 2, 3, 4$ Los enteros positivos y negativos y las fracciones son **números racionales**. Entre los ejemplos se incluyen: $-2, -1.5, -1\frac{2}{3}, -1, -\frac{3}{4}, -\frac{1}{2}, 0, \frac{1}{2}, \frac{3}{4}, 1, 2, 2.5, 2\frac{3}{4}$
Suma y resta Los estudiantes representan y usan símbolos en problemas para desarrollar el sentido y la destreza para hacer sumas y restas antes de desarrollar algoritmos. El **modelo de fichas de colores** requiere la comprensión de los opuestos. El **modelo de recta numérica** ayuda a hacer la conexión con los números racionales como cantidades. A veces es útil volver a expresar un problema de suma como una resta, o un problema de resta como una suma.	Una ficha de color (negro) representa números positivos y una de otro color (rojo) representa números negativos. **Tablero de fichas de Julia** *Toño le debe a su hermana, Julia, $6 por ayudarle a cortar el césped. Él gana $4 repartiendo periódicos. ¿Está Toño en "números rojos" o en "números negros"?* Las fichas negras y rojas de un tablero representan ingresos y gastos. Toño está en "números rojos" por 2 dólares o tiene $^-2$ dólares. Este problema se puede representar con la oración numérica $^-6 + 4 = {}^-2$. La siguiente recta numérica representa un cambio de temperatura de $^-4°F$ a $^+45°F$. El signo del cambio muestra la dirección del cambio. $^-4° + n° = {}^+45°$ ó $^-4° + {}^+49° = {}^+45°$ Al calcular $^+12 + {}^-8$, el resultado será el mismo que el que obtienes si restas $^+8$ en el problema $^+12 - {}^+8$. Cuando calculas $^+5 - {}^-7$, el resultado es el mismo que el que obtienes si sumas $^+7$ en el problema $^+5 + {}^+7$.
Multiplicación La multiplicación se puede explorar contando las veces que ocurre un movimiento de tamaño fijo a lo largo de la recta numérica.	*Si un corredor pasa el punto 0 corriendo hacia la izquierda a 6 metros por segundo, ¿dónde estará 8 segundos más tarde?* Esto se puede representar como 8 saltos de $^-6$ en la recta numérica. $^-6 + {}^-6 + {}^-6 + {}^-6 + {}^-6 + {}^-6 + {}^-6 + {}^-6 = {}^-48$ ó $8 \times {}^-6 = {}^-48$
División Una multiplicación se puede usar para escribir dos divisiones relacionadas.	Sabes que $5 \times {}^-2 = {}^-10$. Puedes escribir divisiones relacionadas: $^-10 \div {}^-2 = 5$ y $^-10 \div 5 = {}^-2$. Al desarrollar la división con base en esta relación con la multiplicación, los estudiantes pueden decidir si el signo de la respuesta a un problema de división es positivo o negativo.
Orden de las operaciones Los matemáticos han establecido reglas para el orden en que las operaciones $(+, -, \times, \div)$ deben llevarse a cabo.	1. Calcula las expresiones en paréntesis. 2. Calcula el exponente. 3. Haz todas las multiplicaciones y divisiones en orden de izquierda a derecha. 4. Haz todas las sumas y restas en orden de izquierda a derecha. $3 + 4 \times \underline{(6 \div 2)} \times 5 - 7^2 + 6 \div 3 =$ $3 + 4 \times 3 \times 5 - \underline{7^2} + 6 \div 3 =$ $3 + 4 \times 3 \times 5 - 49 + \underline{6 \div 3} =$ $\underline{3 + 60} - 49 + 2 =$ $\underline{63 - 49} + 2 =$ $\underline{14 + 2} = 16$
Propiedad conmutativa Esta propiedad no es pertinente para la resta o la división.	El orden de los sumandos no importa. $5 + 4 = 4 + 5$ $\qquad -2 + 3 = 3 + (-2)$ El orden de los factores no importa. $5 \times 4 = 4 \times 5$ $\qquad -2 \times 3 = 3 \times (-2)$ El orden importa en la resta. $5 - 4 \neq 4 - 5$ $\qquad -2 - 3 \neq 3 - (-2)$ El orden importa en la división. $5 \div 4 \neq 4 \div 5$ $\qquad -2 \div 3 \neq 3 \div (-2)$
Propiedad distributiva Esta propiedad se muestra y representa al hallar áreas de rectángulos.	Esta propiedad muestra que la multiplicación se *distribuye* sobre la suma. $6 \times (12 + 8) = (6 \times 12) + (6 \times 8)$

52

Labsheet 1ACE   Exercises 9 and 10

For each set of rational numbers in Exercises 9 and 10, draw a number line and locate the points. Remember to draw your number line with an appropriate *scale* and then plot the points.

HINT: It might help you think about a scale for your number lines if you wrote all numbers in either fraction or decimal form.

9. $\frac{-2}{8}$, $\frac{1}{4}$, $^-1.5$, $1\frac{3}{4}$

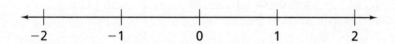

HINT: What would be a good way to scale the number line for Exercise 9—halves or fourths?

10. $^-1.25$, $\frac{-1}{3}$, 1.5, $\frac{-1}{6}$

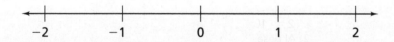

HINT: What would be a good way to scale the number line for Exercise 10—halves, thirds, fourths, sixths, or twelfths?

Labsheet 1ACE   Exercise 48

48. Find the value for each labeled point on the number line. Then use the values to calculate each change.

   a. *A* to *B*

   b. *A* to *C*

   c. *B* to *C*

   d. *C* to *A*

   e. *B* to *A*

   f. *C* to *B*

Labsheet 1ACE   Exercise 78

78. At the start of December, Kenji had a balance of $595.50 in his checking account. The following is a list of transactions he made during the month.

Date	Transaction	Balance
December 1		$595.50
December 5	Writes a check for $19.95	
December 12	Writes a check for $280.88	
December 15	Deposits $257.00	
December 17	Writes a check for $58.12	
December 21	Withdraws $50.00	
December 24	Writes checks for $17.50, $41.37, and $65.15	
December 26	Deposits $100.00	
December 31	Withdraws $50.00	

a. Complete the table.

b. What was Kenji's balance at the end of December?

c. When was his balance the greatest? When was his balance the least?

Labsheet 2.4   Fact Family Table

a	b	$a + b = c$	$a = c - b$	$b = c - a$	c

Labsheet 2ACE Exercises 15 and 16

The chip board below has 10 black and 13 red chips.

HINT: Remember black equals a negative and red equals a positive.

15. What is the value shown on the board?

16. Write a number sentence to represent each situation. Then find the new value of the chip board.

    a. Remove 5 red chips from the original board.

       What will be the value of the chip board?

       Write a number sentence to show your work.

    b. Then add 5 black chips.

       What will be the value of the chip board?

       Write a number sentence to show your work.

    c. Then add 4 black chips and 4 red chips.

       What will be the value of the chip board?

       Write a number sentence to show your work.

Labsheet 3.4   Integer Product Game

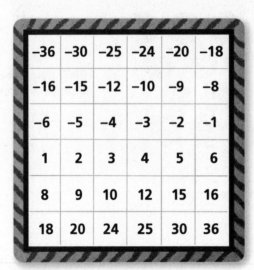

Factors:

−6 −5 −4 −3 −2 −1   1   2   3   4   5   6

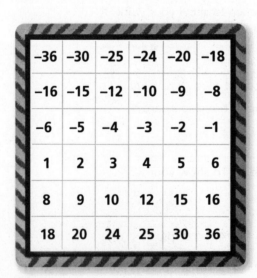

Factors:

−6 −5 −4 −3 −2 −1   1   2   3   4   5   6

Labsheet 3ACE   Exercise 1

1. At some international airports, trains carry passengers between the separate terminal buildings. Suppose that one such train system moves along a track like the one below.

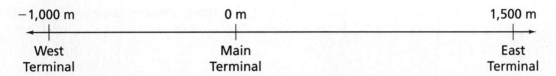

−1,000 m   0 m   1,500 m

West   Main   East
Terminal   Terminal   Terminal

a. A train leaves the main terminal going **east** (towards the East Terminal) at **10 meters per second.**

Where <u>will</u> it be (in meters) in **10 seconds?**

When <u>will</u> it reach the **East Terminal?**

How many meters does the train need to travel to get from the Main Terminal to the East Terminal?

If it travels 10 meters per second, how many seconds will it take the train to get from the Main Terminal to the East Terminal?

b. A train passes the Main Terminal going **east** (towards the East Terminal) at **10 meters per second.**

Where was that train **15 seconds ago?**

HINT: Where was it 1 second ago?

Where was it 2 seconds ago?

When <u>was</u> it at the **West Terminal?**

How many meters is the West Terminal from the Main Terminal?

If the train travels at 10 meters per second, how long will it take to travel that many meters?

Labsheet 3ACE Exercise 1

c. A train leaves the Main Terminal going **west** (towards the West Terminal) at **10 meters per second.**

Where <u>will</u> it be in **20 seconds?**

HINT: What coordinate will it be at?

When <u>will</u> it reach the **West Terminal?**

How many meters does the train need to travel to get from the Main Terminal to the West Terminal?

If it travels 10 meters per second, how many seconds will it take the train to get from the Main Terminal to the West Terminal?

d. A train passes the Main Terminal going **west** (towards the West Terminal) at **10 meters per second.**

When <u>was</u> it at the **East Terminal?**

Where <u>was</u> it **20 seconds ago?**

Labsheet 4ACE   Exercises 66–69

For Exercises 66–69, write equivalent expressions to show two different ways to find the area of each rectangle. Use the ideas of the Distributive Property.

HINT: Exercise 66 is done for you. Refer to Problem 4.2 to review the Distributive Property.

66.

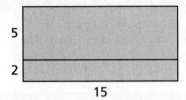

Example: $5(15) + 2(15) = (5 + 2) \times 15 = 7 \times 15$

67.

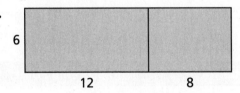

68.

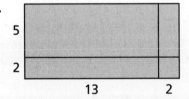

69.

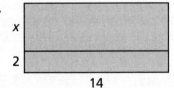

Unit Project | Score Sheet for Dealing Down

Round 1

Cards Dealt	Expression With the Least Quantity	Who Scored a Point

Why That Expression Has the Least Quantity:

Round 2

Cards Dealt	Expression With the Least Quantity	Who Scored a Point

Why That Expression Has the Least Quantity:

Round 3

Cards Dealt	Expression With the Least Quantity	Who Scored a Point

Why That Expression Has the Least Quantity:

Round 4

Cards Dealt	Expression With the Least Quantity	Who Scored a Point

Why That Expression Has the Least Quantity:

Round 5

Cards Dealt	Expression With the Least Quantity	Who Scored a Point

Why That Expression Has the Least Quantity:

Unit Project   Cards for Dealing Down

0	−1	−2	−3	−4
−5	−6	−7	−8	−9
$-\dfrac{1}{2}$	$-\dfrac{1}{3}$	$-\dfrac{1}{4}$	0.5	$\dfrac{1}{3}$
0.25	1	10	5	7
8	2	3	4	−10

Name .... Date .... Class ....

Accentuate the Negative

Check Up 1 *for use after Investigation 1*

1. Use the number line below. Draw and label a point for each number in parts (a)–(c).

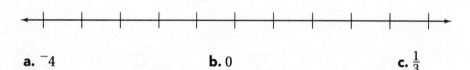

   a. ⁻4   **b.** 0   **c.** $\frac{1}{3}$

In a different color, draw and label the numbers in parts (d) and (e) on the number line above.

   d. the opposite of ⁻4   **e.** the opposite of $\frac{1}{3}$

   f. How do you know that you have correctly located the opposite of ⁻4?

2. At a certain point in a game of Math Fever, the We-Know-It team's score is ⁻150 points.

   Write a number sentence to describe one possible way that the team reached that score.

3. Insert $<$, $>$, or $=$ to make the statements true.

     a. ⁻20 ☐ ⁻25   **b.** ⁻10 ☐ 10

     c. $\frac{^-2}{5}$ ☐ $\frac{^-3}{2}$ **d.** ⁻163 ☐ ⁻162

4. On the number line below, sketch the values of x when $x \le 2.5$.

Partner Quiz *for use after Investigation 2*

1. **Multiple Choice** Which statement below is equivalent to $^-15 - 12$?

   A. $^-15 + 12$ **B.** $12 - ^-15$ **C.** $15 - 12$ **D.** $^-15 + ^-12$

   Explain your choice. _____

   _____

   _____

2. Insert $<$, $>$, or $=$ to make the number statement true.

   $^-\frac{3}{4} \square ^-0.34$

   Explain your choice. _____

   _____

   _____

3. Use the number line below to find the value.

   $^-\frac{4}{5} + ^-1.7$

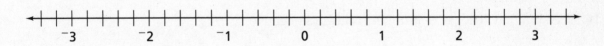

4. Rewrite these numbers in order from least to greatest.

   $^-\frac{5}{4}, 2\frac{1}{4}, ^-\frac{1}{3}, \frac{13}{3}$

Partner Quiz (continued)

5. Lily wrote the equation $n - {}^-11 = 24$. Find the value of n and explain how you found it.

6. Find the distance between -10 and 17 on a number line.

For Exercises 7–14, find each value.

7. $19 - 26$

8. $26 - 19$

9. $12 + {}^-9$

10. ${}^-12 - 9$

11. ${}^-7 - {}^-9$

12. ${}^-9 - {}^-7$

13. ${}^-7 + {}^-9$

14. $7 + {}^-9$

For Exercises 15–18, decide whether the statement is *true* or *false*.

15. The sum of two negative numbers is always negative.

16. The sum of a positive number and a negative number is always negative.

17. The difference of two negative numbers is always negative.

18. A negative number minus a positive number is always negative.

19. Pick a false statement from Exercises 15-18. On the lines below, rewrite the statement as a true statement.

_____

_____

Check Up 2 *for use after Investigation 3*

....

1. A football team loses an average of 3 yards per play. How many yards have they lost after 4 plays? Write a number sentence to show your answer.

2. Together, siblings Brandon, Brooke, Trent, and Trisha owe their parents $100. Write a number sentence to show how much each sibling owes if they share the debt equally. (Be sure to use negative numbers where appropriate.)

For Exercises 3–10, find each value.

3. $6 - 10$

4. $-7 + 15$

5. $-1.2 - (-10)$

6. $21 - (-8)$

7. $\frac{-24}{-6}$

8. $20 \cdot (-6)$

9. $-12 \cdot (-10)$

10. $-27 \div 9$

Unit Test Correlation

Unit Test Item	Problem
Item 1	Problem 1.2
Item 2	Problem 1.4
Item 3	Problem 4.1
Item 4	Problem 2.4
Item 5, parts (a) and (b)	Problem 3.1
Items 5, parts (c), (d), and (e)	Problem 3.3
Item 5, part (f)	Problem 3.2
Item 6	Problem 4.3
Items 7, parts (a) and (b)	Problem 1.4
Item 7, part (c)	Problem 3.1
Item 7, part (d)	Problem 3.3
Item 7, part (e)	Problem 3.3
Item 8	Problem 1.2
Item 9	Problem 1.3

Unit Test

1. Rewrite these numbers in order from least to greatest.

$\frac{2}{5}$,   0, $\frac{^-3}{2}$, $\frac{^-9}{8}$, $\frac{8}{7}$

2. Find each sum or difference.

a. $30 - {}^-17$

b. ${}^-17 - {}^-30$

c. ${}^-150 + 75$

d. $1.5 - 2.7$

e. ${}^-14 + {}^-15$

f. $\frac{3}{4} + \frac{^-1}{2}$

3. Find the value of the expression below. Show your work.
$10 + 9 \cdot (-6) - (-1 + 8)$

4. a. Write two subtraction sentences to complete the fact family for
${}^-8 + n = 62$.

b. Use one of the fact family sentences to find the value of n.

Unit Test (continued)

5. Find each product or quotient.

    a. $13 \cdot (-7)$ **b.** $-8 \cdot (-20)$

    c. $99 \div (-3)$ **d.** $\frac{-36}{-12}$

    e. $-3.6 \div 1.8$ **f.** $\frac{1}{3} \cdot \frac{-5}{7}$

6. Malique wants to take four of her friends to a movie. She knows it costs $5.50 for a ticket and $3.25 for popcorn.

    a. How much will it cost if she pays for the movie and popcorn for all five people?

    b. Write a number sentence to show how you found the total cost.

    c. Write a new number sentence that shows a different way to find the total cost. Explain.

7. Insert $=$ or $\neq$ to make each statement true.

    a. $11 + {}^-20 \,\square\, {}^-20 + 11$ **b.** $12 - {}^-10 \,\square\, {}^-10 - 12$

    c. ${}^-5 \cdot 2 \,\square\, 2 \cdot {}^-5$ **d.** ${}^-16 \div {}^-4 \,\square\, {}^-4 \div {}^-16$

    e. Explain how you decided which symbol to use in parts (a)–(d).

Unit Test (continued)

8. Find the values of x that satisfy the inequality $x + 5 < 7$. Then graph the solutions for x on the number line.

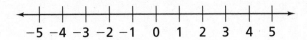

9. The table below gives monthly average low temperatures (in degrees Fahrenheit) from November through March for International Falls, Minnesota.

Average Low Temperatures for International Falls

November	December	January	February	March
17°F	0°F	−9°F	−3°F	10°F

a. What is the mean of the monthly low temperatures? Show your work.

b. What is the difference of the highest and lowest temperatures?

Self Assessment

Mathematical Ideas

After studying the mathematics in this Unit:

1. a. I learned these things about mathematics:

b. Here are page numbers of notebook entries that give evidence of what I have learned, along with descriptions of what each entry shows:

2. a. These are the mathematical ideas that I am still struggling with:

b. This is why I think these ideas are difficult for me:

c. Here are page numbers of notebook entries that give evidence of what I am struggling with, and descriptions of what each entry shows:

Class Participation

I contributed to the classroom **discussion** and understanding of the mathematics in this Unit when I ... (Give examples.)

Self Assessment (continued)

Learning Environment

Rate each learning activity listed below using this scale:

1. I consistently struggled to understand the mathematics and I'm still not sure that I understand it.

2. I struggled somewhat but now I understand more than I did.

3. I had to work, but I feel confident that I understand now.

4. I understood everything pretty easily and I feel confident that I know the mathematics in these problems.

5. Everything came easily. I knew most of the mathematics before we did this.

Learning Activities

____ Problems from the Investigations

____ ACE Homework Assignments

____ Mathematical Reflections

____ Check Ups

____ Partner Quiz

____ Looking Back

____ Unit Test

Check any of the following that you feel are the most helpful in adding to the success of your learning.

☐ Working on my own in class

☐ Discussing a problem with a partner

☐ Working in a small group of 3 or 4 people

☐ Discussing a problem as a whole class

☐ Hearing how other people solved the problem

☐ Summarizing the mathematics as a class and taking notes

☐ Completing homework assignments

Notebook Checklist

Place a ✔ next to each item you have completed.

Notebook Organization

_____ Problems and Mathematical Reflections are labeled and dated.

_____ Work is neat and easy to find and follow.

Vocabulary

_____ All words are listed.   _____ All words are defined or described.

Assessments

_____ Check Up   _____ _____

_____ Partner Quiz   _____ _____

_____ Unit Test   _____ _____

Assignments

_____ _____   _____ _____

_____ _____   _____ _____

_____ _____   _____ _____

_____ _____   _____ _____

_____ _____   _____ _____

_____ _____   _____ _____

_____ _____   _____ _____

_____ _____   _____ _____

_____ _____   _____ _____

Assessment Answers

Check Up 1

1. **a–e.** (See Figure 1.)
   f. Answers may vary. Sample: ⁻4 is the same distance from 0 as 4.
2. Answers will vary. Samples:
   $⁻50 + ⁻50 + ⁻50 = ⁻150$
   $⁻50 + ⁻100 = ⁻150$
   $⁻150 + 200 − 200 = ⁻150$
   $⁻250 + 100 = ⁻150$
3. **a.** $>$ **b.** $<$
   c. $>$ **d.** $<$
4. (See Figure 2.)

Partner Quiz

1. D
   Explanations may vary. Samples: Subtracting a positive number has the same result as adding a negative number.

Or, I found the value of ⁻15 − 12 and the values of each of the expressions to see which matched.

2. $<$
   Explanations may vary. Sample: When both numbers are negative, the number closer to zero is greater.
3. ⁻2.5
   (See Figure 3.)
4. $⁻\frac{5}{4}, ⁻\frac{1}{3}, 2\frac{1}{4}, \frac{13}{3}$
5. $n = 13$. Explanations will vary. Sample: I used the related sentence $24 + ⁻11 = n$ to find n.
6. 27
7. -7 8. 7
9. 3   10. -21
11. 2   12. -2
13. -16 14. -2

Figure 1

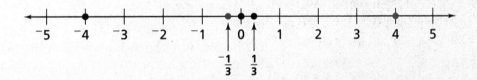

Figure 2

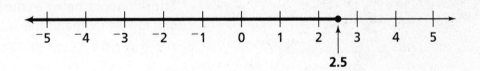

Figure 3

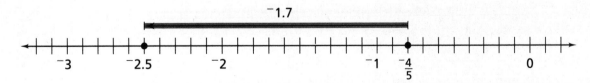

Assessment Answers (continued)

15. True   **16.** False

17. False   **18.** True

19. Answers will vary. Samples:
Exercise 16: The sum of a positive number and a negative number is negative when the absolute value of the negative number is greater than the absolute value of the positive number. Exercise 17: The difference of two negative numbers is negative when the first number is less than the second number.

Check Up 2

1. $-3 \cdot 4 = -12$ **2.** $-100 \div 4 = -25$

3. -4 **4.** 8

5. 8.8   **6.** 29

7. 4   **8.** -120

9. 120   **10.** -3

Unit Test

1. $\frac{-3}{2}, \frac{-9}{8}, 0, \frac{2}{5}, \frac{8}{7}$

2. a. 47   **b.** 13

   c. -75 **d.** -1.2

   e. -29 **f.** $\frac{1}{4}$

3. -51

4. a. $62 - n = {}^-8$ and $62 - {}^-8 = n$

   b. $70 = n$

5. a. -91 **b.** 160

   c. -33 **d.** 3

   e. -2 **f.** $\frac{-5}{21}$

6. a. $43.75

   b. Answers may vary. Samples:
   $5 \cdot 5.50 + 5 \cdot 3.25 = 43.75$ or
   $5 \cdot (5.50 + 3.25) = 43.75$

   c. Answers may vary. Samples: You can use the Commutative Property to rewrite the following expressions:
   $5 \cdot 5.50 + 5 \cdot 3.25$ as
   $5 \cdot 3.25 + 5 \cdot 5.50$;
   $5 \cdot (5.50 + 3.25)$ as $5 \cdot (3.25 + 5.50)$. You can use the Distributive Property to rewrite the expression
   $5 \cdot (5.50 + 3.25) = 43.75$ as
   $5 \cdot 5.50 + 5 \cdot 3.25$.

7. a. $=$ **b.** $\neq$

   c. $=$ **d.** $\neq$

   e. Answers may vary. Sample: Addition and multiplication are commutative, so the statements are equal. Subtraction and division are not commutative, so the statements are not equal.

8. $x < 2$
   (See Figure 4.)

9. a. $(17 + 0 + {}^-9 + {}^-3 + 10) = 15 \div 5$
                                    $= 3$
   The mean temperature is $3°$.

   b. $17 - (-9) = 26$
   The difference between the highest and lowest temperatures is $26°$.

Figure 4

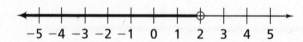

Looking Back Answers

1. a. 200; The BrainyActs answered a 250-point question incorrectly, a 100-point question incorrectly, a 200-point question correctly, and a 200-point question correctly for a total score of 50.

b. −200; The Xtremes answered a 450-point question correctly, a 250-point question incorrectly, and a 200-point question incorrectly for a total score of 0.

c. −350; The ExCells answered a 350-point question incorrectly, a 50-point question correctly, a 200-point question correctly, and a 150-point question incorrectly for a total score of −250.

d. −200; The AmazingM's answered a 350-point question correctly, a 300-point question incorrectly, and a 200-point question incorrectly for a total score of −150.

2. 148 mi
(See Figure 1.)

3. a. Fact family:
$$-2\tfrac{1}{2} + n = -3\tfrac{3}{4}$$
$$n - 2\tfrac{1}{2} = -3\tfrac{3}{4}$$
$$-3\tfrac{3}{4} - n = -2\tfrac{1}{2}$$

$$-3\tfrac{3}{4} - \left(-2\tfrac{1}{2}\right) = n \text{ or } -3\tfrac{3}{4} + 2\tfrac{1}{2} = n$$
Member of the fact family that is easiest to solve for n: $-3\tfrac{3}{4} + 2\tfrac{1}{2} = n$
This is the easiest member of the fact family to use because n is isolated in this equation.
$$n = -1\tfrac{1}{4}$$

b. Fact family:
$$\tfrac{2}{3}n = 10$$
$$n \cdot \tfrac{2}{3} = 10$$
$$n = 10 \div \tfrac{2}{3} \text{ or } n = 10 \cdot \tfrac{3}{2}$$
$$\tfrac{2}{3} = 10 \div n \text{ or } \tfrac{2}{3} = \tfrac{10}{n}$$
Member of the fact family that is easiest to solve for n: $n = 10 \div \tfrac{2}{3}$ or $n = 10 \cdot \tfrac{3}{2}$
This is the easiest member of the fact family to use because n is isolated in this equation.
$$n = 15$$

Figure 1

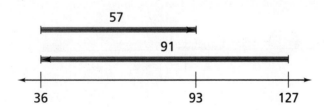

Looking Back Answers *(continued)*

4. When you take the positive number line and flip it over the zero point to get the negative numbers and make marks and labels on the left side of zero to match the marks on the right side, you can see that each negative number is paired with a positive number the same distance from zero on the other side of the number line.

5. **a.** −20 is greater than −35, since −20 lies to the right of −35 on the number line. Also, since 35 is farther to the right of 0 than 20 is, −35 is farther to the left of 0 than −20 is.

   b. $-2\frac{1}{3}$ is greater than $-2\frac{3}{4}$, since $-2\frac{1}{3}$ lies to the right of $-2\frac{3}{4}$ on the number line.

   c. 10.5 is greater than −12.5, since 10.5 lies to the right of −12.5 on the number line. Also, 10.5 is positive, while −12.5 is negative.

6. Students may use either model to demonstrate these calculations.

   a. (See Figure 2.)

   b. (See Figure 3.)

   c. Using the time and motion number line model, if Toni is running 2 meters per second to the left, where will she be in 3 seconds?

   d. Using the time and motion number line model, if Kumiah passes 0 running 2 meters per second to the left, where was she 3 seconds ago?

Figure 2

Figure 3

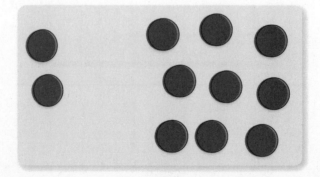

78

Looking Back Answers (continued)

e. Addition: $-2 + 3$
Number Line: Start at -2. Draw an arrow 3 units to the right. End at 1. $-2 + 3 = 1$
Chip Model: Place 2 red chips on a chip board. Add 3 black chips. Simplify the board by removing red-black (opposites) pairs of chips. 1 black chip remains, so $-2 + 3 = 1$.
Multiplication: $3 \cdot (-4)$
Number Line: $3 \cdot (-4)$ can be thought of as 3 groups of -4, or $-4 + (-4) + (-4)$. Start at -4 on the number line. Draw an arrow to the left 4 units to represent another -4. Draw another arrow from there to the left 4 units to represent the last -4. This arrow ends at -12, so $3 \cdot (-4) = -12$.
Chip Model: $3 \cdot (-4)$ is 3 groups of -4, so show 3 groups of 4 red chips, which is -12.

7. a. If both numbers are positive, simply find the sum. If both numbers are negative, find the sum of the absolute values of the two numbers and assign a negative sign.
If one number is positive and one number is negative, find the difference of their absolute values and take the sign of the number with the larger absolute value.

b. If both numbers are positive, find the difference between their absolute values. If the first number is greater than the second number, the difference will be positive. If the first number is less than the second number, the difference will be negative.

If the first number is positive and the second number is negative, find the sum of their absolute values. The answer will be positive.
If the first number is negative and the second number is positive, find the sum of their absolute values. The answer will be negative.
If both numbers are negative, you can rewrite the problem as an addition problem. For example, $^-5 - {}^-3 = {}^-2$ is equivalent to $^-5 + 3 = {}^-2$.

c. The product of two positive numbers is positive.
The product of two negative numbers is positive.
The product of a positive number and a negative number is negative.

d. The quotient of two positive numbers is positive.
The quotient of two negative numbers is positive.
The quotient of a positive number and a negative number is negative.

8. a. Addition and multiplication are commutative operations.
$3 + 4 = 4 + 3$
$3 \times (-4) = -4 \times 3$

b. Multiplication is distributive over addition and subtraction.
$4 \times (3 + 2) = (4 \times 3) + (4 \times 2)$
$4 \times (3 - 2) = (4 \times 3) - (4 \times 2)$

Parent Letters

Labsheets

Assessments

Dear Family,

The next Unit in your child's mathematics class this year is **Stretching and Shrinking: Understanding Similarity.** Its focus is geometry. It teaches students to understand and use the idea of similarity. Students explore what it means for shapes to be mathematically similar.

▶ Unit Goals

In this Unit, students will find relationships among figures that have been stretched or shrunk. They will analyze the resulting changes in properties of the figures, such as area and perimeter. Similarity will also be used to find the heights of real objects (such as buildings and flagpoles).

The Problems are designed to help students begin to reason proportionally. By the end of this Unit, your child will know how to create similar figures, how to determine whether or not two figures are similar, and how to predict the ratios of the lengths and areas of two similar figures. The next Unit develops proportional ideas in numerical contexts.

▶ Helping With Homework and Having Conversations About the Mathematics

In your child's notebook, you can find worked-out examples from problems he or she has done in class, notes on the mathematics of the Unit, and descriptions of the vocabulary words.

You can help with homework and encourage sound mathematical habits as your child studies this Unit by asking questions such as the following:

- *How does the everyday use of the word "similar" differ from its mathematical meaning?*
- *When two figures are similar, what is the same in each figure? What is different in each figure?*
- *When figures are similar, what is the relationship between their areas? Their perimeters?*
- *In what ways can we apply ideas about similarity to solve problems in the everyday world?*

You can help your child with his or her work for this Unit in several ways:

- *Talk with your child about situations that are like those in this Unit – real-world examples of items that are reduced or enlarged, such as models.*
- *Continue to have your child share his or her mathematics notebook with you, showing you the different ideas about similarity that have been recorded.*
- *Share any ways that reductions or enlargements help you in your work or hobbies.*
- *Look over your child's homework; make sure that all questions are answered and all explanations are clear.*

▶ Common Core State Standards

Students develop and use all of the Standards of Mathematical Practice throughout the curriculum. In this Unit, students practice constructing viable arguments and critiquing the reasoning of others as they make conjectures about the similarity of figures and justify their responses to others. This Unit focuses on the Geometry, Ratios & Proportional Relationships, and Expressions & Equations domains in the Common Core State Standards.

A few important mathematical ideas that your child will learn in *Stretching and Shrinking* are given on the next page. As always, if you have any questions or concerns about this Unit or your child's progress in the class, please feel free to call. We are interested in your child and want this year's mathematics experiences to be enjoyable and to promote a firm understanding of mathematics.

Sincerely,

Important Concepts	Examples
Corresponding Corresponding sides or angles have the same relative position in similar figures.	 **Corresponding Sides** AC and DF AB and DE BC and EF **Corresponding angles** A and D B and E C and F
Similarity Two figures are similar if: (1) the measures of their **corresponding** angles are equal and (2) the lengths of their **corresponding** sides increase by the same factor, called the **scale factor**.	The two figures at the right are similar. The corresponding angle measures are equal. The side lengths in Figure B are 1.5 times as long as those in Figure A. So, the scale factor from Figure A to Figure B is 1.5. (Figure A stretches or is enlarged by a factor of 1.5, resulting in Figure B.) 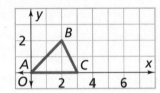 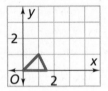 **Figure A** **Figure B** We also say that the scale factor from Figure B to Figure A is $\frac{1}{1.5}$ or $\frac{2}{3}$. (Figure B shrinks by a factor of $\frac{2}{3}$, resulting in figure A.)
Scale Factor The number used to multiply the lengths of a figure to stretch or shrink it into a similar image. A scale factor larger than 1 will enlarge a figure. A scale factor between 0 and 1 will reduce a figure. The scale factor of two similar figures is given by a ratio that compares the corresponding sides: $\frac{\text{length of a side on the image}}{\text{length of a side on the original}}$	If we use a scale factor of $\frac{1}{2}$, all lengths in the image are $\frac{1}{2}$ as long as the corresponding lengths in the original. The base of the original triangle is 3 units. The base of the image is 1.5 units. The scale factor is $\frac{1.5}{3} = \frac{3}{6} = \frac{1}{2}$.
Area and Scale Factor Lengths of similar figures will stretch (or shrink) by a scale factor. Areas of the figures will not change in the same way.	Applying a scale factor of 2 to a figure increases the area by a factor of 4. 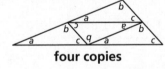 **Original** **four copies** Applying a scale factor of 3 to a figure, increases the area by a factor of 9. The original area is 6 cm². The area of the image is 9 times as large (54 cm²). 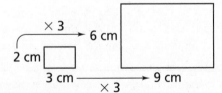

On the **CMP Parent Web Site**, you can learn more about the mathematical goals of each unit. See the glossary, and examine worked-out examples of ACE problems.
http://www.math.msu.edu/cmp/parents/home

Estimada familia:

La siguiente Unidad de la clase de Matemáticas de su hijo(a) de este año es ***Estirar y encoger: Semejanza,*** y se enfocará en la geometría. Enseñará a los estudiantes a entender y aplicar la idea de semejanza. Los estudiantes explorarán lo que significa que las figuras sean matemáticamente semejantes.

▶ Objetivos de la unidad

En esta Unidad, los estudiantes van a hallar relaciones entre figuras que se han estirado o encogido. Analizarán cambios en las propiedades de las figuras, como el área y el perímetro. También, usarán la semejanza para hallar alturas de objetos reales (como edificios y mástiles).

Los Problemas están estructurados para que los estudiantes comiencen a razonar proporcionalmente. Al terminar esta Unidad, su hijo(a) sabrá crear figuras semejantes, determinar si dos figuras son semejantes o no y predecir las razones de la longitudes y las áreas de dos figuras semejantes. La Unidad siguiente desarrolla ideas proporcionales en contextos numéricos.

▶ Ayuda con las tareas

Mientras su hijo(a) estudia esta Unidad, usted puede ayudarlo con la tarea y fomentarle sólidos hábitos matemáticos haciéndole preguntas como las siguientes:

- *¿En qué se diferencia el uso diario de la palabra "semejante" de su significado matemático?*
- *Si dos figuras son semejantes, ¿qué es igual en cada figura? ¿Qué es diferente?*
- *Si dos figuras son semejantes, ¿cuál es la relación entre sus áreas? ¿Y entre sus perímetros?*
- *¿Cómo podemos aplicar las ideas sobre la semejanza para resolver problemas de la vida diaria?*

En el cuaderno de su hijo(a), puede hallar ejemplos resueltos de problemas hechos en clase, notas sobre las matemáticas de la Unidad y descripciones de las palabras del vocabulario.

▶ Conversaciones acerca de las matemáticas de la Unidad

Usted puede ayudar a su hijo(a) con su tarea para esta Unidad de varias maneras:

- *Hable con su hijo(a) sobre situaciones parecidas a las de esta Unidad: ejemplos de la vida diaria de objetos que se encogen o se estiran, como los modelos.*
- *Pida que le muestre su cuaderno de matemáticas y las ideas que haya anotado.*
- *Comenten cómo las disminuciones o los aumentos ayudan en su trabajo o aficiones.*
- *Revise la tarea de su hijo(a) y asegúrese de que responda todas las preguntas y de que sus explicaciones sean claras.*

▶ Estándares estatales comunes

Los estudiantes desarrollan y usan todos los Estándares de prácticas matemáticas a través del currículum. En esta Unidad, los estudiantes elaboran argumentos viables y analizan el razonamiento de los demás mientras desarrollan conjeturas sobre la semejanza de las figuras y justifican sus respuestas. Esta Unidad se enfoca en los dominios de Geometría, Razones y Relaciones proporcionales y Expresiones y ecuaciones de los Estándares estatales comunes.

Algunas ideas importantes de matemáticas que su hijo(a) aprenderá en *Estirar y encoger* se presentan en la página siguiente. Como siempre, si usted tiene cualquier pregunta o preocupación acerca de esta Unidad, o con respecto al progreso de su hijo(a), por favor no dude en llamar. Nos interesa su hijo(a) y queremos que las experiencias matemáticas de este año sean divertidas y promuevan una comprensión sólida de las matemáticas.

Sinceramente,

Conceptos importantes	Ejemplos

Correspondientes
Los lados o ángulos correspondientes tienen la misma posición relativa en figuras semejantes.

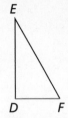

Lados correspondientes
AC y DF
AB y DE
BC y EF

Ángulos correspondientes
A y D
B y E
C y F

Semejanza
Dos figuras son semejantes si:
(1) las medidas de sus ángulos **correspondientes** son iguales y
(2) las longitudes de sus lados **correspondientes** aumentan por el mismo factor, llamado **factor de escala**.

Las dos figuras de la derecha son semejantes.

Las medidas del ángulo correspondiente son iguales.

Las longitudes de los lados de la Figura B son 1.5 veces más largas que las de la Figura A.

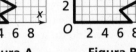

Figura A   **Figura B**

Por tanto, el factor de escala de la Figura A respecto a la Figura B es 1.5 (la Figura A se estira o se encoge por un factor de 1.5, dando como resultado la Figura B).

También decimos que el factor de escala de la Figura B respecto a la Figura A es $\frac{1}{1.5}$ ó $\frac{2}{3}$. (La Figura B disminuye en un factor de $\frac{2}{3}$, dando como resultado la Figura A.)

Factor de escala
El número que se usa para multiplicar las longitudes de una figura para encogerla o agrandarla a una imagen semejante.

Un factor de escala mayor que 1 aumentará la figura. Un factor de escala entre 0 y 1 reducirá la figura.

El factor de escala de dos figuras semejantes está dado por la razón que compara los lados correspondientes:
$\frac{\text{longitud de un lado de la imagen}}{\text{longitud de un lado del original}}$

Si usamos un factor de escala de $\frac{1}{2}$, todas las longitudes de la imagen son $\frac{1}{2}$ de las longitudes correspondientes del original.

La base del triángulo original es 3 unidades.

La base de la imagen es 1.5 unidades.

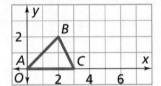

El factor de escala es $\frac{1.5}{3} = \frac{3}{6} = \frac{1}{2}$.

Área y factor de escala
Las longitudes de figuras semejantes aumentarán (o disminuirán) por un factor de escala. Las áreas de las figuras no cambiarán de la misma manera.

Aplicar un factor de escala de 2 a una figura aumenta el área por un factor de 4.

Original

cuatro copias

Aplicar un factor de escala de 3 a una figura, aumenta el área por un factor de 9. El área original es 6 cm². El área de la imagen es 9 veces mayor (54 cm²).

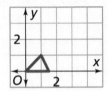

En el **sitio web CMP Parent**, puede encontrar más información sobre los objetivos matemáticos de cada unidad. Consulte el glosario y examine los ejemplos resueltos de los problemas ACA.
http://www.math.msu.edu/cmp/parents/home

Labsheet 1.1A Super Sleuth (right-handed version)

P is the anchor point.

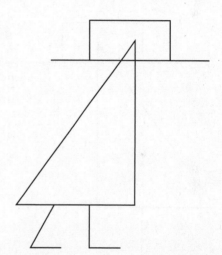

•
P

Labsheet 1.1B   Super Sleuth (left-handed version)

P is the anchor point.

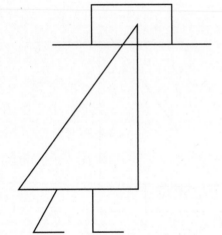

P

Labsheet 1.2   Super Sleuth Figure and Two Copies

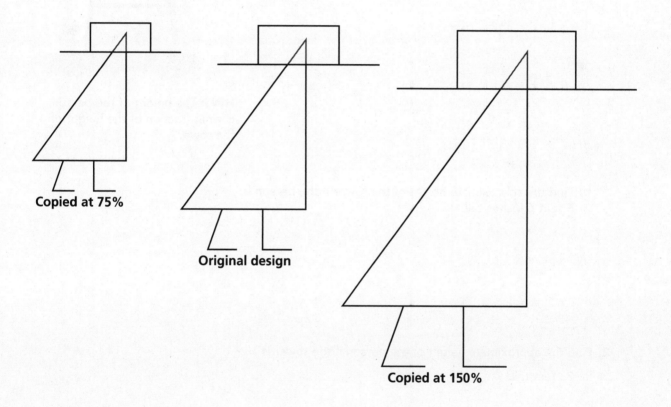

Copied at 75%

Original design

Copied at 150%

Labsheet 1ACE   Exercises 1–2

For Exercises 1 and 2, use the drawing at the right, which shows a person standing next to a ranger's outlook tower.

    1. a. Find the approximate height of the tower if the person is **6 feet tall**.

HINT: The height of the person is what fraction of the height of the tower?

    b. Find the approximate height of the tower if the person is **5 feet 6 inches** tall.

    2. Find the approximate height of the person if the tower is

    a. 28 feet tall.

    b. 36 feet tall.

Labsheet 1ACE   Exercises 3, 4, 12 (right-handed version)

3. Square *ABCD*

•
P

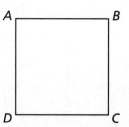

4. Parallelogram *ABCD*

•
P

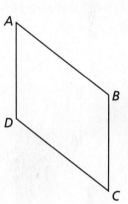

12. Hexagon *ABCDEF*

•
P

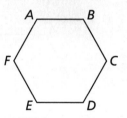

Labsheet 1ACE Exercises 3, 4, 12 (left-handed version)

3. Square *ABCD*

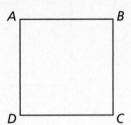

●
P

4. Parallelogram *ABCD*

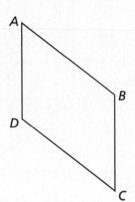

●
P

12. Hexagon *ABCDEF*

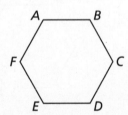

●
P

Labsheet 2.1   Coordinates of Game Characters

	Mug Wump	Zug	Lug	Bug	Glug
Rule	*(x, y)*	*(2x, 2y)*	*(3x, y)*	*(3x, 3y)*	*(x, 3y)*
Point	**Part 1**				
A	(0, 1)	(0, 2)			
B	(2, 1)	(4, 2)			
C	(2, 0)				
D	(3, 0)				
E	(3, 1)				
F	(5, 1)				
G	(5, 0)				
H	(6, 0)				
I	(6, 1)				
J	(8, 1)				
K	(6, 7)				
L	(2, 7)				
M	(0, 1)				
	Part 2 (Start Over)				
N	(2, 2)				
O	(6, 2)				
P	(6, 3)				
Q	(2, 3)				
R	(2, 2)				
	Part 3 (Start Over)				
S	(3, 4)				
T	(4, 5)				
U	(5, 4)				
V	(3, 4)				
	Part 4 (Start Over)				
W	(2, 5) (make a dot)				
X	(6, 5) (make a dot)				

Labsheet 2.2   Mug's Hat

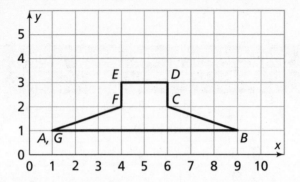

	Mug's Hat	Hat 1	Hat 2	Hat 3	Hat 4	Hat 5
Point	**(x, y)**	**(x + 2, y + 3)**	**(x − 1, y + 4)**	**(x + 2, 3y)**	**(0.5x, 0.5y)**	**(2x, 3y)**
A	(1, 1)					
B	(9, 1)					
C						
D						
E						
F						
G						

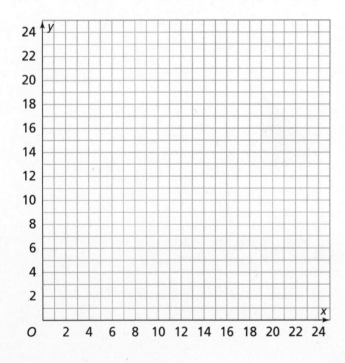

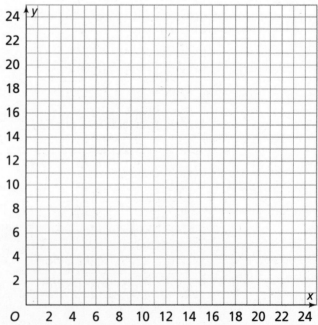

Labsheet 2.3   Wump Mouths and Noses

Labsheet 2ACE Exercise 1

Rule	Mug Wump (x, y)	Glum (1.5x, 1.5y)	Sum (3x, 2y)	Tum (4x, 4y)	Crum (2x, y)
Point	**Mouth**				
M	(2, 2)				
N	(6, 2)				
O	(6, 3)				
P	(2, 3)				
Q	(2, 2) (connect Q to M)				
	Nose (Start Over)				
R	(3, 4)				
S	(4, 5)				
T	(5, 4)				
U	(3, 4) (connect U to R)				

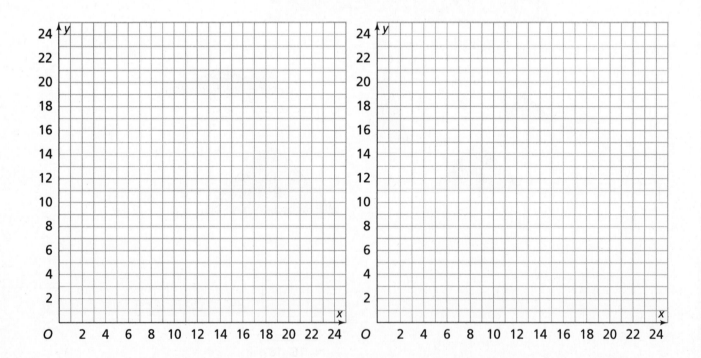

Labsheet 2ACE   Exercise 1

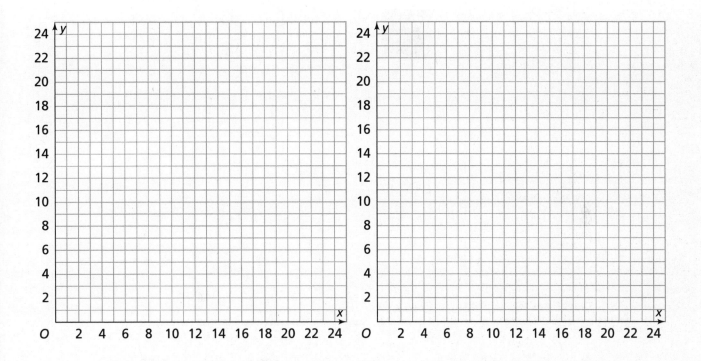

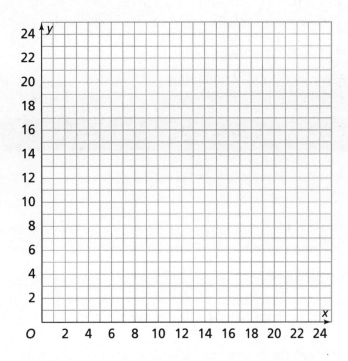

Labsheet 2ACE   Exercise 3

3. **a.** Draw triangle *ABC* with vertex coordinates *A*(0, 2), *B*(6, 2), and *C*(4, 4) on the grid below.

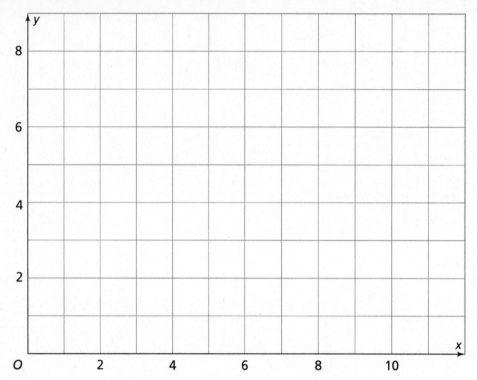

b. Apply the rule (**1.5x, 1.5y**) to the vertices of triangle *ABC* to get triangle *PQR*.

   P (,   )   *Q* (,   )   *R* (,   )

Draw triangle *PQR* on the grid.

Fill in the table. Then write statements that compare the corresponding measurements (side lengths, perimeter, area, angle measures) of the two triangles.

Triangle	Side Lengths	Perimeter	Area	Angle Measures
ABC				
PQR				

Statement 1:

Statement 2:

Statement 3:

Labsheet 2ACE   Exercise 3

c. Apply the rule (**2x, 0.5y**) to the vertices of triangle *ABC* to get triangle *FGH*.

F (,   )

G (,   )

H (,   )

Draw triangle *FGH* on the grid on the previous page.

Fill in the table. Then write statements that compare the corresponding measurements (side lengths, perimeter, area, angle measures) of the two triangles.

Triangle	Side Lengths	Perimeter	Area	Angle Measures
ABC				
FGH				

Statement 1:

Statement 2:

Statement 3:

d. Which triangle, *PQR* or *FGH*, seems **similar** to triangle *ABC*?

Why?

Labsheet 2ACE Exercise 34

Coordinates for Mug and Variations

Rule	(x, y)	(2x, 2y)	(−2x, −2y)
Head Outline	(−4, −2)		
	(−2, −2)		
	(−2, −3)		
Nose	(−1, 1)		
Mouth	(−2, −1)		
Eyes	(−2, 2)		

Labsheet 3 Rep-Tile Recording Sheet

Sketch of How the Figures Fit Together	Scale Factor	Area	Perimeter

Labsheet 3.1   Quadrilaterals for Rep-Tiles

Sketch and make several copies of each of the following shapes:

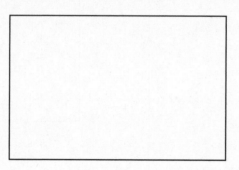

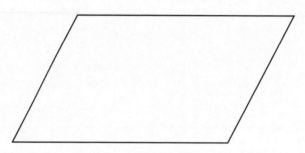

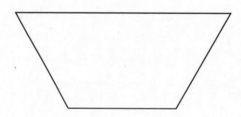

Labsheet 3.2A   Triangles

Labsheet 3.2B   Large Triangles

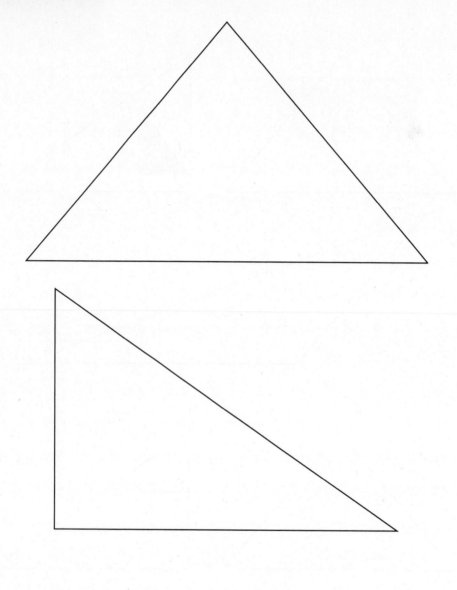

Labsheet 3.3A   Problem 3.3 Figures

Question A

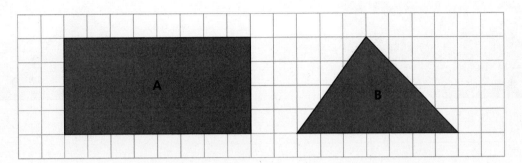

Question C

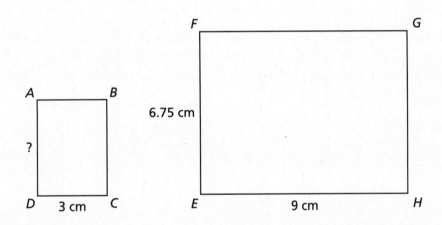

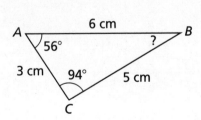

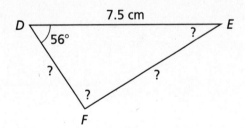

Labsheet 3.3B   Figures on a Grid

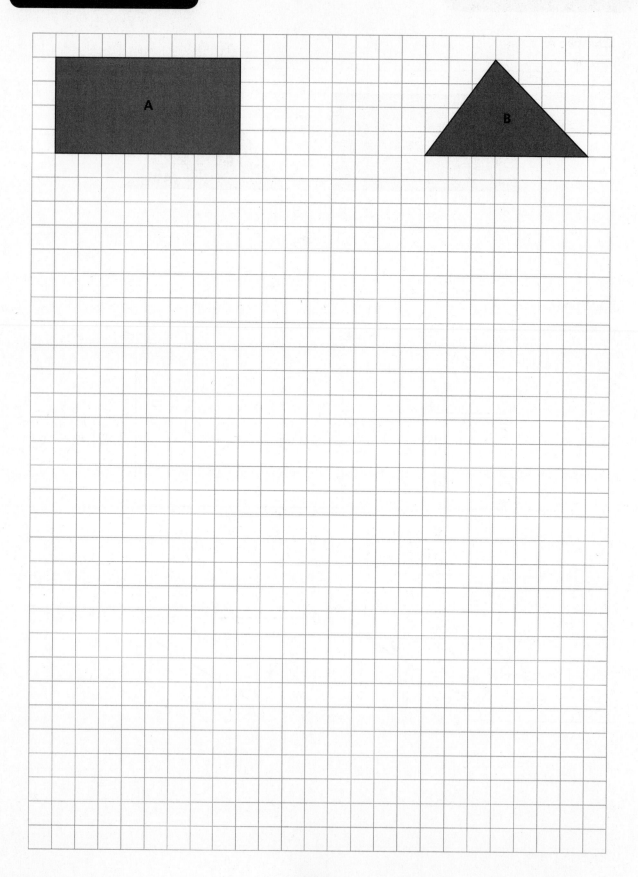

Labsheet 3.3C   Polygon Sets

Rectangle Set

A

B

C

Parallelogram Set

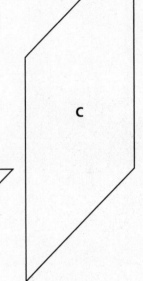

A

B

C

Decagon Set

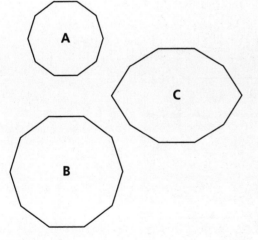

A

B

C

Star Set

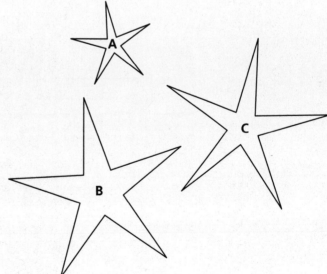

A

B

C

Labsheet 3.4   River Diagrams

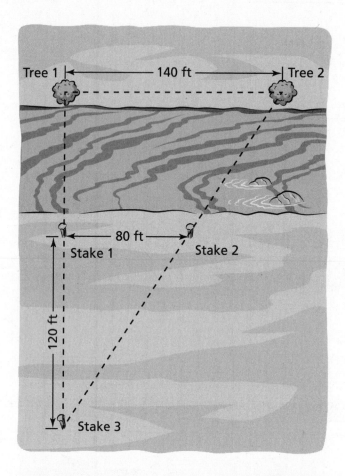

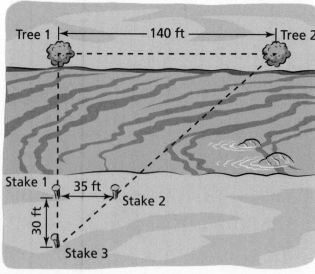

Labsheet 3ACE   Exercise 1

1. Look for **rep-tile** patterns in the designs below. For each design,

   • Tell whether the *small quadrilaterals* are **similar** to the *large quadrilateral*. Explain.

   • If the quadrilaterals are similar, give the **scale factor** from each *small quadrilateral* to the *large quadrilateral*.

a.

Similar? (yes/no):

Explain:

Scale Factor:

b.

Similar? (yes/no):

Explain:

Scale Factor:

c.

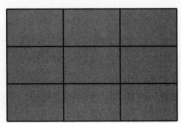

Similar? (yes/no):

Explain:

Scale Factor:

d.

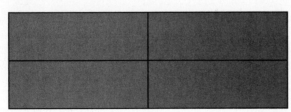

Similar? (yes/no):

Explain:

Scale Factor:

Labsheet 3ACE   Exercise 4

1. Look for **rep-tile** patterns in the designs below. For each design,

- Tell whether the *small triangles* are **similar** to the *large triangle*. Explain.
- If the triangles are similar, give the **scale factor** from each *small triangle* to the *large triangle*.

a.

Similar? (yes/no):

Explain:

Scale Factor:

b.

Similar? (yes/no):

Explain:

Scale Factor:

c.

Similar? (yes/no):

Explain:

Scale Factor:

d.

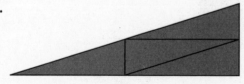

Similar? (yes/no):

Explain:

Scale Factor:

Labsheet 3ACE Exercise 6

6. Draw line segments that divide each of the polygons into four congruent polygons that are similar to the original polygon.

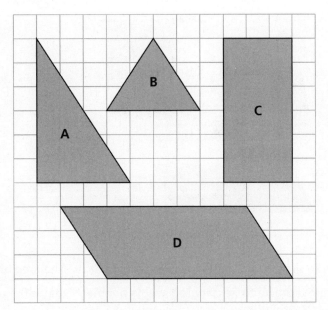

Labsheet 3ACE   Exercise 7

7. Use the figures below.

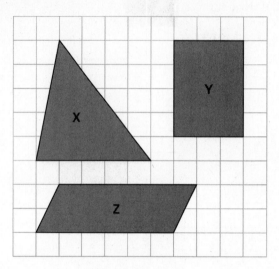

a. Sketch a triangle similar to Triangle X with an area that is $\frac{1}{4}$ the area of Triangle X.

b. Sketch a rectangle similar to Rectangle Y with a perimeter that is 0.5 times the perimeter of Rectangle Y.

c. Sketch a parallelogram similar to Parallelogram Z with side lengths that are 1.5 times the side lengths of Parallelogram Z.

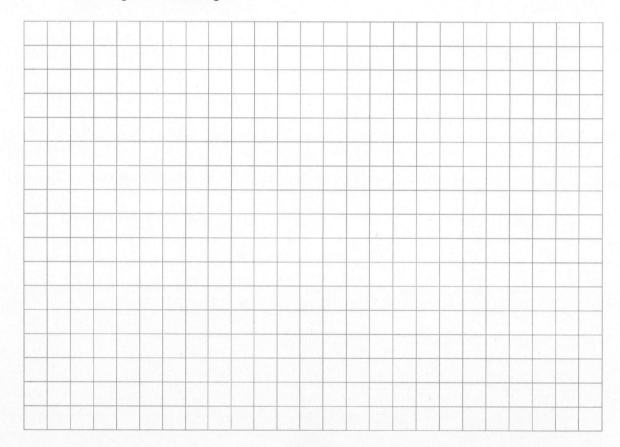

Labsheet 4.1   Ratio Recording Sheet

Figure	Length	Width	Length-to-Width Ratio
Rectangle A			
Rectangle B			
Rectangle C			
Rectangle D			

Figure	Length	Width	Length-to-Width Ratio
Parallelogram E			
Parallelogram F			
Parallelogram G			

Labsheet 4.2   Triangles

Triangle A

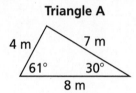

4 m   7 m
61°   30°
8 m

Triangle B

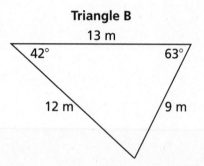

13 m
42°   63°
12 m   9 m

Triangle C

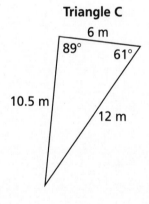

6 m
89°   61°
10.5 m
12 m

Triangle D

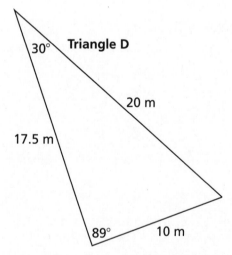

30°
20 m
17.5 m
89°   10 m

Labsheet 4.3   Similar Polygons

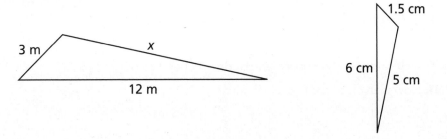

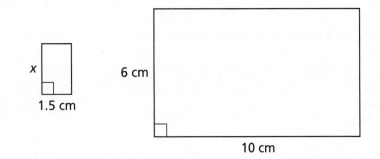

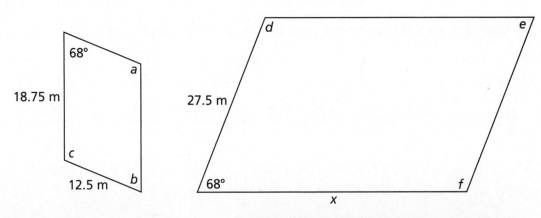

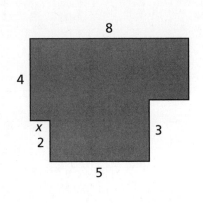

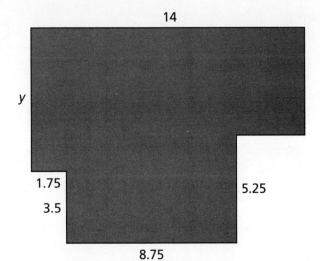

Labsheet 4ACE Exercise 12

1. Suppose you want to buy new carpeting for your bedroom. The bedroom floor is a **9-foot-by-12-foot** rectangle. Carpeting is sold by the **square yard**.

   a. How much carpeting, **in square yards,** do you need to buy?

   HINT: How many feet are there in 1 yard?

   HINT: What are the dimensions of the bedroom in yards?

   b. Carpeting costs $**22 per square yard.** How much will the carpet cost?

Unit Project   Table of Coordinates

Point	Original Picture (x, y)	Image (x, y)
A		
B		

Check Up 1 *for use after Investigation 1*

The coach took a digital photo of the new cycling team bike. She sent a 4 cm-by-6 cm photo to each team member.

1. If the photo were enlarged to 150% of its original size, what would be its new length and width?

2. Suppose you want to make a 2 cm-by-3 cm copy of the original photo. What percent should you use?

3. How will the angles in the original photo compare to the corresponding angles in the smaller photo?

4. How will the perimeter of the original photo compare to that of the smaller photo?

5. Find the areas of the original and the smaller photos. How do these areas compare?

Partner Quiz *for use after Investigation 2*

1. Ryan drew a one-eyed triangle character on dot paper. Ashley used the rule $(3x, 3y)$ to enlarge Ryan's drawing, and she drew the character below.

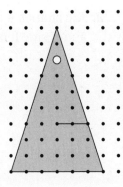

a. Simone saw Ashley's drawing and doubled all the lengths to create her own character. On the grids below, sketch Ryan's original character and Simone's new version of Ashley's character.

Ryan's One–eyed Character   **Simone's One–eyed Character**

b. Are Ryan's and Simone's characters similar? Explain.

c. Write a rule that would create Simone's character from Ryan's character.

Partner Quiz (*continued*)

2. Are shapes A and B similar? Explain why or why not. Include information about side lengths, angle measures, and scale factor.

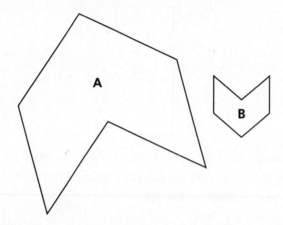

3. Megan wanted to make a new video game character. Use Labsheet 2.1: Coordinates of Game Characters to help you with this question.

   a. Write a rule that would transform Mug (x, y) into Slug, who is very wide and not very tall.

   b. Megan wanted Slug to move up (but not over) on the grid. What rule could do this for her?

   c. Is Slug similar to Mug? Why or why not?

Check Up 2 *for use after Investigation 3*

....

1. Which rectangles below are similar? Explain why.

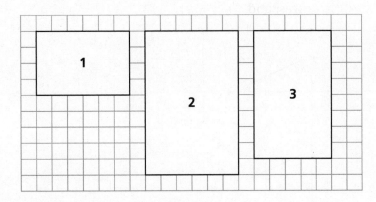

2. The triangles at the right are similar.

a. Use the side lengths of triangle *DEF* and the fact that the triangles are similar to find the lengths of sides *AC* and *AB* and the measure of angle *E*.

side *AC* = _____

side *AB* = _____

angle *E* = _____

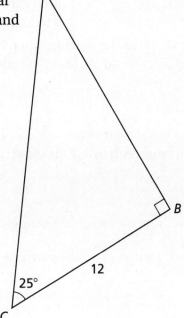

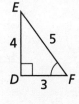

b. What is the scale factor from triangle *DEF* to triangle *ABC*?

c. What is the scale factor from triangle *ABC* to triangle *DEF*?

d. How many times greater is the perimeter of triangle *ABC* than that of triangle *DEF*?

e. How many times greater is the area of triangle *ABC* than that of triangle *DEF*?

3. Rectangle Z is sketched below.

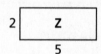

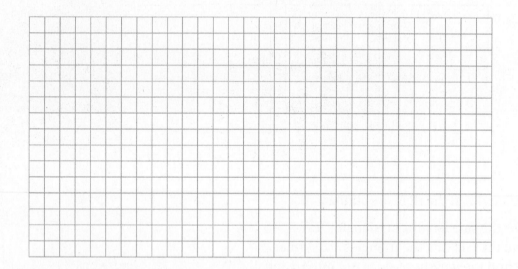

a. Rectangle M is similar to rectangle Z. The scale factor from Z to M is 2. Draw and label rectangle M on the grid above.

b. Rectangle T is similar to rectangle Z. The scale factor from Z to T is 3. Draw and label rectangle T on the grid above.

c. How does the scale factor of 2 change the **area** and **perimeter** of rectangle Z?

d. How does the scale factor of 3 change the **area** and **side lengths** of rectangle Z?

Labsheet CU2   Check Up 2

1. Which rectangles (1, 2, and 3) below are similar?

HINT: Look at your notes. What has to be true for shapes to be similar?

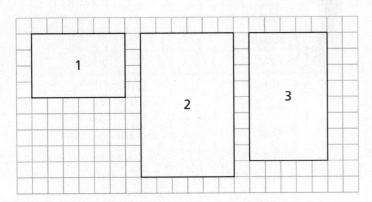

Explain how you know if two rectangles are similar.

Unit Test Correlation

Unit Test Item	Problem
Item 1	Problem 3.1
Item 2	Problem 3.1
Item 3	Problem 3.1
Item 4	Problem 3.1
Item 5, parts (a) and (b)	Problem 2.2
Item 6	Problem 2.3
Item 7, part (a)	Problem 4.3
Item 7, part (b)	Problem 4.1
Item 7, part (c)	Problem 4.2
Item 8	Problem 4.4

Unit Test

Use the following diagrams of the floor plans for a tree house before and after reduction and enlargement by a copier to answer Exercises 1–4.

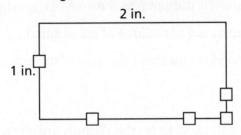

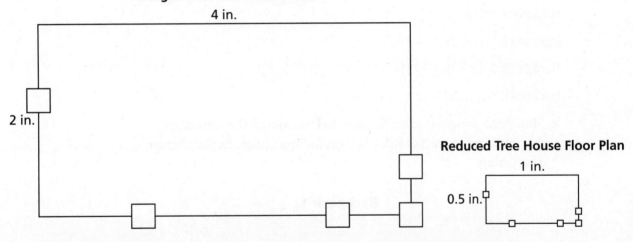

1. What is the scale factor from the original design to the enlarged design?

2. What is the scale factor from the original design to the reduced design?

3. Circle the statement that tells how the perimeter of the enlarged design compares to the perimeter of the original design. Then explain your answer.

   A. The perimeter of the enlarged design is $\frac{1}{2}$ of the perimeter of the original.

   B. The perimeter of the enlarged design is the same as the perimeter of the original.

   C. The perimeter of the enlarged design is twice the perimeter of the original.

   D. The perimeter of the enlarged design is four times the perimeter of the original.

Unit Test (continued)

4. Circle the statement that tells how the area of the reduced design compares to the area of the original design. Then explain your answer.

F. The area of the reduced design is $\frac{1}{2}$ of the area of the original.

G. The area of the reduced design is the same as the area of the original.

H. The area of the reduced design is $\frac{1}{4}$ of the area of the original.

J. The area of the reduced design is four times the area of the original.

5. The following rules for drawing backpacks for the Wumps are given below:

Backpack 1: (x, y)

Backpack 2: $(2x, 2y)$

Backpack 3: $(x + 8, y - 2)$

Backpack 4: $(x, 2y)$

a. Backpack 1 is plotted on the grid below. Match the remaining Backpacks 2–4 with graphs A–C on the next page. Explain your reasoning.

Backpack 1

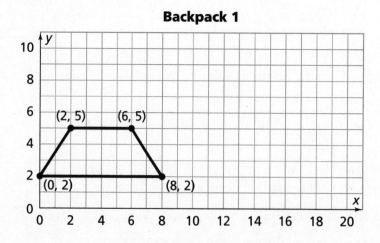

Unit Test (continued)

A.

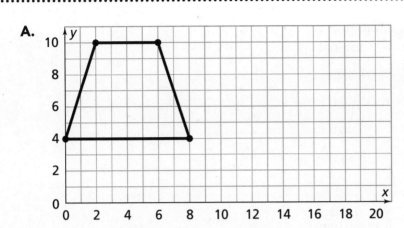

B.

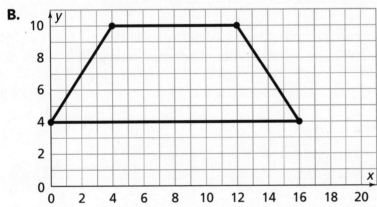

C.

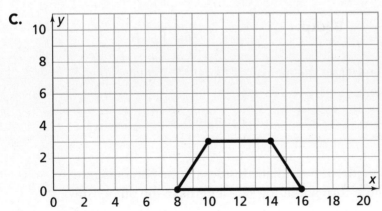

b. Which backpacks are similar? Explain.

Name .... Date .... Class ....

Stretching and Shrinking

Unit Test (continued)

6. Consider the two polygons below.

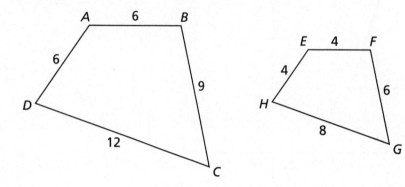

Does the diagram provide enough information to determine whether the two polygons are similar? If not, what additional information would you need?

7. The parallelograms below are similar.

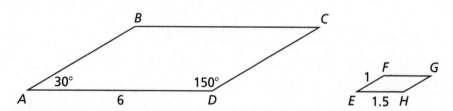

a. Find the length of side *AB* and the measure of angle *E*. Explain how you found your answers.

side *AB* = _____   angle *E* = _____

b. Find the ratio of the lengths of two adjacent sides in one parallelogram. Then find the ratio of the corresponding side lengths in the other. How do the ratios compare?

c. Find the ratio of a pair of corresponding sides in the two parallelograms. What information does this ratio tell you about the two parallelograms? Explain.

Unit Test (continued)

8. Use the diagram below to determine the height of the flagpole.

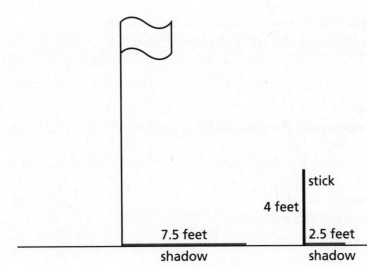

4 feet

stick

7.5 feet
shadow

2.5 feet
shadow

Self Assessment

Mathematical Ideas

After studying the mathematics in this Unit:

1. a. I learned these things about mathematics:

    b. Here are page numbers of notebook entries that give evidence of what I have learned, along with descriptions of what each entry shows:

2. a. These are the mathematical ideas that I am still struggling with:

    b. This is why I think these ideas are difficult for me:

    c. Here are page numbers of notebook entries that give evidence of what I am struggling with, and descriptions of what each entry shows:

Class Participation

I contributed to the classroom **discussion** and understanding of the mathematics in this Unit when I ... (Give examples.)

Self Assessment (continued)

Learning Environment

Rate each learning activity listed below using this scale:

1. I consistently struggled to understand the mathematics and I'm still not sure that I understand it.

2. I struggled somewhat but now I understand more than I did.

3. I had to work, but I feel confident that I understand now.

4. I understood everything pretty easily and I feel confident that I know the mathematics in these problems.

5. Everything came easily. I knew most of the mathematics before we did this.

Learning Activities

_____ Problems from the Investigations

_____ ACE Homework Assignments

_____ Mathematical Reflections

_____ Check Ups

_____ Partner Quiz

_____ Looking Back

_____ Unit Test

Check any of the following that you feel are the most helpful in adding to the success of your learning.

☐ Working on my own in class

☐ Discussing a problem with a partner

☐ Working in a small group of 3 or 4 people

☐ Discussing a problem as a whole class

☐ Hearing how other people solved the problem

☐ Summarizing the mathematics as a class and taking notes

☐ Completing homework assignments

Notebook Checklist

Place a ✔ next to each item you have completed.

Notebook Organization

_____ Problems and Mathematical Reflections are labeled and dated.

_____ Work is neat and easy to find and follow.

Vocabulary

_____ All words are listed.   _____ All words are defined or described.

Assessments

_____ Check Up   _____ _____

_____ Partner Quiz   _____ _____

_____ Unit Test   _____ _____

Assignments

_____ _____   _____ _____

_____ _____   _____ _____

_____ _____   _____ _____

_____ _____   _____ _____

_____ _____   _____ _____

_____ _____   _____ _____

_____ _____   _____ _____

_____ _____   _____ _____

_____ _____   _____ _____

_____ _____   _____ _____

Assessment Answers

Check Up 1

1. **a.** 6 cm by 9 cm
   b. 50%
   c. The corresponding angles in both photos will have the same measures: all 90°.
   d. The perimeter of the original is 20 cm. The perimeter of the reduced image is 10 cm.
   The perimeter of the original is 2 times that of the reduced photo. OR The perimeter of the reduced photo is $\frac{1}{2}$ that of the original.
   e. The area of the original is 24 cm^2. The area of the reduced image is 6 cm^2.
   The area of the original is 4 times that of the reduced photo. OR The area of the reduced photo is $\frac{1}{4}$ that of the original.

Check Up 2

1. Rectangle 1 is similar to Rectangle 2. The ratio of length to width for both rectangles is 3 to 2. Corresponding sides in Rectangles 1 and 2 differ by a scale factor of 1.5. The corresponding angles in Rectangles 1 and 2 have the same measure (all 90°). The perimeter of Rectangle 2 is 1.5 times the perimeter of Rectangle 1. The area of Rectangle 2 is $1.5^2 = 2.25$ times the area of Rectangle 1.
2. **a.** side $AC = 20$; side $AB = 16$; angle E: 65°
   b. 4
   c. $\frac{1}{4}$

d. The perimeter of triangle ABC is 4 times the perimeter of triangle DEF.
e. The area of triangle ABC is 16 times the area of triangle DEF.

3. **a.** Students will draw rectangle M with side lengths of 4 and 10.
   b. Students will draw rectangle T with side lengths of 6 and 15.
   c. The area of the new triangle is four times as great as that of Z; the perimeter is twice as that of Z.
   d. The area of the new triangle is nine times as great as that of Z; the side lengths are three times those of Z.

Partner Quiz

1. **a.**

Ryan's One–eyed Character

Assessment Answers (continued)

Simone's One–eyed Character

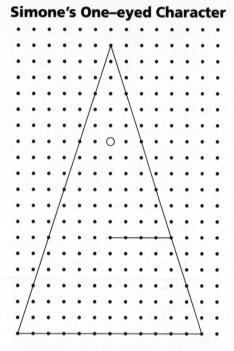

b. Ryan's and Simone's characters are similar: the shapes are the same, corresponding angles have the same measure, and the corresponding sides grow by the same scale factor. The scale factor from Ryan's character to Simone's character is 6.
Note: If students use the transitive property to answer this question (Since Ryan's character is similar to Ashley's and Ashley's is similar to Simone's, then Ryan's is similar to Simone's.), you may want to ask them to support the answer with an explanation based on the properties of similar figures.

c. $(6x, 6y)$

2. Shapes A and B are similar. They have the same basic shape, corresponding angles are equal, and the side lengths of shape A are 3 times the corresponding side lengths of B.
Note: Students may determine this by measuring, tracing, or cutting out the two shapes to compare their angles and sides.

3. a. Any rule in which the coefficient of x is relatively large compared to the coefficient of y will work.
Possible answers: $(5x, 2y)$, $(3x, y)$, or $(10x, 0.5y)$

b. Students should add some positive number to the second coordinate in their rule from Part A.
Possible answers: $(5x, 2y + 4)$, $(3x, y + 3)$, or $(10x, 0.5y + 8)$

c. Slug is not similar to Mug because Slug is stretched more horizontally than vertically. The figures have different shapes.

Unit Test

1. The enlarged design is related to the original design by a scale factor of 2.

2. The reduced design is related to the original design by a scale factor of $\frac{1}{2}$.

3. C. The perimeter of the enlarged figure is 12 units. The perimeter of the original is 6 units. So, $12 \div 6 = 2$.

4. H. The area of the reduced figure is 0.5 square units. The area of the original is 2 square units. So, $0.5 \div 2 = 0.25$

Assessment Answers (continued)

5. a. (See Figure 1.)
Backpack 2 matches with Graph B.
Backpack 3 matches with Graph C.
Backpack 4 matches with Graph A.

b. Backpacks 1, 2, and 3 are similar.
Corresponding angles on all three
trapezoids have equal measure.
The scale factor from Backpack 1
to Backpack 2 is 2. The scale factor
from Backpack 1 to Backpack 3 is 1.
These two backpacks are identical;
only the location of the backpacks
on the grid changes.

6. No. You need to know the angle
measures, so you can see if
corresponding angles have equal
measure. This is necessary to determine
if two shapes are similar.

7. a. Side AB is 4 because each side of
parallelogram $ABCD$ is 4 times the
length of each side of parallelogram
$EFGH$. Side AB corresponds with
side EF of the smaller parallelogram,
so since side EF is 1 unit long, side
AB is 4 units long. Angle E is 30°
because it corresponds with Angle A
of the larger parallelogram.

b. $\frac{EF}{EH} = \frac{1}{1.5} = \frac{2}{3}$
Since the parallelograms are
similar, $\frac{AB}{AD} = \frac{2}{3}$ also. OR $\frac{EH}{EF} = 1.5$
Since the parallelograms are
similar, $\frac{AD}{AB} = 1.5$ also.

c. Side EH of the smaller parallelogram
corresponds with side AD of the
larger parallelogram.
The ratio can be written as
$\frac{EH}{AD} = \frac{1.5}{6}$ or as $\frac{AD}{EH} = \frac{6}{1.5}$.
The first ratio tells us that the smaller
parallelogram, $EFGH$, is $\frac{1}{4}$ the size of
the larger parallelogram, $ABCD$.
The second ratio tells us that the
larger parallelogram, $ABCD$, is
4 times the size of the smaller
parallelogram, $EFGH$.

8. $\frac{x}{4} = \frac{7.5}{2.5}$, so $x = 12$; The flagpole is
12 feet high.

Figure 1

Wump Backpacks

Backpack 1	Backpack 2	Backpack 3	Backpack 4
(x, y)	(2x, 2y)	(x + 8, y − 2)	(x, 2y)
(0, 2)	(0, 4)	(8, 0)	(0, 4)
(8, 2)	(16, 4)	(16, 0)	(8, 4)
(6, 5)	(12, 10)	(14, 3)	(6, 10)
(2, 5)	(4, 10)	(10, 3)	(2, 10)
(0, 2)	(0, 4)	(8, 0)	(0, 4)

Looking Back Answers

1. a. Triangles A, C, G, and K are similar with the following scale factors:
A to C: approx. 0.7
C to A: approx. 1.4
(in fact, it is $\sqrt{2}$)
A to G: approx. 0.4
G to A: approx. 2.4
A to K: approx. 0.3
K to A: approx. 3.5
C to G: 0.6
G to C: $\frac{5}{3}$
C to K: 0.4
K to C: 2.5
G to K: $\frac{2}{3}$
K to G: 1.5
Triangles E and F are similar, with a scale factor of 1.

b. Answers will vary depending on which triangles students choose. In general, the perimeters of the triangles will compare in the same way as the side lengths—their ratios will be the scale factor. The areas compare by the square of the scale factor.

c. None of triangles A, C, G, and K is similar to either E or F.

d. Parallelograms B and H are similar. The scale factor from B to H is 0.4. From H to B the scale factor is 2.5.

e. There is only one pair of similar parallelograms. The perimeter of B is 2.5 times the perimeter of H. (This is the same as the scale factor.) The area of B is 6.25 times the area of H. (This is the square of the scale factor.)

f. Any pair of parallelograms other than B and H will be nonsimilar.

2. a. Rules i, ii, iv, and v will all give similar triangles.

b. Rule i gives a triangle with a scale factor of 3.
Rule ii gives a triangle with a scale factor of 1.
Rule iv gives a triangle with a scale factor of 2.
Rule v gives a triangle with a scale factor of 1.5.

3. a. No. The ratio of the sides in the original is 0.6. In the desired image, the ratio of sides is $\frac{2}{3}$.

b. Yes. The ratio of the sides in both the original and the image is 0.6. The scale factor from the original to the image is 3.5.

4. Answers will vary. Sample questions: "Are all the pairs of corresponding angles congruent in the two figures?" "Is the scale factor between corresponding sides the same for all pairs?" "Is the ratio of sides within each figure the same?"

5. a. The perimeter of shape B will be k times the perimeter of shape A.

b. The area of shape B will be k^2 times the area of shape A.

6. a. Answers will vary. Possible answer: The lengths of any two corresponding sides are related by the scale factor. If we form a ratio of the lengths of a pair of sides in the original figure, the ratio of the lengths of the corresponding sides in the image will be the same.

b. Corresponding angles are congruent.

7. a. True; all angles in an equilateral triangle are 60° and the ratio of any two sides is 1.

b. False; while the angles are all congruent in any two rectangles, the ratio of the sides could be anything.

c. True; squares are rectangles with sides of equal length. This means the ratio of the sides must be 1.

d. False; isosceles triangles can have angles of any measure less than 180°. Therefore, any two isosceles triangles may not have angles with equal measure.

Parent Letters

Labsheets

Assessments

Dear Family,

The next Unit in your child's mathematics class this year is **Comparing and Scaling: Ratios, Rates, Percents, and Proportions**. Students work within many different problem situations to make comparisons using ratios, fractions, percents, and rates. Students explore these concepts by making sense of surveys, scaling recipes for different numbers of people, analyzing prices for better deals, and calculating commissions from the selling prices of cars.

▶ Unit Goals

This Unit has two broad goals. One is to help students develop the ability to compare quantitative information by using ratios, fractions, decimals, rates, unit rates, and percents. Another is to encourage students to use those comparisons to scale rates and ratios up and down.

Additionally, in this Unit students will learn different ways of reasoning in proportional situations, as well as how to recognize when such reasoning is appropriate.

▶ Homework and Conversations About the Mathematics

In your child's notebook, you can find problems that were completed in class, notes on the mathematics of the Unit, and descriptions of the vocabulary words.

You can help with homework and encourage sound mathematical habits during this Unit by asking questions such as:

- *Why is a ratio a good means of comparison? How can you scale a ratio up or down?*
- *How can you use proportions to solve problems?*
- *When quantities have different units of measure, how can you compare them?*
- *When can you use subtraction to make a comparison? When can you use division?*

You can help your child with his or her work for this Unit in several ways:

- Ratios, proportions, and percents are everywhere. When you see one of these concepts in a newspaper or magazine, point it out to your child. Discuss with your child what information the numbers give about the situation.
- If you keep track of your car mileage, you may want to share this with your child. If you use other modes of transportation, such as a bus or subway, you may want to discuss the cost of the transportation per week, per month, and per year.
- Ask your child to pick a question in the Unit that was interesting to him or her. Discuss the question together.

▶ Common Core State Standards

While all of the Standards of Mathematical Practice are developed and used by students throughout the curriculum, this Unit focuses on reasoning abstractly and quantitatively. Students attend to finding the meaning of quantities, not just computing them. *Comparing and Scaling* focuses on the Ratios and Proportional Relationships domain. As students explore ratios, rates, percents, and proportions, several standards from the Expressions & Equations domain are also addressed.

Some of the important mathematical ideas that your child will learn in *Comparing and Scaling* are listed on the back of this letter.

If you have any questions or concerns about this Unit or your child's progress in the class, please feel free to contact me. All of us here are interested in your child and want to ensure that this year's mathematics experiences are enjoyable and promote a firm understanding of mathematics.

Sincerely,

Important Concepts	Examples
Ratio A comparison of two quantities	Ratios can be written in several forms. You can write the ratio of 3 cups of water to 2 cups of lemonade concentrate as 2 to 3, 2 : 3, or $\frac{2}{3}$.
Proportions A proportion is a statement of equality between two ratios.	*Kendra takes 70 steps on the treadmill to run 0.1 mile. When her workout is done, she has run 3 miles. How many steps has she taken?* Proportion: $\frac{70 \text{ steps}}{0.1 \text{ mile}} = \frac{x \text{ steps}}{3 \text{ miles}}$ $\frac{70 \text{ steps} \times 30}{0.1 \text{ miles} \times 30} = \frac{21,00 \text{ steps}}{3 \text{ miles}}$ Solution of the proportion
Two Types of Ratios Ratios can be *part-to-part* or *part-to-whole* comparisons. Part-to-whole comparisons can be written as fractions or percents. Part-to-part comparisons can be written in fraction form, but do not represent a fraction.	*The ratio of concentrate to water in a mix for lemonade is 3 cups concentrate to 16 cups water. What fraction of the mix is concentrate?* $\frac{3}{16}$ is the part-to-part comparison. This does not mean that the fraction of mix that is concentrate is $\frac{3}{16}$. Find the total, 19 cups, to write the fraction of the mix that is concentrate. Write a part-to-whole comparison using a fraction, $\frac{3}{19}$, or a percent, $3 \div 19 = 0.15789\ldots \approx 15.8\%$, to describe the part that is concentrate.
Rate A comparison of measures with two different units	Examples of rates: miles to gallons, sandwiches to people, dollars to hours, calories to ounces, kilometers to hours
Unit Rate A rate in which the second quantity is 1 unit	Students sometimes find unit rates difficult because they have two options when dividing the two numbers of a rate. Tracking the units helps students think through such situations. The goal is to build flexibility in using either set of unit rates to compare the quantities. *Sascha rides 6 miles in 20 minutes during the first leg of his bike ride. During the second leg, he rides 8 miles in 24 minutes. During which leg is Sascha faster?* $\frac{6 \text{ miles}}{20 \text{ minutes}} = 0.3$ miles per minute $\qquad \frac{8 \text{ miles}}{24 \text{ minutes}} = 0.333$ miles per minute The times, 1 minute, are the same, so 8 miles in 24 minutes is faster. You can divide the other way as well: $\frac{20 \text{ minutes}}{6 \text{ miles}} = 3.333$ minutes per mile $\qquad \frac{24 \text{ minutes}}{8 \text{ miles}} = 3$ minutes per mile The distances, 1 mile, are the same, and 3 minutes per mile is faster.
Scaling Ratios (and Rates) Finding a common denominator or common numerator to make comparisons easier	*Which is cheaper, 3 roses for \$5 or 7 roses for \$9?* Scale the costs to be the same by finding a common denominator. Use a common multiple of 5 and 9: $\frac{3 \text{ roses}}{\$5} = \frac{3 \text{ roses} \times 9}{\$5 \times 9} = \frac{27 \text{ roses}}{\$45}, \frac{7 \text{ roses}}{\$9} = \frac{7 \text{ roses} \times 5}{\$9 \times 5} = \frac{35 \text{ roses}}{\$45}$ 7 roses for \$9 gives more roses for the same amount of money. Or, scale the numerators to be the same: $\frac{3 \text{ roses}}{\$5} = \frac{3 \text{ roses} \times 7}{\$5 \times 7} = \frac{21 \text{ roses}}{\$35}, \frac{7 \text{ roses}}{\$9} = \frac{7 \text{ roses} \times 3}{\$9 \times 3} = \frac{21 \text{ roses}}{\$27}.$ 21 roses for \$27 is cheaper than 21 roses for \$35.
Proportional Relationship A relationship in which you multiply one variable by a constant number to find the value of another variable	*The price of one pizza is \$13.* To find the cost *C* of any number of pizzas *n*, multiply the number of pizzas by 13. The unit rate 13 is also called the *constant of proportionality, k*. The relationship appears as a straight line on a graph. The equation can be written as $y = kx$. In this case, $C = 13n$.

Estimada familia:

La siguiente Unidad de la clase de Matemáticas de su hijo(a) de este año es ***Comparaciones y escalas:
Razones, tasas, porcentajes y proporciones***. Los estudiantes trabajan con varias situaciones de
problemas para hacer comparaciones usando razones, fracciones, porcentajes y tasas. Los estudiantes
exploran esos conceptos hallando sentido en encuestas, aumentando proporcionalmente las
cantidades de recetas para distintos números de porciones, analizando precios para hallar los tratos
más convenientes y calculando las comisiones correspondientes a los precios de venta de los carros.

Objetivos de la unidad

Esta Unidad tiene dos amplios objetivos. Uno es ayudar a los estudiantes a desarrollar la
capacidad de comparar información cuantitativa usando razones, fracciones, números decimales,
tasas, tasas por unidad y porcentajes. Otra es alentar a los estudiantes a que usen esas
comparaciones con la finalidad de aumentar y reducir proporcionalmente las tasas y razones.

Además, en esta Unidad los estudiantes aprenderán distintas maneras de razonar en situaciones
proporcionales, así como a reconocer cuándo es apropiado tal razonamiento.

Tareas y conversaciones acerca de las matemáticas

Usted puede ayudar a su hijo(a) con la tarea y fomentar en él o ella algunos hábitos matemáticos
firmes durante esta Unidad, haciéndole preguntas como las siguientes:

- ¿Por qué una razón es un buen medio de comparación? ¿Cómo se aumenta o disminuye una
  razón proporcionalmente?
- ¿Cómo usarías proporciones para resolver problemas?
- Cuando las cantidades tienen distintas unidades de medida, ¿cómo las comparas?
- ¿Cuándo usarías una resta para hacer una comparación? ¿Cuándo usarías una división?

Usted puede ayudar a su hijo(a) con su trabajo para esta Unidad de varias maneras:

- Las razones, las proporciones y los porcentajes están en todos lados. Cuando vea uno de
  estos conceptos en un periódico o una revista, muéstreselo a su hijo(a). Comente con él o ella
  qué información proporcionan los números acerca de la situación.
- Si lleva la cuenta de las millas que su auto recorre por unidad de combustible, puede
  compartir esta actividad con su hijo(a). Si usa otros medios de transporte, como el autobús o
  el subterráneo, puede comentar con él o ella el costo por semana, mes o año.
- Pida a su hijo(a) que escoja una pregunta de la Unidad que haya sido especialmente
  interesante para él o ella. Comenten la pregunta.

Estándares estatales comunes

Aunque los estudiantes desarrollan y usan todos los Estándares de prácticas matemáticas a
través del currículum, esta Unidad se concentra en razonar cuantitativa y abstractamente. Los
estudiantes se dedican a hallar el sentido de las cantidades y no sólo a calcularlas. *Comparaciones
y escalas* se concentra en el dominio Razones y relaciones proporcionales. A medida que los
estudiantes exploran razones, tasas, porcentajes y proporciones, se abordan diversos estándares
del dominio Expresiones y ecuaciones.

Algunas ideas importantes de matemáticas que su hijo(a) aprenderá en *Razones, tasas,
proporciones y relaciones* se presentan en el reverso de esta carta. Todos estamos interesados
en su hijo(a) y queremos asegurarnos de que sus experiencias de matemáticas de este año sean
agradables y promuevan un firme entendimiento de esta materia.

Sinceramente,

Conceptos importantes	Ejemplos
Razón Comparación de dos cantidades.	Las razones se pueden escribir de varias formas. Puedes escribir la razón de 3 tazas de agua a 2 tazas de concentrado de limonada como 2 a 3, 2 : 3 ó $\frac{2}{3}$.
Proporciones Una proporción es un enunciado de igualdad entre dos razones.	Kendra da 70 pasos en la caminadora para correr 0.1 milla. Cuando termina su ejercicio ha corrido 3 millas. ¿Cuántos pasos dio? Proporción: $\dfrac{70 \text{ pasos}}{0.1 \text{ milla}} = \dfrac{x \text{ pasos}}{3 \text{ millas}}$ $\dfrac{70 \text{ pasos} \times 30}{0.1 \text{ millas} \times 30} = \dfrac{2100 \text{ pasos}}{3 \text{ millas}}$ Solución de la proporción
Dos tipos de razones Las razones pueden ser comparaciones de *parte a parte* o de *parte a todo*. Las comparaciones de parte a todo pueden escribirse como fracciones o porcentajes. Las comparaciones de parte a parte pueden escribirse en forma fraccionaria, pero no representan una fracción.	La razón del concentrado al agua en una mezcla para limonada es de 3 tazas de concentrado a 16 tazas de agua. ¿Qué fracción de la mezcla es concentrado? $\frac{3}{16}$ es la comparación parte a parte. Esto no significa que la fracción de mezcla que es concentrado sea $\frac{3}{16}$. Halla el total, 19 tazas, para escribir la fracción de la mezcla que corresponde al concentrado. Escribe una comparación de parte a todo usando una fracción, $\frac{3}{19}$, o un porcentaje, $3 \div 19 = 0.15789... \approx 15.8\%$ para describir la parte que es concentrado.
Tasa Una comparación de medidas con dos unidades distintas.	Ejemplos de tasas: millas a galones, sándwiches a personas, dólares a horas, calorías a onzas, kilómetros a horas
Tasa por unidad Tasa en la que la segunda cantidad es 1 unidad.	A veces, las tasas por unidad se les dificultan a los estudiantes porque tienen dos opciones al dividir los dos números de una tasa. Llevar el control de las unidades ayuda a los estudiantes a pensar para esclarecer tales situaciones. La finalidad es lograr flexibilidad al usar cualquier conjunto de tasas por unidad para comparar las cantidades. Sascha recorre en bicicleta 6 millas en 20 minutos en la primera etapa de su recorrido. En la segunda etapa, recorre 8 millas en 24 minutos. ¿En qué etapa es Sascha más rápido? $\dfrac{6 \text{ millas}}{20 \text{ minutos}} = 0.3$ millas por minuto $\qquad \dfrac{8 \text{ millas}}{24 \text{ minutos}} = 0.333$ millas por minuto Los tiempos, 1 minuto, son los mismos, así que 8 millas en 24 minutos es más rápido. También puedes dividir a la inversa: $\dfrac{20 \text{ minutos}}{6 \text{ millas}} = 3.333$ minutos por milla $\qquad \dfrac{24 \text{ minutos}}{8 \text{ millas}} = 3$ minutos por milla Las distancias, 1 milla, son las mismas, y 3 minutos por milla es más rápido.
Razones (y tasas) a escala Hallar un común denominador o común numerador para facilitar las comparaciones.	¿Qué es más barato, 3 rosas por $5 ó 7 rosas por $9? Ajusta los costos para que sean los mismos hallando un común denominador. Usa un múltiplo común de 5 y 9: $\dfrac{3 \text{ rosas}}{\$5} = \dfrac{3 \text{ rosas} \times 9}{\$5 \times 9} = \dfrac{27 \text{ rosas}}{\$45}$, $\dfrac{7 \text{ rosas}}{\$9} = \dfrac{7 \text{ rosas} \times 5}{\$9 \times 5} = \dfrac{35 \text{ rosas}}{\$45}$ 7 rosas por $9 da más rosas por la misma cantidad de dinero. O ajusta los numeradores de manera que sean los mismos: $\dfrac{3 \text{ rosas}}{\$5} = \dfrac{3 \text{ rosas} \times 7}{\$5 \times 7} = \dfrac{21 \text{ rosas}}{\$35}$, $\dfrac{7 \text{ rosas}}{\$9} = \dfrac{7 \text{ rosas} \times 3}{\$9 \times 3} = \dfrac{21 \text{ rosas}}{\$27}$ 21 rosas por $27 es más barato que 21 rosas por $35.
Relación proporcional Una relación en la que una variable se multiplica por una constante para hallar el valor de otra variable.	El precio de una pizza es $13. Para hallar el costo, C, de cualquier número de pizzas, n, multiplica el número de pizzas por 13. La tasa por unidad 13 también se llama constante de proporcionalidad, k. La relación aparece como una línea recta en una gráfica. La ecuación se puede escribir como $y = kx$. En este caso, $C = 13n$.

Labsheet 1ACE   Exercise 1

1. In a comparison taste test of two juice drinks, 780 people preferred Cranberry Blast. Only 220 people preferred Melon Splash. Complete each statement.

   a. There were ☐ more people who preferred Cranberry Blast.

   (**HINT:** How many people preferred Cranberry Blast and how many preferred Melon Splash?).

   b. In the taste test, ☐% of the people preferred Cranberry Blast.

   (**HINT:** What was the total number of people who participated in the taste test?)

   c. People who preferred Cranberry Blast outnumbered those who preferred Melon Splash by a ratio of ☐ to ☐.

   (**HINT:** Remember that a ratio is a comparison. The problem is asking you to compare people who preferred Cranberry Blast to people who preferred Melon Splash by writing a ratio.)

Labsheet 1ACE   Exercise 10

10. Compare these four mixes for apple juice.

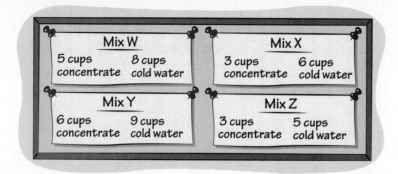

a. Which mix would make the most "appley" juice? Explain your reasoning.
(**HINT:** What would make a juice more "appley?")

b. Suppose you make a single batch of each mix (W, X, Y, and Z). What fraction of
each batch is concentrate?
(**HINT:** What is the total number of cups added to each batch?)

Mix W: Mix X:

Mix Y: Mix Z:

Name .... Date .... Class ....

Labsheet 1ACE

Exercise 10

c. Rewrite your answers to part (b) as percents.

Mix W:

Mix X:

Mix Y:

Mix Z:

d. Suppose you make only 1 cup of Mix W. How much water and how much concentrate do you need?
(**Hint:** For Mix W, the current batch makes 13 cups, where there are 5 cups concentrate and 8 cups water.)

What fraction of the mix is water?

How can you then determine how much concentrate and water you need to get only one total cup?

Now answer the question: How much water and how much concentrate do you need?

Labsheet 2.2   Royal and Howdy's Pizzerias

Pizza Prices

Number of Pizzas	1	2	3	4	5	10	15	20	100	150	200
Price of Royal Pizza						$120					
Price of Howdy's Pizza							$195				

Labsheet 2.2   Royal and Howdy's Pizzerias

Howdy's Pizza Prices

Number of Pizzas	1	2	3	4	5	10	15
Price if Howdy's Delivers							
Price for Pick-Up							$195

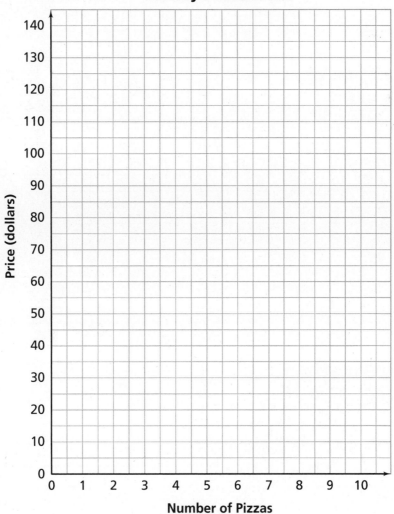

Howdy's Pizza Prices

Labsheet 2.3   Cost of Oranges Rate Table and Graph

Cost of Oranges at FreshFoods

Number of Oranges, n	10		1	20	11	
Cost, C	$2	$1				$2.60

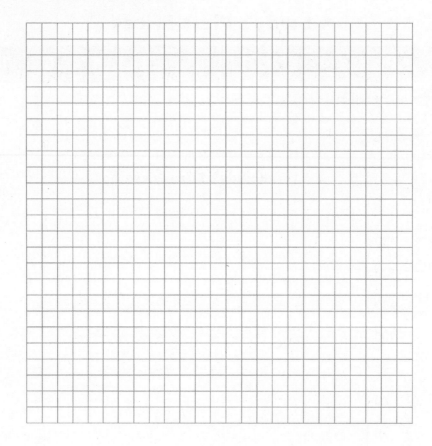

Labsheet 2.3   Cost of Oranges Rate Table and Graph

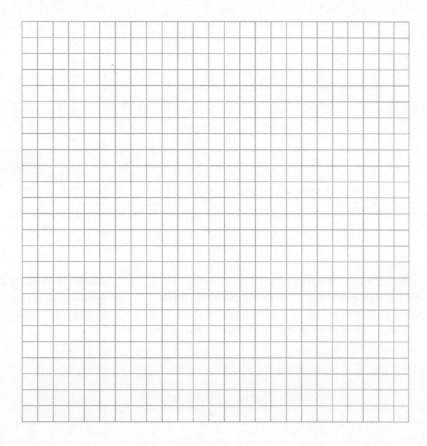

Labsheet 2ACE   Exercises 5 and 6

5. Maralah can drive her car **580 miles** at a steady speed
using **20 gallons of gasoline**. Complete the **rate table**
to show the number of miles she can drive her car at
this speed. Be careful to use correct measurement units.

Maralah's Driving Distance

Gallons	Miles Driven
1	
2	
3	
4	116
5	
6	
7	
8	
9	
10	
⋮	
20	580

6. Joel can drive his car **450 miles** at a steady speed
using **15 gallons of gasoline**. Complete the **rate table**
showing the number of miles he can drive his car at
this speed. Be careful to use correct measurement units.

Joel's Driving Distance

Gallons	Miles Driven
1	
2	
3	
4	
5	150
6	
7	
8	
9	
10	
⋮	
15	450

Labsheet 2ACE   Exercises 10 and 27

10. Complete the table below.

Prices of Songs

Number of Songs, *n*	35		50	1	70	
Cost, *C*	$26.25	$3				$15

27. Complete the table below.

Containers Needed by Volume

Volume of Container (liters)	10	4	2	1	$\frac{1}{2}$	$\frac{1}{4}$	$\frac{1}{10}$
Number of Containers Needed							

Labsheet 3.1A   Ticket Prices

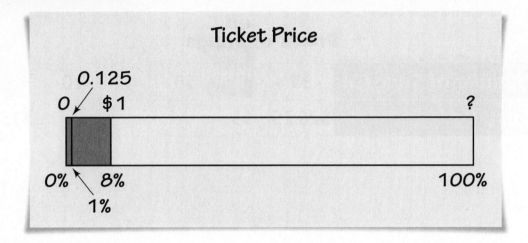

Ticket Price

Percent	8% (tax)	1%	100% (original ticket price)	108% (total price)
Dollars	1	0.125		

Labsheet 3.1B Carla's Used Car Prices

Carla's Used Cars

Model	Markup	Commission	Buying Price	Selling Price
Sedan	$300			
SUV	$500			
Convertible	$950			

Labsheet 3.2   Conversions

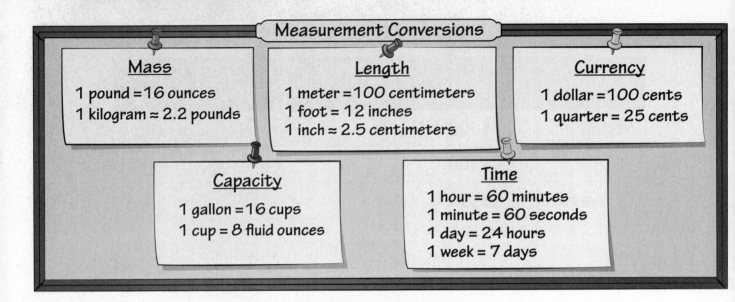

Measurement Conversions

Mass
1 pound = 16 ounces
1 kilogram ≈ 2.2 pounds

Length
1 meter = 100 centimeters
1 foot = 12 inches
1 inch ≈ 2.5 centimeters

Currency
1 dollar = 100 cents
1 quarter = 25 cents

Capacity
1 gallon = 16 cups
1 cup = 8 fluid ounces

Time
1 hour = 60 minutes
1 minute = 60 seconds
1 day = 24 hours
1 week = 7 days

Sean's Walking Rate

Distance (miles)	$\frac{3}{4}$		
Time (hours)	$\frac{1}{4}$	1	$1\frac{1}{3}$

Labsheet 3.3   Chimp Food Mixes

Baby Chimp Food Mix

Scoops of High-Fiber Food			1
Scoops of High-Protein Food		1	
Total Scoops in Mix	100		

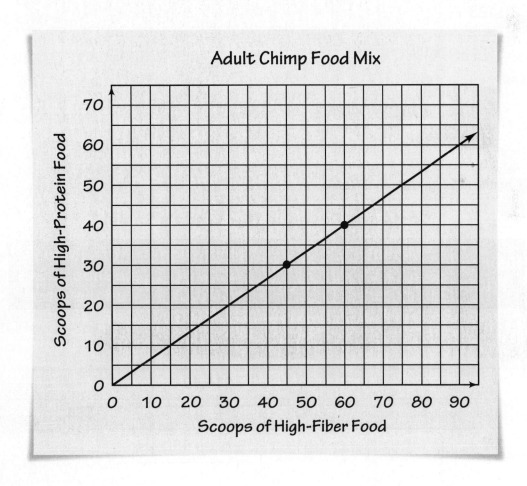

Labsheet 3ACE   Exercises 11–13

11. Find the missing values in the table.

Costs and Revenue (for Roberto's Sales)

Buying Price	Markup (80% of buying price)	Selling Price	Commission (25% of markup)	Profit (Money the shop makes on the sale)
$100	$80	$180	$20	$60
$10				
$55				
$125				

12. Find the missing values in the table.

Costs and Revenue (for Linda's Sales)

Buying Price	Markup (80% of buying price)	Selling Price	Commission (25% of markup)	Profit (Money the shop makes on the sale)
	$48			
		$252		
			$14.40	
				$54
$N				

Labsheet 3ACE   Exercises 11–13

13. For each arrow in the figure below, write a mathematical rule describing how to get from one value to the next value. The first one is done for you.

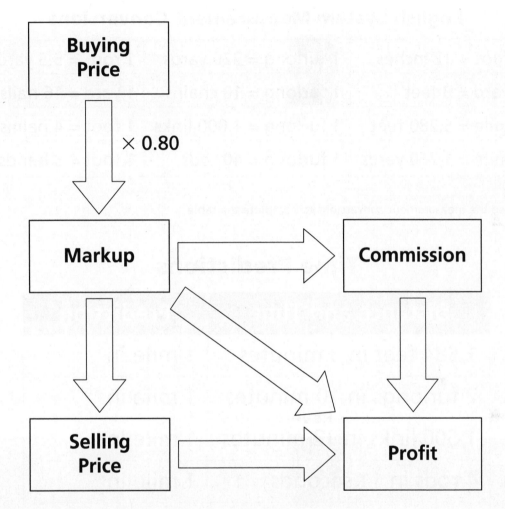

Labsheet 3ACE   Exercise 19

19. The United States uses the English system of measurement. The English system has many old conversions that are rarely used.

English System Measurement Conversions

1 foot = 12 inches	1 furlong = 220 yards	1 rod = 5.5 yards
1 yard = 3 feet	1 furlong = 10 chains	1 yard = 16 nails
1 mile = 5,280 feet	1 furlong = 1,000 links	1 foot = 4 palms
1 mile = 1,760 yards	1 furlong = 40 rods	1 foot = 3 hands

Use the measurement conversions to complete the table.

Time Predictions

	Distance and Time	Prediction
a.	1,584 feet in 3 minutes	1 mile in
b.	2 furlongs in 10 minutes	1 mile in
c.	1,500 links in 12 minutes	1 mile in
d.	4 rods in 11 seconds	1 mile in
e.	5 chains in 1 minute	1 mile in

Labsheet 3ACE   Exercises 51 and 52

51. e. Use the table. Draw a graph with the amounts of high-protein food on the *y*-axis and the amounts of high-fiber food on the *x*-axis.

Orangutan Food Mix

Scoops of High-Protein Food	21	24	27	18	33
Scoops of High-Fiber Food	7	8	9	6	11

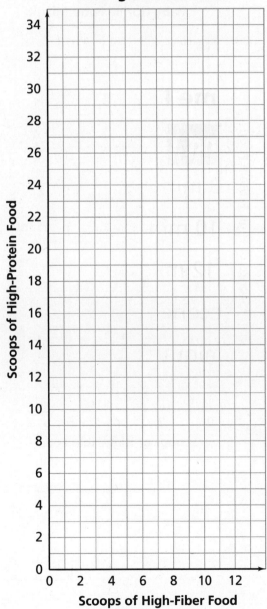

Orangutan Food Mix

Labsheet 3ACE Exercises 51 and 52

52. b. The ratio of high-fiber food to high-protein food for baby gorillas is 30% to 70%. Fill in the table below.

Baby Gorilla Food Mix

Scoops of High-Protein Food		14	1		x
Scoops of High-Fiber Food	3			1	

c. Graph the relationship between high-protein food and high-fiber food.

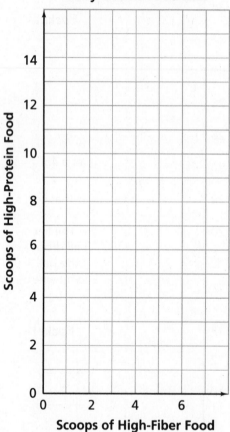

Baby Gorilla Food Mix

Unit Project   Student's Guide, Part 1

Kim made up a game called *Paper Pool*. Her "tables" are rectangles traced on grid paper. There are "pockets" at each corner of the table. The pool table pockets are labeled A (bottom left corner), B (bottom right corner), C (upper right corner), and D (upper left corner). One of Kim's Paper Pool Tables is shown below.

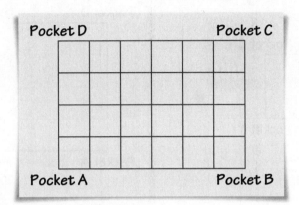

Kim's game has the following guidelines:

- The ball always starts at Pocket A.
- To move the ball, "hit" it as if you were playing pool.
- The ball always moves on a 45° diagonal across the grid.
- When the ball hits a side of the table, it bounces off at a 45° angle and continues to move.
- If the ball moves to a corner, it falls into the pocket at that corner.

Kim has played her Paper Pool game on the table below. The lines show the path that the ball traveled on the table. She notices that the ball dropped in Pocket D and that the ball has a total of 5 hits: the initial hit to get the ball moving, three hits from the ball bouncing off the sides of the table, and one hit when the ball hits into the pocket and drops.

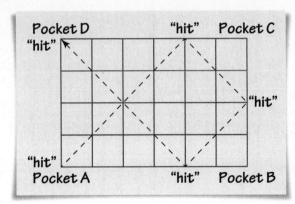

Unit Project   Student's Guide, Part 1

Draw the path a ball would take on the two Paper Pool Tables below. Record what pocket the ball drops into, how many hits occur on its journey, and the dimensions of the tables, giving the bottom length first and the side length second.

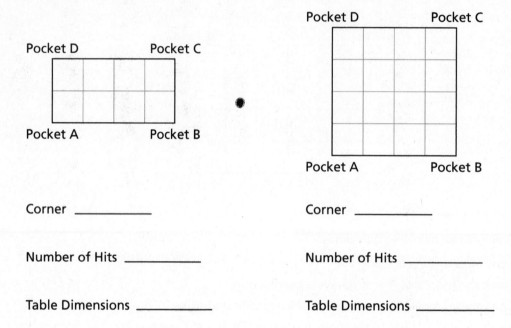

Corner _____

Number of Hits _____

Table Dimensions _____

Corner _____

Number of Hits _____

Table Dimensions _____

After playing Paper Pool on several different-sized tables, Kim wonders if there is a way to predict which pocket the ball would drop into and how many hits would occur by the time the ball drops.

Unit Project   Student's Guide, Part 2

Investigate:

Explore the questions about Paper Pool that are listed below.

- Into what pocket will the ball drop?
- How many hits will occur by the time the ball drops?

Each question is asking you to notice what is happening to the ball as it travels on the Paper Pool tables. Some tables are provided (Labsheets Paper Pool A–C) to get you thinking about these questions. Make conjectures about what pocket the ball will drop into and how many hits will occur by the time the ball drops. You may need to draw additional tables on grid paper to check out any ideas you have and to test any conjectures you make.

When you think you can predict outcomes, write a rule that you could use to determine what will happen to the ball as it travels on the Paper Pool table. This means that your rule should tell you, *without drawing the path*, the number of hits and the dropping pocket for the ball on a Paper Pool table of any size. Remember:

- The ball always starts in the bottom left hand corner of the table (at Pocket A).
- The ball travels on a diagonal path across the square grids.
- If the ball hits the side of the table, it bounces off at a 45° angle.
- When the ball comes to a pocket, it drops in.

Report:

When you have finished exploring different-sized Paper Pool tables and have reached some conclusions, write a report on your work. Be sure to include the following:

1. A summary of the rules you found, why you think your rules are correct, and anything else you discovered. (You might discuss what you noticed as you examined the paths for the different tables and what helped you to arrive at your rules.)

2. For each rule given, draw one new Paper Pool table (not one from the ones given to you) that shows that your rule accurately predicts what happens.

3. Include your drawings of ball paths on the given Paper Pool tables as well as any additional Paper Pool Tables you made to help you write your rules.

4. Include any tables, charts, or other tools you used to help you organize your information and look for patterns that would lead to rules.

5. Explain any other patterns or ideas about Paper Pool tables and the path of the ball that you observed. (For example, on which tables does the ball's path follow the same basic course? For which tables does the design traced by the ball's path look the same?)

Unit Project   Student's Guide, Part 3

Extension Question

Can you predict the length of the path of the ball will travel on any size Paper Pool table? Suppose each time the ball crosses a square, the distance it travels is "one diagonal unit." How many diagonal units is the path of the ball?

One Diagonal
Unit

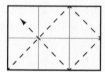

Length of Path:
6 Diagonal units

Unit Project   Paper Pool A

D ___ C

A ___ B

Corner _____
# of Hits _____
Table Dimensions _____

D ___ C

A ___ B

Corner _____
# of Hits _____
Table Dimensions _____

D ___ C

A ___ B

Corner _____
# of Hits _____
Table Dimensions _____

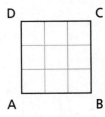

D ___ C

A ___ B

Corner _____
# of Hits _____
Table Dimensions _____

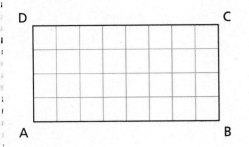

D ___ C

A ___ B

Corner _____
# of Hits _____
Table Dimensions _____

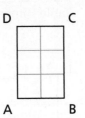

D ___ C

A ___ B

Corner _____
# of Hits _____
Table Dimensions _____

D ___ C

A ___ B

Corner _____
# of Hits _____
Table Dimensions _____

D ___ C

A ___ B

Corner _____
# of Hits _____
Table Dimensions _____

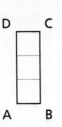

D ___ C

A ___ B

Corner _____
# of Hits _____
Table Dimensions _____

D ___ C

A ___ B

Corner _____
# of Hits _____
Table Dimensions _____

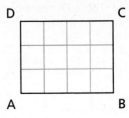

D ___ C

A ___ B

Corner _____
# of Hits _____
Table Dimensions _____

Unit Project   Paper Pool B

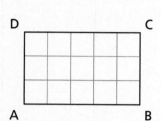

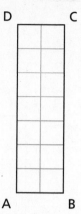

D   C

A   B

Corner _____
# of Hits _____
Table Dimensions _____

Corner _____
# of Hits _____
Table Dimensions _____

Corner _____
# of Hits _____
Table Dimensions _____

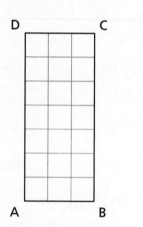

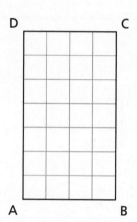

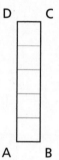

Corner _____
# of Hits _____
Table Dimensions _____

Corner _____
# of Hits _____
Table Dimensions _____

Corner _____
# of Hits _____
Table Dimensions _____

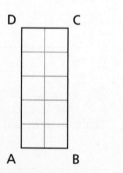

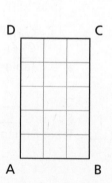

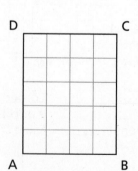

Corner _____
# of Hits _____
Table Dimensions _____

Corner _____
# of Hits _____
Table Dimensions _____

Corner _____
# of Hits _____
Table Dimensions _____

Comparing and Scaling

Unit Project

Unit Project   Paper Pool C

D   C

A   B

Corner _____
# of Hits _____
Table Dimensions _____

D   C

A   B

Corner _____
# of Hits _____
Table Dimensions _____

D   C

A   B

Corner _____
# of Hits _____
Table Dimensions _____

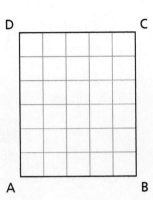

D   C

A   B

Corner _____
# of Hits _____
Table Dimensions _____

D   C

A   B

Corner _____
# of Hits _____
Table Dimensions _____

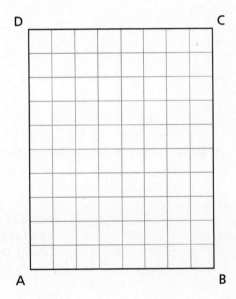

D   C

A   B

Corner _____
# of Hits _____
Table Dimensions _____

Check Up *for use after Investigation 1*

1. In a survey, Eric, the team manager, asked all 120 soccer players in the league which drink they preferred during and after the game.

Drink	During Game	After Game
Sports Beverage	70	10
Juice	10	80
Water	40	30

Ricardo, the soccer league director, made the following statements based on Eric's survey. For each statement, tell if it is accurate and explain how you made each decision.

a. **During** the game, players prefer juice to water by a ratio of 4 to 1.

b. 25% of the players prefer water **after** the game.

c. More than half of the players prefer a sports drink **during** the game.

Check Up (continued)

2. a. Ryan took 15 minutes to type his 450-word report. At this rate, how many words could he type in 20 minutes? Show how you arrived at your answer.

b. Two of these proportions correctly represent how to solve the problem. Circle the two that are correct.

$$\frac{450}{15} = \frac{x}{20} \qquad\qquad \frac{x}{450} = \frac{15}{20} \qquad\qquad \frac{20}{15} = \frac{450}{x} \qquad\qquad \frac{20}{x} = \frac{15}{450}$$

3. Find the value of x that will make each proportion true.

a. $\frac{3}{4} = \frac{24}{x}$ **b.** $\frac{2}{3} = \frac{x}{15}$

c. $\frac{x}{5} = \frac{5}{25}$ **d.** $\frac{4}{x} = \frac{10}{30}$

Partner Quiz *for use after Investigation 2*

A group of students were planning a picnic for the 30 members of their homeroom. They investigated prices for food and drink at two stores and listed their findings in a table.

Food and Drink Prices

Item	Streamline Market		Bulky Store	
	Quantity	Cost	Quantity	Cost
Cola	6 cans (12 ounces each)	$1.99	a case of twenty-four cans (12 ounces each)	$6.99
Ground Beef (for hamburgers)	1 pound (makes four hamburgers)	$1.39	10 patties (1/4 pound each)	$4.99
Hamburger Buns	8-count package	$1.49	12-count package	$2.09
Potato Chips	small bag (1.5 ounces)	$.89	Fun Pack (eight 1.5-ounce bags)	$6.99

1. How much would it cost to make 30 hamburger patties with ground beef purchased from Streamline? Show your work.

2. How much would 30 hamburger patties cost at Bulky's? Show your work.

3. Which store offers the better buy for cola? Explain how you decided.

Partner Quiz (continued)

4. You need to purchase enough hamburger buns to make 30 sandwiches. Buns come in packages of 8 or 12, depending where you shop. Which store offers the better buy for 30 buns? Can you get an even better deal by combining purchases at both stores? Explain how you decided.

5. The meal at the picnic will include the following items:
- One 12-ounce can of cola
- One hamburger **and** bun
- One small bag of potato chips (1.5 ounce bag)

Additional facts about the picnic are—
- The school cafeteria donated mustard, ketchup, relish, onions, paper plates and napkins.
- The students will buy *each item* at whichever store has the best price.
- There are 30 people attending the picnic.

Use the table on the previous page. How much should the students charge each person in order to cover the food expenses? Show how you determined the amount.

Name .... Date .... Class ....

Comparing and Scaling

Partner Quiz (continued)

6. **a.** Which graph represents the cost of hamburgers at Bulky's store? Explain.

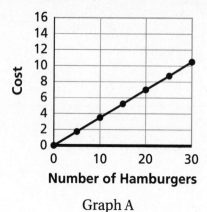

Graph A

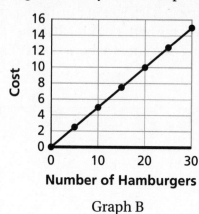

Graph B

b. Match each equation with one of the graphs above. Explain how you made your match.

$C = 0.5n$ $C = 0.35n$

c. Explain how you could use the graph or equation to determine the cost for a given number of hamburgers.

Unit Test Correlation

Unit Test Item	Problem
Item 1	Problem 1.1
Item 2, part (a)	Problem 1.4
Item 2, parts (b) and (c)	Problem 2.3
Item 3	Problem 2.3
Item 4	Problem 3.1
Item 5	Problem 1.2
Item 6	Problem 2.3
Item 7	Problem 3.2
Item 8	Problem 1.3

Name .... Date .... Class ....

Unit Test *for use after Investigation 3*

1. The table below shows the medal count of four countries at the 2012 Summer Olympics. Use the data to complete each statement.

Country	Gold Medals	Total Medals
United States of America	46	104
Russian Federation	24	82
Australia	7	35
Canada	1	18

SOURCE: The London Organising Committee of the Olympic Games and Paralympic Games Limited

a. The ratio of United States gold medals to Russia gold medals was about ■ to 1.

b. Canada had about ■ as many total medals as Australia.

c. About ■ % of Australia's total medals were gold.

Unit Test (continued)

....

2. There are 64 pretzels in a 16-ounce bag of chocolate-covered pretzels.

    a. Write and solve a proportion that you can use to find the number of chocolate covered pretzels in a 5-ounce bag.

    b. What is the number of chocolate-covered pretzels per ounce?

    c. How many ounces does each pretzel weigh?

Unit Test (continued)

3. The local Farm Market sells peppers at five for $2.25.

   a. Complete the rate table.

Number of Peppers	1	2	3	4	5	10	15	20	100
Cost					2.25				

   b. How many peppers could you buy for $20?

   c. Describe what the graph of this data would look like and name a point on the graph.

   d. Write an equation that relates the number of peppers, n, and the cost, C.

   e. What is the constant of proportionality? How do you know?

Unit Test (continued)

4. Many U.S. employees received a 3% raise in 2012. Suppose an employee made $47,000 in 2011 and received a 3% raise. What she did make in 2012? Show two different ways to answer the question.

5. Danielle wants to paint her daughter's room pink. She has been told two different plans:
- Plan A: Use 5 parts white and 2 parts red
- Plan B: Use 4 parts white and 1 part red

Which plan will give her paint that is the *least* red? Explain what the numbers in your calculations mean.

Unit Test (continued)

6. The train ride at the zoo covers a distance of $2\frac{1}{2}$ miles in $\frac{1}{3}$ of an hour.

   a. How many miles per hour does the train go?

   b. How far can the train travel in 3 hours? Show your work.

7. Nancy wants to put a birdseed mix in her birdfeeder. The mix is 20% wild bird seed and 80% sunflower seed. Her birdfeeder can hold 8 cups of birdseed. How much wild bird seed does she need to fill the birdfeeder?

8. The engine in Paul's weed whacker uses an oil–gas mixture. The owner's manual recommends mixing the oil and gasoline together, using the size of the oil container to guide how much of each to use. It states to use $\frac{1}{8}$ part oil with 4 parts gasoline. Paul buys a 32-ounce container of oil. How large of a container will he need to hold the mixture if the amount of oil he uses is $\frac{1}{8}$ of the oil container?

Self Assessment

Mathematical Ideas

After studying the mathematics in this Unit:

1. a. I learned these things about mathematics:

    b. Here are page numbers of notebook entries that give evidence of what I have learned, along with descriptions of what each entry shows:

2. a. These are the mathematical ideas that I am still struggling with:

    b. This is why I think these ideas are difficult for me:

    c. Here are page numbers of notebook entries that give evidence of what I am struggling with, and descriptions of what each entry shows:

Class Participation

I contributed to the classroom **discussion** and understanding of the mathematics in this Unit when I ... (Give examples.)

Self Assessment (continued)

Learning Environment

Rate each learning activity listed below using this scale:

1. I consistently struggled to understand the mathematics and I'm still not sure that I understand it.

2. I struggled somewhat but now I understand more than I did.

3. I had to work, but I feel confident that I understand now.

4. I understood everything pretty easily and I feel confident that I know the mathematics in these problems.

5. Everything came easily. I knew most of the mathematics before we did this.

Learning Activities

_____ Problems from the Investigations

_____ ACE Homework Assignments

_____ Mathematical Reflections

_____ Check Ups

_____ Partner Quiz

_____ Looking Back

_____ Unit Test

Check any of the following that you feel are the most helpful in adding to the success of your learning.

☐ Working on my own in class

☐ Discussing a problem with a partner

☐ Working in a small group of 3 or 4 people

☐ Discussing a problem as a whole class

☐ Hearing how other people solved the problem

☐ Summarizing the mathematics as a class and taking notes

☐ Completing homework assignments

Notebook Checklist

Place a ✔ next to each item you have completed.

Notebook Organization

_____ Problems and Mathematical Reflections are labeled and dated.

_____ Work is neat and easy to find and follow.

Vocabulary

_____ All words are listed.   _____ All words are defined or described.

Assessments

_____ Check Up   _____ _____

_____ Partner Quiz   _____ _____

_____ Unit Test   _____ _____

Assignments

_____ _____   _____ _____

_____ _____   _____ _____

_____ _____   _____ _____

_____ _____   _____ _____

_____ _____   _____ _____

_____ _____   _____ _____

_____ _____   _____ _____

_____ _____   _____ _____

_____ _____   _____ _____

Assessment Answers

Check Up

The problems in this Check Up were designed to be answered with the use of a calculator. The Check Up can be used any time after Investigation 1.

1. a. Not accurate. Should be 10 to 40 or 1 to 4 OR Students might say that the order of the ratio should be switched to "water to juice".

  b. Accurate. Explanations may vary.
  One example: $\frac{30}{120} = \frac{1}{4} = 25\%$

  c. Accurate. Explanations may vary.
  One example: $\frac{70}{120} > \frac{60}{120} = \frac{1}{2}$

2. a. 600. Work may vary. One example: $15 \cdot 30 = 450$, so $20 \cdot 30 = 600$.

  b. $\frac{450}{15} = \frac{x}{20}$ and $\frac{20}{x} = \frac{15}{450}$

3. a. $x = 32$ **b.** $x = 10$
  c. $x = 1$ **d.** $x = 12$

Partner Quiz

The Partner Quiz can be given at any time after Investigation 2.

1. 4 burgers cost $1.39
  1 burger costs $0.3475
  30 burgers cost $10.425, or $10.43

  or

  $\frac{30 \text{ burgers}}{4 \text{ per pound}} = 7.5$ pounds

  $7.5 \times \$1.39 = \$10.425$, or $10.43

2. 10 patties for $4.99
  30 patties for $14.97

3. Streamline: 6 cans for $1.99, 24 cans for $7.96
  Bulky: 24 cans for $6.99

4. Streamline: 8 buns for $1.49, 32 buns for $5.96
  Bulky: 12 buns for $2.09, 36 buns for $6.27
  Buying from both: 2 packs from Bulky: 24 buns for $4.18; 1 pack from Streamline: 8 buns for $1.49; Total of 32 buns for $5.67.

5. If students buy the same item at different stores to save as much as possible: $\frac{\$51.39}{30 \text{ people}} = \$1.713$, or about $1.72 per person. (See Figure 1). If students do not think they can buy the same item at different stores to save as much as possible: $\frac{\$53.04}{30 \text{ people}} = \$1.768$, or about $1.77 per person. (See Figure 2, next page.)

Figure 1

	Streamline	Bulky	# of items	Cost
Cola	one 6-pack for $1.99	one 24-pack for $6.99	30	$8.98
Burger	30 burgers cost $10.43	30 patties for $14.97	30	$10.43
Buns	one 8-pack of buns for $1.49	two 12-packs of buns for $4.18	32	$5.67
Chips	6 bags at $.89 each for $5.34	three 8-packs for $20.97	30	$26.31
			Total	**$51.39**

Assessment Answers *(continued)*

6. a. Graph A represents Streamline Market. Graph B represents Bulky Store. You can use the answers for questions 1 and 2 and help answer this question. It costs about $10.43 for 30 hamburgers at Streamline Market. This corresponds to the ordered pair representing the cost of 30 hamburgers on Graph A. It costs almost $15 for 30 hamburgers at Bulky Store, which corresponds with the ordered pair representing the cost of 30 hamburgers on Graph B.

b. The equation $C = 0.5n$ matches Graph B, because the slope is $\frac{1}{2}$ that means you are moving along the x-axis twice what you are moving along the y-axis. For example, if you start at the ordered pair $(0, 0)$ and go up 10 on the y-axis (Cost), you would need to go right 20 on the x-axis (Number of Hamburgers) for the slope to be $\frac{1}{2}$. Graph B is the only

graph that has a point at $(20, 10)$. That means the equation $C = 0.35n$ matches Graph A.

c. You could use the graph of either store to find the cost of any number of hamburgers by finding the desired number of hamburgers on the x-axis and seeing where that intersects with the line. You could use the equations of either store by substituting the desired number of hamburgers into the equation for x to determine y, which represents the cost.

Unit Test

The problems in this Unit Test were designed to be answered with the use of a calculator. The Unit Test can be used any time after Investigation 3.

1. a. 2 **b.** $\frac{1}{2}$ **c.** 20

2. a. Proportions may vary. $\frac{64}{16} = \frac{x}{5}$; $x = 20$

b. 4 **c.** $\frac{1}{4}$

Figure 2

	Streamline	Bulky	# of items	Cost
Cola	five 6-packs = 30 cans for $9.95	two 24-packs = 48 cans for $13.98	30	$9.95
Burger	30 burgers cost $10.43	30 patties for $14.97	30	$10.43
Buns	four 8-packs = 32 buns for $5.96	three 12-packs = 36 buns for $6.27	32	$5.96
Chips	30 bags at $.89 each for $26.70	four 8-packs = 32 bags for $27.96	30	$26.70
			Total	$53.04

Assessment Answers (continued)

3. a. (See Figure 3.)   **b.** 44

c. An increasing straight line from (0,0) by 0.45 up for each 1 over. Descriptions and points may vary based on student explanations. (1, 0.45)

d. $C = 0.45n$

e. 0.45, it is the unit rate. Explanations may vary. One possible explanation: The price of 1 pepper is $.45.

4. $47,000 \times 0.03 = 1,410$

$1,410 + 47,000 = 48,410$, so $48,410

OR

$47,000 \times 1.03 = 48,410$, so $48,410

5. Plan B:

$2 : 5 = 0.4$ red to 1 white

$1 : 4 = 0.25$ red to 1 white

Students might also scale up using part-to-whole-ratios and come up with 35 parts total and 14 parts red for Plan A and 35 parts total and 7 parts red for Plan B.

6. a. 7.5 miles per hour

b. 22.5 miles

7. 1.6 cups of wild bird seed

8. 132 ounce container

Figure 3

Number of Peppers	1	2	3	4	5	10	15	20	100
Cost	$.45	$.90	$1.35	$1.80	$2.25	$4.50	$6.75	$9.00	$45.00

Looking Back Answers

1. a. *Difference*: This is done by subtracting the number of walkers from the number of bus riders, which answers the question of "How many more students ride the bus than walk?" For Mr. Archer's room, the difference is 5 students.

Ratio: A ratio can also be used to compare the number of bus riders to the number of walkers. For Mr. Archer's room, the ratio is 20 : 15 or 4 : 3.

Fractions: The first fraction is constructed by writing the number of walkers in the numerator. The denominator would be the total students from the room. The second fraction would have the number of bus riders in the numerator and the total students from the room in the denominator. After writing the fractions, they are then compared. For Mr. Archer's room, the fractions are $\frac{4}{7}$ and $\frac{3}{7}$. You can say that the number of walkers is $\frac{3}{4}$ of the students who ride the bus.

Percent: Percent can also be used to determine the number of bus riders and walkers out of 100. For Mr. Archer's room, the percent of bus riders is 57% and the percent of walkers is 43%.

Unit rate or scaling: These can be found by dividing the number of walkers into the number of bus riders and determining that there are 1.3 bus riders for every walker, or the number of bus riders is 1.3 times the number of walkers.

The best statement would probably be a ratio, as you are trying to compare two parts: bus riders to walkers.

b. One could compare the number of bus riders and walkers between homerooms through the use of percents. Percents allow you to compare both bus riders and walkers out of 100, so that the difference in total students between the homerooms would not matter. Mr. Archer's homeroom had 57% bus riders and 43% walkers compared to 61% bus riders and 39% walkers in Ms. Brown's homeroom. The ratio of bus riders to walkers can be compared between rooms, such as 4 to 3 (or 12 to 9) for Mr. Archer's and 14 to 9 for Ms. Brown's.

A comparison can also be made by the unit rate or scale factor, so first determine the number of walkers per bus ride or bus riders per walker for each homeroom: 1.3 bus riders per walker for Mr. Archer and 1.6 bus riders per walker for Ms. Brown. The difference of bus riders and walkers could also be compared between homerooms. The difference is 5 for each teacher.

The best method seems to be percent, as the number of students in each homeroom is not the same. Percents show the numbers in amounts "out of 100."

c. 12 students; using equivalent ratios, $\frac{5}{3} = \frac{20}{\blacksquare}$. The scale factor is 4.

Looking Back Answers (continued)

d. 180 bus riders and 120 walkers. The total bus riders from the 3 homerooms is 54 and the total walkers from the 3 homerooms is 36. The total number of students in the 3 homerooms is 90. Using equivalent fractions for bus riders, $\frac{54}{90} = \frac{\blacksquare}{300}$. The scale factor is $3\frac{1}{3}$.

e. 270 bus riders and 180 walkers. The ratio of bus riders to walkers at East is 3 to 2.

2. a. Dog food is cheaper per pound. Dog food costs $.49 per pound and cat food costs $.60 per pound.

b. A cat is cheapest to feed. The cost per pound of cat food is $.60 and a cat eats $\frac{1}{3}$ pound per day. Therefore, it costs $.20 per day to feed a cat. Dog food costs $.49 per pound. A small dog eats $\frac{1}{2}$ pound per day and therefore costs about 24.5 cents a day, while a large dog eats $1\frac{1}{4}$ pounds per day and therefore costs about $.61 per day to feed.

c. Cat food. For cat food, $20 \times \frac{1}{3}$, or $6\frac{2}{3}$ lbs per day. Since the bag holds 10 lbs, it will last $10 \div 6\frac{2}{3}$, or 1.5 days. For dog food, $30 \times \frac{1}{2} + 20 \times 1\frac{1}{4} = 40$ lbs/day used. Since the bag holds 50 lbs, it will last $50 \div 40 = 1.25$ days.

d. About 20.67 bags of cat food (21 opened) and 24.8 bags of dog food (25 opened). There are 31 days in January. Since 1 bag of dog food lasts 1.25 days, 24.8 bags will be needed. Since one bag of cat food lasts 1.5 days, 20.67 bags will be needed.

e. The 5-lb. bag will cost $22.50. At the new store, the cost of Bow Chow per pound is $.45. Therefore, for 50 lbs, it will cost $0.45 \times 50 = 22.50$, or $22.50.

f. The new store is the better deal. It costs $22.50 for a 50-lb. bag, but at the old store, it costs $24.50. Therefore, the owner will save $2.00 on a 50-lb. bag if he/she shops at the new store.

3. You need to look at what the question is asking. Ratios are used when you are comparing two quantities, such as two parts of a mix and want to know the scale between them. Percents are used when you compare two things in different amounts. Differences are used when you talk about a discrepancy between two amounts. Rates are used when you want to talk about a direct comparison between two sets. When you want to compare number of girls to number of boys, a ratio would be appropriate. When you want to know how much bigger or farther one thing is from another, using differences is appropriate. When you want to know the number of something per some other unit, such as the number of Calories per cookie, then a rate would be appropriate. When you want to how many people out of 100, then a percent would be appropriate.

4. 3 to 5 can also be expressed as 3 : 5. You can also express it using the fraction $\frac{3}{5}$, or the percent 60%. 3 to 5 can also be expressed as 0.6 per unit.

5. a. Possible answers: 12 to 9, 4 to 3, 240 to 180, 8 to 6, 48 to 36

b. 4 to 3

Looking Back Answers *(continued)*

6. Find the scale factor between the two given numbers in the same numerator and denominator location and then multiply by the scale factor. For example, to solve $\frac{5}{8} = \frac{12}{\blacksquare}$, find the scale factor between 12 and 5 ($12 \div 5 = 2.4$), then multiply 8 by 2.4, which is 19.2. To solve $\frac{5}{8} = \frac{\blacksquare}{24}$, find the scale factor between 24 and 8 ($24 \div 8 = 3$) and multiply 5 by 3 to get 15. Strategies include finding the scale factor or equivalent fractions.

7. a. With the recipe, you scale up or down the quantity of ingredients needed based on the numbers of people the recipe can feed in original form. To change recipes to feed a given number of people, you need to multiply the amount of each ingredient by the ratio of the number of people you want to feed to the number of people you can feed using the original recipe. For example, to scale up a recipe that serves 4 to serve 12, multiply each quantity by 3. Similarly, to scale down a recipe that serves 20 to serve 4, multiply each quantity by $\frac{4}{20}$ (or $\frac{1}{5}$).

b. Compare the differences on the map and use the scale factor given in the legend to determine the actual distance (multiply the distance you find on a map using a ruler by the ratio/scale factor given on the map). For example, the distance between two cities on a map is 0.25 inches. If the scale factor is 1 inch = 100 miles, then the actual distance is 25 miles.

c. Use a proportion to determine the cost per unit of weight (ounces o pounds). Then the unit rates of cost per weight can be compared to determine which is the better deal or more economical.

d. You can multiply the coordinates by scale factors to make larger or smaller copies of the design. The copies would then be similar to the original. The scale factor would be the ratio of one side of the design to the corresponding side of a similar figure of the design.

Parent Letters

Labsheets

Assessments

Dear Family,

The next Unit in your child's mathematics class this year is **_Moving Straight Ahead: Linear Relationships_**. In this Unit, students are developing skills in areas that are traditionally known as algebra. This Unit introduces them to situations that can be modeled with linear relationships and graphed with straight lines. In the Grade 8 Unit _Thinking With Mathematical Models_, they will revisit the use of linear models before shifting the focus to nonlinear relationships.

Unit Goals

In this Unit, students identify, represent, and interpret linear relationships. They learn to recognize linear relationships by the constant rate of change between two variables in a verbal context, table, graph, and equation. This idea is introduced by way of an experiment in which students determine their walking rates. This experiment focuses on rates, which students have already studied, in order to access the central ideas surrounding constant rate of change between two variables. Students then learn to solve linear equations and write equations for lines.

Helping With Homework and Conversations About the Mathematics

In your child's notebook, you can find worked-out examples, notes on the mathematics of the Unit, and descriptions of the vocabulary words.

You can help with homework and encourage sound mathematical habits as your child studies this Unit by asking questions such as:

- _What are the variables in the problem, and how are they related?_
- _How can I recognize a linear pattern if it is represented in a problem, in a table, in a graph, or with an equation?_
- _How can I use these representations to answer given questions?_

You can help your child with his or her work for this Unit in several ways:

- _Ask your child to describe some real-world situations in which linear relationships are used. Here are some examples:_
  - The distance traveled in a vehicle moving at a constant speed
  - The amount of water in a sink that is draining at a constant rate
- _Look at your child's mathematics notebook. Read some of the explanations they have written and, if they aren't clear, talk with your child about why you think they may need more explanation._
- _Look at your child's homework; make sure all questions are answered and explanations are clear._

Common Core State Standards

Students develop and use all of the Standards for Mathematical Practice throughout the curriculum. In this Unit, particular attention is paid to modeling with mathematics as students solve problems involving linear relationships using tables, graphs, and equations. _Moving Straight Ahead_ focuses largely on the Expressions and Equations domain. As students explore linear relationships, parts of the Ratio and Proportional Reasoning and Functions domains are also addressed.

A few important mathematical ideas that your child will learn in _Moving Straight Ahead_ are given on the next page. As always, if you have any questions or concerns about this Unit or your child's progress in the class, please feel free to call. We are interested in your child and want this year's mathematics experiences to be enjoyable and to promote a firm understanding of mathematics.

Sincerely,

Important Concepts	Examples

Linear Relationships
A relationship is linear if there is a constant rate of change between the two variables. That is, for each unit change in x, there is a constant change in y.

Tables
In the table, the **constant rate of change** can be observed as a pattern of consistent change in the variables.

For Gilberto's walking rate, as the time increases by 1 second, the distance increases by 2 meters. The constant rate of change is 2 meters per second.

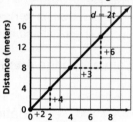

Gilberto's Walking Rate

Time (seconds)	Distance (meters)
0	0
1	2
2	4
3	6

Graphs
If we graph the data, the constant rate of change between the two variables shows up as a straight line. This constant rate of change is called the **slope of the line**. It is the ratio of change between the two variables. For any two points on the line,

$$\text{slope} = \frac{\text{vertical change}}{\text{horizontal change}}.$$

Gilberto's Walking Rate

Here, the slope is $\frac{4}{2}$ or $\frac{6}{3}$ or $\frac{2}{1}$.

Equations
In the symbolic representation, the constant rate of change shows up as the **coefficient** of the independent variable.

Here, the coefficient of t is 2.

Gilberto: $d = 2t$

y-intercept
On a graph, the y-intercept is the point at which the graph of a line crosses the y-axis (vertical axis).

Cost of Bike Rental

Suppose the cost to rent bikes is $150 plus $10 per bike. Symbolically, we can write $C = 150 + 10n$, where C is the cost in dollars and n is the number of bikes. The y-intercept is at (0, 150) because for 0 bikes, the cost is $150. This means there is a fixed charge in addition to the cost per bike. The y-intercept is the constant term in the equation. The slope (or constant rate of change) of the line is 10, the coefficient of n.

Solving Equations
To solve an equation, students write a series of equivalent equations until it is easy to read the value of the variable. Equivalent equations have the same solutions. Equality is maintained by adding, subtracting, multiplying, or dividing by the same quantity on each side of the equation. For multiplication and division, the quantity must not be zero. These procedures are called the **properties of equality**.

For the equation $C = 150 + 10n$, if C is 750, what is the value of n?

Equation	Reason
$750 = 150 + 10n$	Original equation
$750 - 150 = 150 - 150 + 10n$	Subtract 150 from each side to undo adding 150.
$600 = 10n$	Simplify.
$\frac{600}{10} = \frac{10n}{10}$	Divide each side by 10 to undo multiplying by 10.
$60 = n$	Simplify.

Note that if you replace n with 60 in each step, the equation is true. For example, the original equation simplifies to $750 = 750$.

190

Estimada familia:

La siguiente Unidad de la clase de matemáticas de su hija(o) este año es **Seguir adelante: Relaciones lineales**. En esta Unidad, los estudiantes desarrollan destrezas en áreas que tradicionalmente se conocen como álgebra. Esta Unidad les presenta situaciones que se pueden demostrar con relaciones lineales y representar gráficamente con líneas rectas. En la Unidad del Grado 8 *Pensar con modelos matemáticos*, ellos retomarán el uso de los modelos lineales antes de enfocarse en las relaciones no lineales.

▶ Objetivos de la unidad

En esta Unidad, los estudiantes identifican, representan e interpretan relaciones lineales. Aprenden a reconocer las relaciones lineales según la tasa de cambio constante entre dos variables en un contexto verbal, en tablas, en gráficas y en ecuaciones. Esta idea se presenta en la forma de un experimento en el que los estudiantes determinan sus velocidades de caminata. Este experimento se concentra en las tasas y las velocidades, que los estudiantes ya han estudiado, con el fin de acceder a las ideas más importantes que rodean a la tasa de cambio constante entre dos variables. Luego, los estudiantes aprenden a resolver ecuaciones lineales y a escribir ecuaciones para rectas.

▶ Tareas y conversaciones acerca de las matemáticas

Usted puede ayudar a su hijo(a) con la tarea y fomentarle algunos hábitos matemáticos firmes a medida que trabaja en esta Unidad, haciéndole preguntas como:

- *¿Cuáles son las variables del problema y cómo están relacionadas?*
- *¿Cómo se puede reconocer un patrón lineal si está representado en un problema, en una tabla, en una gráfica o en una ecuación?*
- *¿Cómo se usan estas representaciones para responder a preguntas dadas?*

Usted puede ayudar a su hijo(a) con su tarea para esta Unidad en varias formas:

- *Pida a su hijo(a) que describa algunas situaciones de la vida diaria en las que se usen relaciones lineales. Estos son algunos ejemplos:*
  - La distancia recorrida por un vehículo que se mueve a una velocidad constante
  - La cantidad de agua en un lavabo que se drena a una velocidad constante
- *Revise el cuaderno de matemáticas de su hijo(a). Lea algunos de las explicaciones que ha escrito y, si no son claras, hable con él o ella acerca de por qué usted piensa que son necesarias mayores explicaciones.*
- *Revise la tarea de su hijo(a); asegúrese de que todas las preguntas estén respondidas y de que las explicaciones sean claras.*

▶ Estándares estatales comunes

Los estudiantes desarrollan y usan todos los Estándares de Prácticas Matemáticas a lo largo del curso. En esta Unidad, se presta especial atención a la representación con matemáticas a medida que los estudiantes resuelven problemas que incluyen relaciones lineales usando tablas, gráficas y ecuaciones. *Seguir adelante* se concentra principalmente en la rama de las Expresiones y ecuaciones. A medida que los estudiantes exploran las relaciones lineales, también se abordan las ramas del Razonamiento con razones y el razonamiento proporcional, y las Funciones.

Algunas importantes ideas matemáticas que su hijo(a) aprenderá en *Seguir adelante* se presentan en la siguiente página. Como siempre, si usted tiene cualquier pregunta o preocupación acerca de esta Unidad, o con respecto al progreso de su hijo(a) en clase, por favor no dude en llamar. Estamos interesados en su hijo(a) y queremos que él o ella disfrute las experiencias matemáticas de este año, además de promover un entendimiento firme de las matemáticas.

Sinceramente,

Conceptos importantes	Ejemplos

Relaciones lineales
Una relación es lineal si hay una tasa de cambio constante entre dos variables.
Es decir, por cada unidad de cambio en x, hay un cambio constante en y.

Tablas
En la tabla, la **tasa de cambio constante** se puede observar como un patrón de cambio constante en las variables.

Para hallar la velocidad de caminata de Gilberto, a medida que la velocidad se incrementa en 1 segundo, la distancia se incrementa en 2 metros. La tasa de cambio constante es de 2 metros por segundo.

Velocidad de caminata de Gilberto

Tiempo (segundos)	Distancia (metros)
0	0
1	2
2	4
3	6

Gráficas
Si representamos gráficamente los datos, la tasa de cambio constante entre las dos variables aparece como una línea recta. Esta tasa de cambio constante se llama **pendiente de la recta.** Es la razón de cambio entre las dos variables. Para dos puntos cualesquiera de la recta,

$$\text{pendiente} = \frac{\text{cambio vertical}}{\text{cambio horizontal}}.$$

Velocidad de caminata de Gilberto

Aquí, la pendiente es $\frac{4}{2}$ ó $\frac{6}{3}$ ó $\frac{2}{1}$.

Ecuaciones
En la representación simbólica, la tasa de cambio constante aparece como el **coeficiente** de la variable independiente.

Aquí, el coeficiente de t es 2.

Gilberto: $d = 2t$

Intercepto en y
En una gráfica, el intercepto en y es el punto en el que la gráfica de una recta cruza el eje de las y (eje vertical).

Costo de alquiler de bicicletas

Supón que el costo de alquiler de las bicicletas es $150 más $10 por bicicleta. Simbólicamente, podemos escribir $C = 150 + 10$, *donde C es* el costo en dólares y n es el número de bicicletas. El intercepto en y está en (0, 150) porque por 0 bicicletas, el costo es de $150. Esto significa que hay un cargo fijo además del costo por bicicleta. El intercepto en y es el término constante de la ecuación. La pendiente (o tasa de cambio constante) de la recta es 10, el coeficiente de n.

Resolver ecuaciones
Para resolver una ecuación, los estudiantes escriben una serie de ecuaciones equivalentes hasta que les sea fácil leer el valor de la variable. Las ecuaciones equivalentes tienen las mismas soluciones. La igualdad se mantiene sumando, restando, multiplicando o dividiendo por la misma cantidad en cada lado de la ecuación. Para la multiplicación y la división, la cantidad debe ser distinta de cero. Estos procedimientos se llaman **propiedades de la igualdad.**

En la ecuación $C = 150 + 10n$, si C es 750, ¿cuál es el valor de n?

Ecuación	Razón
$750 = 150 + 10n$	Ecuación original
$750 - 150 = 150 - 150 + 10n$	Se resta 150 de cada lado para cancelar la suma de 150.
$600 = 10n$	Se simplifica.
$\frac{600}{10} = \frac{10n}{10}$	Se divide cada lado por 10 para cancelar la multiplicación de 10.
$60 = n$	Se simplifica.

Observa que si reemplazas n con 60 en cada paso, la ecuación es verdadera. Por ejemplo, la ecuación original se simplifica a $750 = 750$.

Labsheet 1.2 Walking Rates

A. Here are the walking rates that Gilberto, Alana, and Leanne found in their experiment.

Name	Walking Rate
Alana	1 meter per second
Gilberto	2 meters per second
Leanne	2.5 meters per second

1.

Walking Rates

Time (seconds)	Distance (meters)		
	Alana	Gilberto	Leanne
0			
1			
2			
3			
4			
5			
6			
7			
8			
9			
10			

Labsheet 1.2   Walking Rates

2.

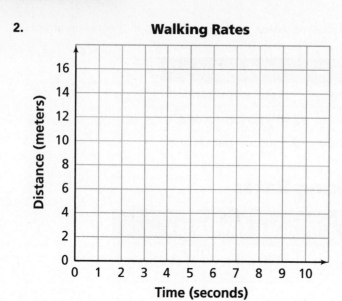

Labsheet 1.3   Pledge Plans

A. 1.

Pledge Plans

Distance (km)	Amount of Money		
	Alana	Gilberto	Leanne
0			
1			
2			
3			
4			
5			
6			

2.

Pledge Plans

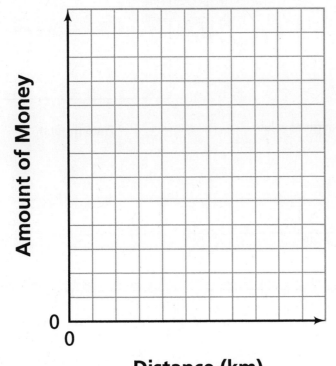

Amount of Money

Distance (km)

Labsheet 1ACE Exercise 4

4. Mike makes the following table of the distances he travels during the first day of the trip.

    a. Suppose Mike continues riding at this rate. Write an **equation** for the distance (D) Mike travels after *t* hours.

        D =

Cycling Distance

Time (hours)	Distance (miles)
0	0
1	6.5
2	13
3	19.5
4	26
5	32.5
6	39

    b. Sketch a **graph** of the equation.

        How did you choose the range of values for the time axis?

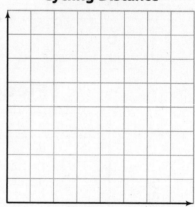

Cycling Distance

Distance (miles)

Time (hours)

        How did you choose the range of values for the distance axis?

Labsheet 1ACE   Exercise 4

c. How can you find the distances Mike travels in 7 hours ($t = 7$) and in $9\frac{1}{2}$ hours ($t = 9.5$), using the table?

> **Hint:** Extend the table provided and then tell how you would use it to find the distance Mike traveled in an hour.

Using the graph?

> **Hint:** See part (b).

Using the equation?

> **Hint:** See part (a).

d. How can you find the **numbers of hours** it takes Mike to travel 100 miles ($D = 100$) and 237 miles ($D = 237$), using the table?

Using the graph?

Using the equation?

Labsheet 1ACE   Exercise 4

e. For parts (c) and (d), what are the advantages and disadvantages of using each model—a table, a graph, and an equation—to find the answers?

Form	Advantages	Disadvantages
Table		
Graph		
Equation		

f. Compare the rate at which Mike rides with the rates at which Jose, Mario, and Melanie ride.

Mike's rate of riding:

Hint: How do you find the rate? What is Mike's rate of riding? What is Jose's rate? Mario's? Melanie's?

Jose's rate of riding:

Mario's rate of riding:

Melanie's rate of riding:

Who rides the fastest?

How can you determine this from the tables?

From the graphs?

From the equations?

Labsheet 1ACE   Exercise 6

6. The graph represents the walkathon pledge
   plans for three sponsors.

   a. Describe each sponsor's pledge plan.

   Sponsor A:

   Sponsor B:

   Sponsor C:

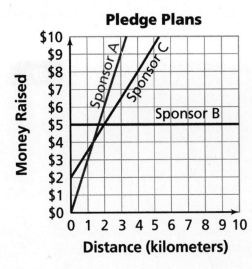

Pledge Plans

b. What is the number of **dollars per kilometer** each sponsor pledges?

   Sponsor A:

   Hint: If you are stuck, write an
   equation for each pledge plan and
   explain what each number or
   variable in the equation represents.

   Sponsor B:

   Sponsor C:

Labsheet 1ACE   Exercise 6

c. What does the point where the line crosses the **y-axis** mean to each sponsor?

Hint: Use part (a).

Sponsor A:

Sponsor B:

Sponsor C:

d. Write the coordinates of two points on each line.

Sponsor A:

Sponsor B:

Sponsor C:

What information does each point represent for the sponsor's pledge plan?

Hint: What quantity does each coordinate of a point represent?

e. Does each relationship represent a proportional relationship?

Labsheet 1ACE   Exercise 12

12. Jamal's parents give him money to spend at camp. Jamal spends the same amount of money on snacks each day. The table shows the amount of money, in dollars, he has left at the end of each day.

Snack Money

Days	Money Left
0	$20
1	$18
2	$16
3	$14
4	$12
5	$10
6	$8

a. How much money does Jamal have at the start of camp? Explain.

b. How much money does he spend each day? Explain.

> **Hint:** How can you use a table to find the unit rate of dollars spent per day?

c. Is the relationship between the number of days and the amount of money left in Jamal's wallet a linear relationship? Explain.

Labsheet 1ACE   Exercise 12

d. Assume that Jamal's spending pattern continues. Check your answer to part (c) by sketching a graph of this relationship.

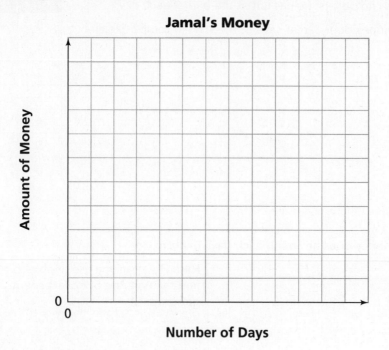

e. Write an equation that represents this relationship.

$M =$

Explain what information the variables represent.

Explain what information the numbers represent.

Labsheet 2.2   Henri and Emile's Race

A. Emile walks 2.5 meters every 1 second. Henri walks 1 meter every second.

1.

Time (seconds)	Distance (meters)	
	Henri	Emile
0		
5		
10		
15		
20		
25		
30		
35		
40		
45		

2.

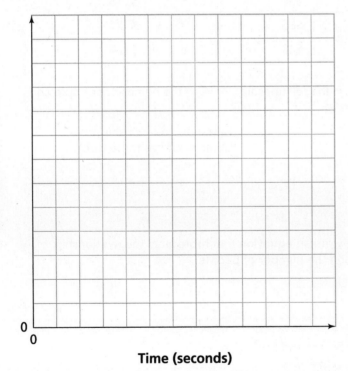

Distance (meters)

Time (seconds)

Labsheet 2ACE   Exercise 4

The student council asks for cost estimates for a skating party to celebrate the end of the school year.

5. The following tables represent the costs from two skating companies: Rollaway Skates and Wheelie's Skates and Stuff.

Rollaway Skates

Number of People	Cost
0	$0
1	$5
2	$10
3	$15
4	$20
5	$25
6	$30
7	$35
8	$40

Wheelie's Skates and Stuff

Number of People	Cost
0	$100
1	$103
2	$106
3	$109
4	$112
5	$115
6	$118
7	$121
8	$124

a. For each company, is the relationship between the number of people and cost **linear**? Explain.

> **Hint:** For a relationship to be linear, what has to be true?

b. For each company, write an **equation** that represents the relationship between the cost and the number of people.

Rollaway Skates: $C =$

Wheelie's Skates and Stuff: $C =$

What is the dependent variable?

What is the independent variable?

Labsheet 2ACE   Exercise 4

c. Describe how you can use the **table** or a **graph** to find when the costs of the two plans are equal.

> **Hint:** Making a graph for both companies on the same axes may help you answer this question.

Skating Company Costs

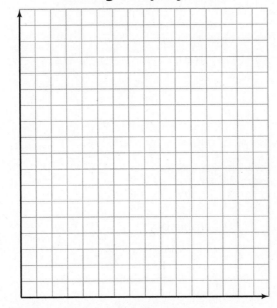

Cost (C)

People (p)

How can this information help the student council decide which company to choose?

> **Hint:** How would you decide which company to choose?

Labsheet 3.2   Pouch-and-Coin Situations

A. In parts (1)–(6) below, each pouch contains the same number of $1 gold coins. Also, the total number of coins on eah side of the equation is the same.

- Find the number of gold coins in each pouch. Write down your steps so that someone else could follow your steps to find the number of coins in a pouch.

- Describe how you can check your answer. That is, how do you know you have found the correct number of gold coins in each pouch?

1.

2.

3.

Labsheet 3.2 Pouch-and-Coin Situations

4.

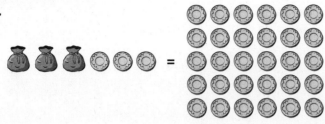

5.

6.

Labsheet 3.3 Pouch-and-Coin Equations

A. For each situation, find the number of coins in each pouch. Record your answers in the table below.

- In the second column, use your method from Problem 3.2 to find the number of gold coins in each pouch.
- In the third column, write an equation that represents the situation. Use x to represent the number of gold coins in each pouch. Use the number 1 to represent each coin. Then, use your equation to find the number of gold coins in each pouch.
- Check your answer.

Picture	Solution Using Coins and Pouches	Solution Using Equations	Check Your Answer
1.			
2.			
3.			
4.			

Labsheet 3ACE   Exercise 1

1. Ms. Chang's class decides to use the *Cool Tee's* company to make their T-shirts. The following equation represents the relationship between cost C and the number of T-shirts n.

$$C = 2n + 20$$

   a. The class wants to buy 25 T-shirts from *Cool Tee's*. Describe how you use a **table** and a **graph** to find the cost of 25 T-shirts.

   Hint: If you are unsure, try using a table or a graph and then explain.

T-shirt Cost

n (T-shirts)	0	1	5	10	15	20	25
C (cost)	$20						

How can you use the **table**?

T-shirt Cost

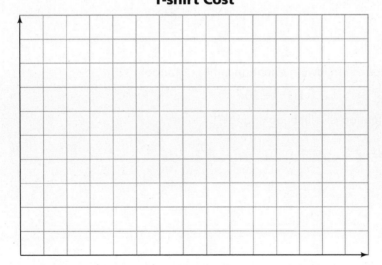

Cost (C)

Number of T-Shirts (n)

How can you use the **graph**?

Labsheet 3ACE   Exercise 1

b. Suppose the class has $80 to spend on T-shirts. Describe how you can use a table and a grpah to find the number of T-shirts the class cn buy.

Hint: Refer to your graph and table from part (a).

How could you use the **table**?

How could you use the **graph**?

c. Taleah writes the following equation in her notebook:

$$C = 2(15) + 20$$

What information is Taleah looking for?

d. Keisha uses the **coordinates** (30, 80) to find information about the cost of the T-shirts. What information is she looking for?

Labsheet 3ACE   Exercise 41

In Symbols	On a Number Line	In Words
a. $x > -4$		
b. $x \leq 2$		all numbers less than or equal to 2
c. $3 < x$		
d.		
e.		all numbers greater than negative 3

Labsheet 3ACE   Exercise 54

Airplane Flight Times

Distance (mi)	NYC to SF Time (h)	SF to NYC Time (h)
0		
200		
400		
600		

Labsheet 3ACE   Exercise 54

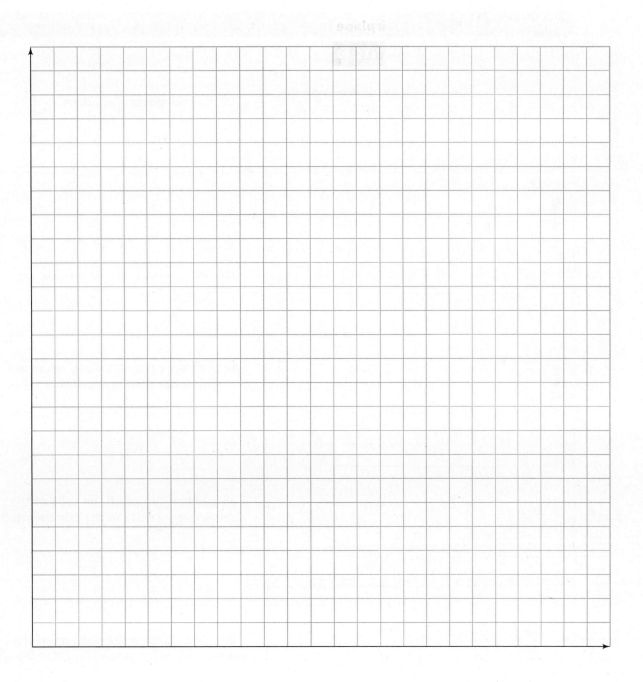

Labsheet 3ACE   Exercise 58

	In Symbols	On a Number Line	In Words
a.			all positive numbers
b.	$x^2 < 9$		all numbers whose squares are less than 9
c.			all numbers whose absolute values are greater than or equal to 2
d.	$x^3 > x$		all numbers for which the cube of the number is greater than the number itself
e.	$x + \frac{1}{x} > 1$		all numbers for which the sum of the number and its reciprocal is greater than 1

Labsheet 4.1   Stair Measurement Table

A. 1. Determine the steepness of a set of stairs in your school or home. To calculate the steepness you will need to:

- measure the rise and run of at least two steps in the set of stairs.
- make a sketch of the stairs, and label the sketch with the measurements you found.
- find the ratio of rise to run.

	Rise	Run	Ratio of Rise to Run	Sum of Rise and Run
Step 1				
Step 2				
Step 3				
Step 4				

Labsheet 4.2   Linear Relationships

Given Representation	Slope	y-Intercept	Equation
Graph 1 graph			
Graph 2 graph			
Table 1 <table><tr><td>x</td><td>−6</td><td>−4</td><td>−2</td><td>0</td><td>2</td><td>4</td></tr><tr><td>y</td><td>−10</td><td>−7</td><td>−4</td><td>−1</td><td>2</td><td>5</td></tr></table>			
Table 2 <table><tr><td>x</td><td>1</td><td>2</td><td>3</td><td>4</td><td>5</td><td>6</td></tr><tr><td>y</td><td>4.5</td><td>4.0</td><td>3.5</td><td>3.0</td><td>2.5</td><td>2.0</td></tr></table>			
Equation 1 $y = 2.5x + 5$			$y = 2.5x + 5$
Equation 2 $y = 20 - 3x$			$y = 20 - 3x$

Labsheet 4ACE Exercise 7

3. Seven possible descriptions of lines are listed below

   i. positive slope   **v.** negative slope

   ii. y-intercept equals 0   **vi.** passes through the point (1, 2)

   iii. slope of zero   **vii.** positive y-intercept

   iv. negative y-intercept

For each equation, **list _all_ of the descriptions i–vii** (above) that describe the
<u>graph of that equation</u>. Part (a) has been done for you as an example.

> **Hint:** Graphing these equations on
> graph paper or a graphing calculator
> may help you answer the questions.

a. $y = 2x$

   i. positive slope: 2 is a positive number.

   iii. y-intercept equals 0: The line passes through the point (0, 0).

   iv. passes through the point (1, 2): When $x = 1$, $y = 2$, so the line passes
                      through the point (1, 2).

b. $y = 3 - 3x$

c. $y = 2x + 3$

d. $y = 5x - 3$

e. $y = 2$

Labsheet 4.4 Linear Logic Activity

The graph below shows two intersecting lines.

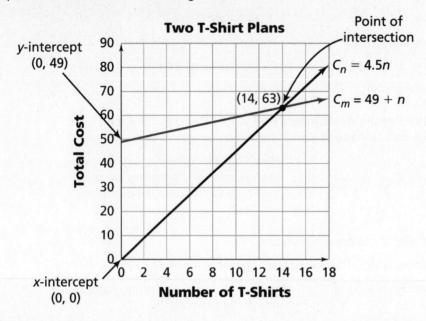

Complete the idea web by connecting related terms. On each connecting line you draw, write a description of the relationship.

y-intercept

x-intercept

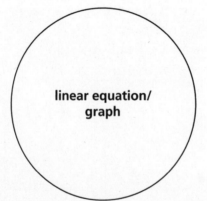

linear equation/ graph

slope

point of intersection

Unit Project   Wasted Water Experiment

Time (s)	Amount of Water (ml)
5	
10	
15	
20	
25	
30	
35	
40	
45	
50	
55	
60	

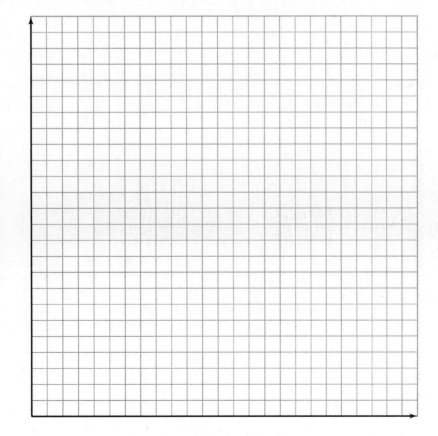

Amount of Water (ml)

Time (s)

Unit Project   Ball Bounce Experiment

Drop Height (cm)	Bounce Height (cm)

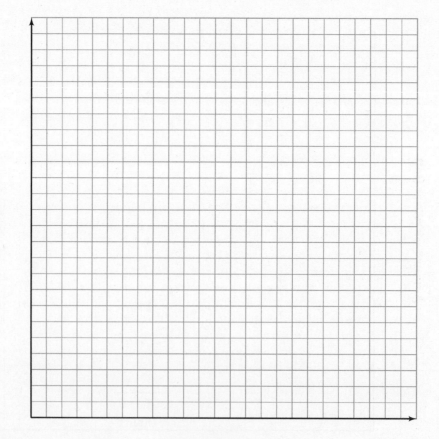

Bounce Height (cm)

Drop Height (cm)

Name .... Date .... Class ....

Moving Straight Ahead

Check Up 1 *for use after Investigation 1*

....

1. **a.** Which of the following tables represent linear relationships?
   Circle your choice(s).

Table 1	
Time (s)	Distance (m)
0	5
1	10
2	12
3	16
4	20

Table 2	
Distance (km)	Money ($)
0	0
1	10
2	20
3	30
4	40

Table 3	
Days	Money ($)
0	10
1	8
2	6
3	4
4	2

   b. Write an equation for one of the tables that represents a linear relationship.

   c. Which table(s), if any, represents a proportional relationship? Explain.

2. Each graph below represents a linear relationship between time and distance.
   For each graph, what is the rate of change?

a.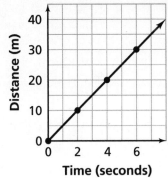

b.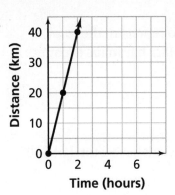

c.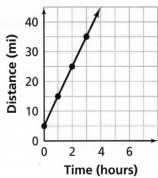

Rate: _____   Rate: _____   Rate: _____

Check Up 1 (continued)

3. a. Jason is participating in a walkathon. He writes the equation $m = 2d + 50$ to represent the amount of money he collects from each sponsor for walking d kilometers. What number represents the rate of change?

b. Cierra is keeping track of the amount of money in her lunch account each week. She writes the equation $A = -6w + 40$. What number represents the rate of change?

4. Mark opens a bank account with $20. He plans to put in $5 each week.

a. Complete the table below to show the **total** amount of money Mark has in his bank account from 0 to 10 weeks.

Time (weeks)											
Money ($)											

b. Use the grid to make a graph that matches the table.

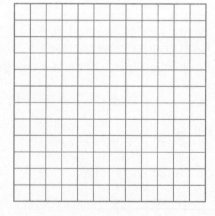

c. Write an equation to represent the **total** amount of money Mark has in his account over time.

d. In which week will Mark have a total of $60? Explain your reasoning.

Partner Quiz *for use after Investigation 2*

1. The graph of the money Jake earns while babysitting is shown below.

Jake's Babysitting

Money Jake Made (vertical axis)

Hours (horizontal axis)

a. Put a scale on each axis that makes sense for this situation. Explain why you chose the scales you did.

b. Based on the scale you chose in part (a), what would the equation of the graph be?

c. If the line of this graph were steeper, what would it tell you about the money Jake is making? Write an equation for such a line.

Partner Quiz (continued)

2. Rachael's backyard swimming pool is being emptied by a pump. The amount of water in the pool W in gallons at any time t in hours is given by the following equation:

$$W = 9,000 - 250t$$

   a. How many gallons of water are being pumped out each hour? Explain how you got your answer.

   b. After 11 hours, how much water is left in the pool? Explain.

   c. How much water was in the pool at the start? Explain.

   d. How long will it take to empty the pool? Explain.

3. Jabal and Michael are walking to school and agree to leave their homes at the same time. Jabal leaves his house walking 2 meters per second. Michael leaves his house walking 2.5 meters per second. Jabal's house is 100 meters closer to school than Michael's house. After how long are the boys walking together? Show all your work.

Labsheet PQ Partner Quiz

2. Rachael's backyard swimming pool is being emptied by a pump. The amount of water in the pool W (measured in gallons) at any time t (measured in hours) is given by the following equation:

$W = -250t + 9{,}000$

a. How many **gallons of water** are being pumped out **each hour**?

Explain how you got your answer.

b. After 11 hours, **how much water is left** in the pool?

Explain.

c. How much water was in the pool **at the start**?

Explain.

d. How long will it take the pool to **empty** (when $W = 0$)?

Explain.

Check Up 2 *for use after Investigation 3*

....

1. Find the value of the indicated variable.

    a. Suppose $y = 2x + 10$. Find y if $x = -2$.

    b. Suppose $y = 2x - 2.5$. Find x if $y = 10$.

2. Solve each equation to find the value of x.

    a. $4x + 10 = 22$

    b. $3x + 9 = 6x$

    c. $2(x + 3) = 18$

    d. $2x + 15 = 27 - 4x$

Name .... Date .... Class ....

Moving Straight Ahead

Check Up 2 (continued)

3. LaShawn wants to buy some music online. There are two plans to choose from. The first plan is a flat rate of $1.29 per download. The second plan has a membership fee of $21 and a fee of $.99 per download. Let x be the number of downloads and C be the cost.

$$\text{Plan 1: } C = 1.29x$$

$$\text{Plan 2: } C = 21 + 0.99x$$

a. When are the costs of the two plans equal to each other? Explain.

b. What is the y-intercept of the line for each equation? What does it mean in this context?

c. What is the constant rate of change for each relationship? What does it mean in this context?

d. For Plan 1, how many downloads are possible if the total cost is at most $15? Explain.

Unit Test Correlation

Unit Test Item	Problem
Item 1, parts (a) and (b)	Problem 4.2
Item 2	Problem 1.2
Item 3, parts (a), (b), and (c)	Problem 3.4
Item 4	Problem 3.4
Item 5	Problem 4.2
Item 6, parts (a) and (b)	Problem 1.3
Item 6, parts (c), (d), (e), and (f)	Problem 4.2
Item 6, parts (g) and (h)	Problem 3.5

Unit Test

1. Use the graph at the right.

   a. Find the slope of the line.

   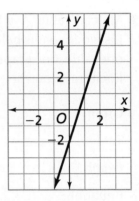

   b. Find the equation of the line.

2. Does the table below represent a linear relationship? If so, write an equation for that relationship. If not, explain.

Time (s)	Distance (m)
0	11
3	17
7	25
9	29
10	31

3. Solve each equation for x. Show your work.

   a. $3x + 8 = 35$ **b.** $12 + 5x = 7x + 3$ **c.** $3(x + 1) = 12$

4. **Multiple Choice** Which of the following expressions is not equivalent to the others? Explain.

   A. $6(x - 1) + 5$ **B.** $6x - 1$ **C.** $6(1 - x) + 5$ **D.** $5 + 6x - 6$

Unit Test (continued)

5. Match a table (A–D) with a graph (E–H) and an equation (J–M).
List your results below in four groups, where each group contains
one table, one graph, and one equation that all represent the same
linear relationship.

Group 1:

Table: _____

Graph: _____

Equation: _____

Group 2:

Table: _____

Graph: _____

Equation: _____

Group 3:

Table: _____

Graph: _____

Equation: _____

Group 4:

Table: _____

Graph: _____

Equation: _____

A.

x	y
−2	−5
−1	−3
0	−1
1	1
2	3

B.

x	y
−2	3
−1	2
0	1
1	0
2	−1

C.

x	y
−2	1.5
−1	1.5
0	1.5
1	1.5
2	1.5

D.

x	y
−2	−3
−1	−1
0	1
1	3
2	5

E.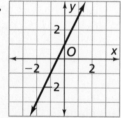

F.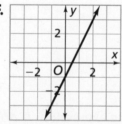

G.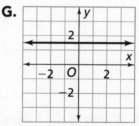

H.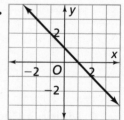

J. $y = 1.5$ **K.** $y = 2x - 1$ **L.** $y = 2x + 1$ **M.** $y = -x + 1$

Unit Test (continued)

6. To encourage new customers, a new movie theater is offering different ways to pay for a movie.

   - Members: $75 a year plus $2 per movie

   - Nonmembers: $5.75 to see a movie

   a. Make one table that shows the number of movies n and the cost for members C_1. Make another table that shows the number of movies n and the cost for nonmembers C_2. For both tables, include values of n from 0 to 50 movies, in increments of 10.

   b. On the same set of axes, graph the relationship between cost and number of movies for members and for nonmembers.

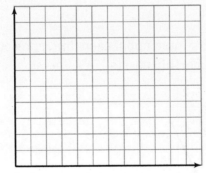

Unit Test (continued)

c. Write equations that you can use to calculate the cost for members C_1 and nonmembers C_2 for any number of movies n.

Equation for members: _____

Equation for nonmembers: _____

d. What is the slope of each line in part (c)?

Slope of equation for members: _____

Slope of equation for nonmembers: _____

e. What information does the slope of each line represent about the membership and nonmembership costs?

f. Explain how you could find the slope from a table, a graph, and an equation.

g. What information does the y-intercept of each line represent about the membership and nonmembership costs?

h. For what number of movies will the cost be the same for both members and nonmembers? Explain how you found your answer.

Self Assessment

Mathematical Ideas

After studying the mathematics in this Unit:

    1. a. I learned these things about mathematics:

        b. Here are page numbers of notebook entries that give evidence of what I have learned, along with descriptions of what each entry shows:

    2. a. These are the mathematical ideas that I am still struggling with:

        b. This is why I think these ideas are difficult for me:

        c. Here are page numbers of notebook entries that give evidence of what I am struggling with, and descriptions of what each entry shows:

Class Participation

I contributed to the classroom **discussion** and understanding of the mathematics in this Unit when I ... (Give examples.)

Self Assessment (continued)

Learning Environment

Rate each learning activity listed below using this scale:

1. I consistently struggled to understand the mathematics and I'm still not sure that I understand it.

2. I struggled somewhat but now I understand more than I did.

3. I had to work, but I feel confident that I understand now.

4. I understood everything pretty easily and I feel confident that I know the mathematics in these problems.

5. Everything came easily. I knew most of the mathematics before we did this.

Learning Activities

_____ Problems from the Investigations

_____ ACE Homework Assignments

_____ Mathematical Reflections

_____ Check Ups

_____ Partner Quiz

_____ Looking Back

_____ Unit Test

Check any of the following that you feel are the most helpful in adding to the success of your learning.

☐ Working on my own in class

☐ Discussing a problem with a partner

☐ Working in a small group of 3 or 4 people

☐ Discussing a problem as a whole class

☐ Hearing how other people solved the problem

☐ Summarizing the mathematics as a class and taking notes

☐ Completing homework assignments

Notebook Checklist

Place a ✔ next to each item you have completed.

Notebook Organization

_____ Problems and Mathematical Reflections are labeled and dated.

_____ Work is neat and easy to find and follow.

Vocabulary

_____ All words are listed.   _____ All words are defined or described.

Assessments

_____ Check Up   _____ _____

_____ Partner Quiz   _____ _____

_____ Unit Test   _____ _____

Assignments

_____ _____   _____ _____

_____ _____   _____ _____

_____ _____   _____ _____

_____ _____   _____ _____

_____ _____   _____ _____

_____ _____   _____ _____

_____ _____   _____ _____

_____ _____   _____ _____

_____ _____   _____ _____

Assessment Answers

Check Up 1

1. a. Tables 2 and 3 represent linear relationships.

   b. For Table 2: $y = 10x$, where y is the money in dollars and x is the distance in kilometers.
   For Table 3: $y = 10 - 2x$, where y is the money in dollars and x is the time in days.

   c. Table 2; the graph goes through $(0, 0)$, and the ratio of distance to amount of money is the same for each ordered pair.

2. a. 5 meters per second; as x increases by 1 second, y increases by 5 meters.

   b. 20 kilometers per hour; as x increases by 1 hour, y increases by 20 kilometers.

   c. 10 miles per hour; as x increases by 1 hour, y increases by 10 miles.

3. a. The coefficient of d is the rate of change, so Jason collects $2 per kilometer.

   b. The equation can be written as $A = 40 + (-6w)$, so the rate of change is -6 dollars per week.

4. a.

Week	Money in Account
0	$20
1	$25
2	$30
3	$35
4	$40
5	$45
6	$50
7	$55
8	$60
9	$65
10	$70

b.

Mark's Bank Account

c. $y = 20 + 5x$

236

Assessment Answers *(continued)*

d. Week 8; you can use the table to see where $60 appears in the Money in Account column, which is Week 8. If you use the graph, find the point on the line with a y-coordinate of 60, and then find the x-coordinate of that point. If you use the equation, substitute 60 for y (which represents the total amount of money in the account) and solve the equation for x (which represents the week).

Partner Quiz

1. Answers will vary. Sample answers are given for a rate of $4 per hour.
   a. Sample answer:

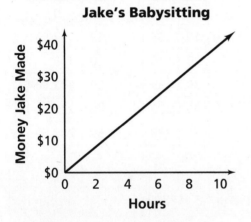

Jake's Babysitting

   b. Sample answer: $y = 4x$
   c. If the line were steeper, it would mean that Jake's rate of dollars per hour is greater. Answers for the equation will vary. Possible answer: $y = 6x$.

2. **a.** 250 gallons are being pumped out of Rachel's pool per hour. The coefficient of t is -250, so as 1 hour passes, W decreases by 250. Students could also make a table of values or a graph and see the same rate of change.

   b. After 11 hours, there are $9000 - 250(11) = 6{,}250$ gallons of water left in the pool. Explanations may vary. Students may use a table, a graph, or numeric reasoning.
   c. When $t = 0$, $W = 9{,}000$, so 9,000 gallons were in the pool at the start.
   d. It takes 36 hours to empty the pool. Students should find the value of t when $W = 0$. They can use a table, a graph, or an equation. If they use an equation, they should set $W = 0$ and solve for t: $9{,}000 - 250t = 0$
$$-250t = -9{,}000$$
$$t = 36$$

3. It takes 200 seconds, or 3 minutes 20 seconds, for Michael to catch up to Jabal. One way to solve this problem is to write an equation for each person's distance from Jabal's home. When the two distances are equal, Jabal and Michael will meet. Jabal's distance from Michael's house is given by the equation $y = 100 + 2x$. Michael's distance from his own house is given by $y = 2.5x$.
   Students may make a table and find the row in which the values for distance are the same. They may graph both equations and see where the lines intersect. They may also set Jabal's and Michael's equations equal to each other and solve for x: $100 + 2x = 2.5x$
$$100 = 0.5x$$
$$x = 200$$

Assessment Answers *(continued)*

Check Up 2

1. **a.** $y = 6$; students may make a table for this equation or may substitute the value for x in the equation.
   b. $x = 6.25$; students may make a table for this equation or may substitute the value for y in the equation and solve for x.

2. **a.** $x = 3$
   b. $x = 3$
   c. $x = 6$
   d. $x = 2$

3. **a.** When LaShawn purchases 70 songs, the cost will be the same for both plans.
   b. Plan 1: The y-intercept is 0, which means that there is no upfront cost. If you buy 0 songs, you pay $0.
   Plan 2: The y-intercept is 21, which means that there is an upfront cost of $21 before you buy any songs.
   c. Plan 1: The constant rate of change is $1.29 per song, the coefficient of x.
   Plan 2: The constant rate of change is $.99 per song.
   d. 11 downloads; *at most* means "less than or equal to," so you can write the inequality $1.29x \leq C$ for Plan 1. If you substitute 15 for C, you get $1.29x \leq 15$. Since the solution is $x \leq 11.63$, and the number of songs must be a whole number, you can download at most 11 songs.

Unit Test

1. **a.** The slope is 3. Encourage students to check several points on the line. For example, the slope using $(0, -2)$ and $(1, 1)$ is 3, as is the slope between $(1, 1)$ and $(2, 4)$.
   b. $y = 3x - 2$

2. Yes. The equation is $y = 2x + 11$.

3. **a.** $x = 9$
   b. $x = 4.5$
   c. $x = 3$

4. C; when simplified, the other three expressions are equivalent to $6x - 1$. When choice C is simplified, the expression is $-6x + 11$.

5. **Note:** Since students are asked to form four groups, the naming of each group is arbitrary. Sample answer:
   Group 1: A, F, K
   Group 2: B, H, M
   Group 3: C, G, J
   Group 4: D, E, L

6. **a.**

n	C_1
0	75
10	95
20	115
30	135
40	155
50	175

n	C_2
0	0
10	57.50
20	115
30	172.50
40	230
50	287.50

   b.

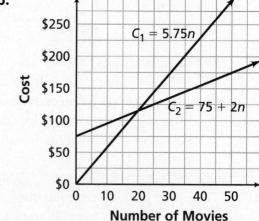

   c. $C_1 = 75 + 2n$
   $C_2 = 5.75n$

Assessment Answers (continued)

d. The slope of the line for members is 2. The slope of the line for nonmembers is 5.75.

e. The slope of each line represents the constant rate of change, or the cost per movie.

f. From the table, you can compare the quantities in any two rows. The slope is the ratio of the change in cost to the change in number of movies. From the graph, you can find the slope using any two points on the line. The slope is the ratio of the vertical change to the horizontal change. From the equations, the slope is the coefficient of n in each equation.

g. The y-intercept represents the cost if a person does not go to the movies at all. For a member, the y-intercept is 75. For a nonmember, the y-intercept is 0.

h. 20 movies
$$75 + 2x = 5.75x$$
$$75 = 3.75x$$
$$20 = x$$

Note: Students may also use the table or graph to answer this question.

Looking Back Answers

1. a. $I = 4.50x$
b. $E = 1.25x + 130$
c. See Figure 1.
d.

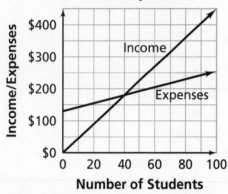

Theater Income and Expenses

y-axis: Income/Expenses — $400, $300, $200, $100, $0

Labels: Income, Expenses

x-axis: 0 20 40 60 80 100

Number of Students

e. Income: As the number of students x increases by 1, income increases by $4.50.
Expenses: As the number of students x increases by 1, expenses increase by $1.25.
For each increase of 10 students, expenses increase by $12.50.

f. Use the answers for part (a) and part (b).
Set $I = E$ and solve for x:
$4.50x = 1.25x + 130$
$x = 40$

g. Profit = Income − Expenses
$= 4.50x - 1.25x - 130$
$= 3.25x - 130$

h. **i.** $1.25x + 130 < 255; x > 100$
ii. $4.50x > 675; x > 150$

2. a. **i.** The purpose of this question is to get students to think about the meaning of slope and the meaning of y-intercept. Student answers will vary, but the following ideas should be included: "When $x = 0$, there is a loss of $115." and "There is a profit of $3 for every one student."
ii. Student responses should include the idea that as the number of students x increases by one, profit increases by 3.
iii. Students should say that 3 represents the slope of the line and -115 represents the y-intercept.

Figure 1

Theater Income and Expenses

Number of Students, x	0	10	20	30	40	50	60	70
Income, I ($)	$0	$45	$90	$135	$180	$225	$270	$315
Expenses, E ($)	$130	$142.50	$155	$167.50	$180	$192.50	$205	$217.50

Looking Back Answers (continued)

b. **i.** Set the profit equation equal to 0 and solve for x:
$$3x - 115 = 0$$
$$x = 38.33$$

ii. Set the profit equation equal to 100 and solve for x:
$$3x - 115 = 100; x = 71.67$$
So, the number of students needed is 72.

Since neither the break-even nor the $100-profit figure occurs for a whole number of students, there might be some disagreement about the "right" answers. Common usage assumes an interpretation of the questions as "What is the minimum number of tickets that needs to be purchased for the theater not to lose money or to earn at least $100 in profit?"

c. First, find the profit equation for Problem 1 by subtracting expenses from income. Then, set this profit equation equal to the profit equation from Problem 2. Solve for x.
$$3.25x - 130 = 3x - 115; x = 60$$
A group of 60 students produces a profit of $65 for either theater.

3. **a.** The variables are: number of students, income, expenses, and profit.

b. income and number of students, expenses and number of students, profit and income, profit and expenses

c. Answers will vary. Responses should include the idea that, in each case, a constant change in the independent variable (x) produces a constant change in the dependent variable (y).

4. All of the relationships are linear. In the tables, the output values (y) change by a constant amount as the input values (x) increase. The graph of each of these relationships is a straight line. The symbolic rule (equation) for each relationship is linear—each contains no exponent larger than one and is of the form $y = mx + b$.

5. The slopes describe how the output values (y) change as the input values (x) change. The y-intercept describes the output value for which the corresponding input value is 0 (where the line intersects the y-axis). The x-intercept describes the input value for which the y-value is 0 (where the line intersects the x-axis).

6. The slopes describe the constant rate of change in the output (y) as the input (x) changes. In the tables, the x-intercepts will be the ordered pairs for which $y = 0$, and the y-intercepts will be the ordered pairs for which $x = 0$.

7. **a.** In Problem 1, part (f), make tables of values for the income and expense expressions and look for a value of x that makes the two expressions equal. In Problem 2, part (c), write profit expressions for each theater as income minus expenses. Then produce tables of values for each profit expression and look for values of x that make the two expressions equal.

b. Graph both equations on the same coordinate grid and find the point of intersection.

c. Set the income and expense expressions equal to one another and solve for x.

Looking Back Answers *(continued)*

8. The purpose of this question is to get students to think about the various useful mathematical tools that they are acquiring and when each is most useful. Varied answers often mention that a graph gives a quick overall picture of a relationship, a table gives specific numerical information more directly, and a formula gives a tool for calculating outputs for any input.

Parent Letters

Labsheets

Assessments

Dear Family,

The next Unit in your child's mathematics class this year is **What Do You Expect?** Students will gain an understanding of experimental and theoretical probabilities and the relationship between them. The Unit also makes important connections between probability and rational numbers, geometry, statistics, science, and business.

Unit Goals

Students will learn to find probabilities by conducting trials and collecting experimental data, and also by analyzing situations to determine theoretical probabilities. Students will be using fractions, decimals, and percents to describe how likely certain events are.

To explore probability, students experiment with coins, number cubes, spinners, and paper cups. They examine simple games of chance to determine whether they are fair. Students analyze basketball free-throw success rates to determine average points per attempt. They also use a tree diagram or organized list to determine which team has a better chance of winning a 7-game series.

Homework and Having Conversations About The Mathematics

In your child's notebook, you can find worked-out examples, notes on the mathematics of the Unit, and descriptions of the vocabulary words.

You can help with homework and encourage sound mathematical habits during this Unit by asking questions such as:

- _What are the possible outcomes that can occur for the events in this situation?_
- _How could I determine the experimental probability of each of the outcomes?_
- _Is it possible to determine the theoretical probability of each of the outcomes?_
- _If so, what are these probabilities?_
- _How can I use probabilities to answer questions or make decisions about this situation?_

You can help your child with his or her work for this Unit in several ways:

- Discuss examples of statements or situations in everyday experiences that relate to the likelihood of certain events. Examples might include weather forecasting, the chances of a baby being a girl, the chances of your favorite college team winning a championship, or the likelihood of winning the lottery.

- Look at sports statistics with your child, and ask questions such as how a batting average or a free-throw average can be used to predict the likelihood of a hit the next time at bat or making two free-throw attempts.

- Look over your child's homework and make sure all questions are answered and that explanations are clear.

Common Core State Standards

While all of the Standards for Mathematical Practice are developed and used by students throughout the curriculum, particular attention is paid to _constructing viable arguments_ and _critiquing the reasoning of others_ as students make conjectures about the probability of events and games. _What Do You Expect?_ focuses largely on the Statistics and Probability domain, and also includes work from the Ratio and Proportional Relationships domain.

A few important mathematical ideas that your child will learn in _What Do You Expect?_ are on the next page. As always, if you have any questions or concerns about this Unit or your child's progress in class, please feel free to call.

Sincerely,

Important Concepts	Examples
Probability A number from 0 to 1 that describes the likelihood that an event will occur.	If a bag contains a red marble, a white marble, and a blue marble, then the probability of drawing a red marble is 1 out of 3 or $\frac{1}{3}$. We would write: $P(\text{red}) = \frac{1}{3}$.
Theoretical Probability A probability obtained by analyzing a situation. If all the **outcomes** (possible results) are equally likely, theoretical probability is the ratio of the number of outcomes you are interested in to the total number of outcomes.	If a number cube has six sides with the possible outcomes of rolling 1, 2, 3, 4, 5, or 6, then the probability of rolling a 3 is 1 out of 6. $P(\text{Rolling a 3}) =$ $\dfrac{\text{number of favorable outcomes}}{\text{number of possible outcomes}} = \dfrac{1 \text{ (there is 1 number 3 on the cube)}}{6 \text{ (there are 6 possible outcomes)}}$
Experimental Probability A probability found as a result of an experiment. This probability is the relative frequency of the **event** (a set of outcomes)—that is, the ratio of the number of times the event occurred compared to the total number of **trials** (one round of an experiment). Experimental probabilities are used to predict behavior over the long run.	You could find the experimental probability of getting a head (H) when you toss a coin by tossing the coin several times and keeping track of the outcomes. If you tossed a coin 50 times and heads occurred 23 times, the relative frequency of heads would be $\frac{23}{50}$. $P(\text{H}) = \dfrac{\text{number of times the event occured}}{\text{number of trials}} = \dfrac{\text{number of heads}}{\text{total number of tosses}} = \dfrac{23}{50}$
Random Events In mathematics, *random* means that any particular outcome is unpredictable, but the long-term behavior exhibits a pattern.	When you roll a number cube, the number that will result is uncertain on any one particular roll, but over a great many rolls, each number will occur about the same number of times.
Strategies for Finding Outcomes When situations involve more than one action, we need to generate the outcomes in a systematic way. An organized list or tree diagram is particularly useful.	**Organized List** Coin 1 Coin 2 Outcome H H H-H H T H-T T H T-H T T T-T **Tree Diagram** Coin 1 Coin 2 Outcome H → H H-H H → T H-T T → H T-H T → T T-T
Area Model A diagram in which fractions of the area correspond to probabilities in a situation. Area models are particularly helpful when the outcomes being analyzed are not equally likely, and larger areas can represent the more likely outcomes. Area models are also most helpful for outcomes involving more than one stage, such as *roll a die* and then *flip a coin*.	If there are three blue blocks and two red blocks in a container and one block is drawn out at a time, without replacing the block drawn each time, the area model at the right shows that the probability of getting two red blocks is $\frac{2}{20}$ or $\frac{1}{10}$. **First Draw** Second Draw: B B B R R B: BB BB BB BR BR B: BB BB BB BR BR R/B: BR BR BR RB RB R: BR BR BR RR RR
Expected Value or Long-Term Average The average payoff over many trials.	A game is played with two number cubes. You score 2 points when a sum of 6 is rolled, 1 point for a sum of 3, and 0 points for anything else. If you roll the cubes 36 times, you could expect to get a sum of 6 about five times and a sum of 3 about twice. This means that you could expect to score $(5 \times 2) + (2 \times 1) = 12$ points for 36 rolls, an average of $\frac{12}{36} = \frac{1}{3}$ point per roll. This is the expected value (or long-term average) of one roll.
Law of Large Numbers Experimental data gathered over many trials should produce probabilities that are close to the theoretical probabilities.	For 1 million flips, exactly 50% heads is improbable. But for 1 million flips, it would be extremely unlikely for the percent of heads to be less than 49% or more than 51%.

Estimada familia:

La siguiente Unidad de la clase de matemáticas de su hijo(a) este año es **¿Qué esperas?** En ella, los estudiantes comprenderán las probabilidades teórica y experimental y la relación entre ambas. Esta Unidad también realiza importantes conexiones entre la probabilidad y los números racionales, la geometría, la estadística, las ciencias y los negocios.

Objetivos de la unidad

Los estudiantes aprenderán a hallar probabilidades al realizar pruebas y recopilar datos experimentales y al analizar situaciones para determinar las probabilidades teóricas. Usarán fracciones, números decimales y porcentajes para describir qué tan probables son los eventos. Para explorar la probabilidad, experimentarán con monedas, cubos numéricos, flechas giratorias y vasos desechables. Examinarán juegos de probabilidad simples para determinar si son justos. Analizarán tasas de aciertos en tiros libres de básquetbol para determinar el promedio de puntos por intento. También usarán un diagrama de árbol o una lista organizada para determinar qué equipo tiene una mayor probabilidad de ganar una serie de 7 partidos.

Tareas y conversaciones acerca de las matemáticas

Usted puede ayudar a su hijo(a) con la tarea y fomentarle hábitos matemáticos firmes durante esta Unidad, haciéndole preguntas como:

- *¿Cuáles son los resultados posibles que pueden ocurrir para los eventos de esta situación?*
- *¿Cómo determinarías la probabilidad experimental de cada uno de los resultados?*
- *¿Es posible determinar la probabilidad experimental de cada uno de los resultados?*
- *Si es así, ¿cuáles son estas probabilidades?*
- *¿Cómo puedes usar las probabilidades para responder preguntas o tomar decisiones sobre esta situación?*

Usted puede ayudar a su hijo(a) con su trabajo para esta Unidad en varias formas:

- Comente ejemplos de enunciados o situaciones de experiencias de la vida diaria que se relacionan con la probabilidad de ciertos eventos. Algunos ejemplos incluyen los pronósticos del clima, las probabilidades de que un bebé sea niña, de que el equipo colegial favorito gane un campeonato o de ganar la lotería.

- Examine estadísticas deportivas junto con su hijo(a) y pregúntele, por ejemplo, si un promedio de bateo o un promedio de tiros libres se puede usar para predecir la probabilidad de un hit en el siguiente turno al bate o de encestar 2 tiros libres.

- Revise la tarea de su hijo(a) y asegúrese de que responda a todas las preguntas y de que sus explicaciones sean claras.

En el cuaderno de su hijo(a) puede encontrar ejemplos resueltos, notas sobre las matemáticas de la Unidad y descripciones de las palabras de vocabulario.

Estándares estatales comunes

Los estudiantes desarrollan y usan todos los Estándares de Prácticas Matemáticas a lo largo del curso. Se presta especial atención a *construir argumentos viables* y *evaluar el razonamiento de otros* a medida que hacen conjeturas sobre la probabilidad de eventos y juegos. *¿Qué esperas?* se enfoca principalmente en la rama de la Estadística y probabilidad, e incluye trabajo de las ramas de las Razones y las relaciones proporcionales.

Algunas importantes ideas matemáticas que su hijo(a) aprenderá en *¿Qué esperas?* se presentan en la siguiente página. Si usted tiene cualquier pregunta o preocupación acerca de esta Unidad, o con respecto al progreso de su hijo(a) en clase, por favor no dude en llamar.

Sinceramente,

Conceptos importantes	Ejemplos

Probabilidad
Un número de 0 a 1 que describe la probabilidad de que un evento ocurra.

Si una bolsa contiene una canica roja, una blanca y una azul, la probabilidad de sacar una canica roja es 1 de 3 ó $\frac{1}{3}$. Escribiríamos: $P(\text{roja}) = \frac{1}{3}$.

Probabilidad teórica
Probabilidad que se obtiene al analizar una situación. Si todos los **resultados** (resultados posibles) son igualmente probables, la probabilidad teórica es la razón del número de resultados que se desean al número total de resultados.

Si un cubo numérico tiene seis caras con los resultados posibles de caer en 1, 2, 3, 4, 5 ó 6, la probabilidad de que caiga en 3 es 1 de 6.

$P(\text{que caiga en 3}) =$

$\dfrac{\text{número de resultados favorables}}{\text{número de resultados posibles}} = \dfrac{1 \text{ (hay 1 número 3 en el cubo)}}{6 \text{ (hay 6 resultados posibles)}}$

Probabilidad experimental
Probabilidad que se halla como resultado de un experimento. Esta probabilidad es la frecuencia relativa de un **evento** (un conjunto de resultados), es decir, la razón del número de veces que el evento ocurrió en comparación con el número total de **pruebas** (un ronda de un experimento). Las probabilidades experimentales se usan para predecir un comportamiento a largo plazo.

Puedes hallar la probabilidad experimental de que una moneda caiga en cara (Ca) cuando la lanzas varias veces y anotas los resultados. Si lanzaste una moneda 50 veces y sacaste cara 23 veces, la frecuencia relativa de caras sería $\frac{23}{50}$.

$P(\text{Ca}) = \dfrac{\text{número de veces que el evento occurrió}}{\text{número de pruebas}} =$

$= \dfrac{\text{número de caras}}{\text{número total de lanzamientos}} = \dfrac{23}{50}$.

Eventos aleatorios
En matemáticas, *aleatorio* significa que cualquier evento en particular es impredecible, pero el comportamiento a largo plazo presenta un patrón.

Cuando tiras un cubo numérico, es incierto el número que resultará en un tiro en particular, pero después de muchos tiros, cada número habrá ocurrido más o menos el mismo números de veces.

Estrategias para hallar resultados
Cuando las situaciones incluyen más de una acción, se tienen que generar resultados de manera sistemática. Una lista organizada o diagrama de árbol es particularmente útil.

Lista organizada

Moneda 1	Moneda 2	Resultado
Ca	Ca	Ca-Ca
Ca	Cr	Ca-Cr
Cr	Ca	Cr-Ca
Cr	Cr	Cr-Cr

Diagrama de árbol

Moneda 1	Moneda 2	Resultado
Ca	Ca	Ca-Ca
	Cr	Ca-Cr
Cr	Ca	Cr-Ca
	Cr	Cr-Cr

Modelo de área
Un diagrama donde fracciones del área corresponden a las probabilidades de una situación. Los modelos de área son útiles cuando los resultados analizados no son igualmente probables y las áreas más grandes pueden representar los resultados más probables. Los modelos de área son útiles para resultados que incluyen más de una etapa, como *lanzar un dado* y luego *lanzar una moneda*.

Si en un recipiente hay tres bloques azules y dos rojos, y se saca un bloque cada vez sin reemplazarlo, el modelo de área de la derecha muestra que la probabilidad de sacar dos bloques rojos es $\frac{2}{20}$ ó $\frac{1}{10}$.

Primer saque

Segundo saque	A	A	A	R	R
A	AA	AA	AA	AR	AR
A	AA	AA	AA	AR	AR
R/A	AR	AR	AR	RA	RA
R	AR	AR	AR	RR	RR

Valor esperado o promedio a largo plazo
El resultado medio de varias pruebas.

En un juego se usan 2 cubos numéricos. Obtienes 2 puntos por un total de 6, 1 punto por un total de 3 y 0 puntos para cualquier otro resultado. Si tiras los cubos 36 veces, puedes esperar obtener una suma de 6 aprox. cinco veces y una suma de 3 aprox. dos veces. Así, puedes esperar obtener $(5 \times 2) + (2 \times 1) = 12$ puntos en 36 tiros, un promedio de $\frac{12}{36} = \frac{1}{3}$ por tiro. Este es el valor esperado (o promedio a largo plazo) de un tiro.

Ley de los números extensos
Los datos experimentales reunidos en muchas pruebas deben producir probabilidades cercanas a las probabilidades teóricas.

En 1 millón de lanzamientos, obtener exactamente 50% de caras es improbable. Pero en 1 millón de lanzamientos, sería muy improbable que el porcentaje de caras fuera menor que 49% o mayor que 51%.

248

Labsheet 1.1   Coin-Toss Results

Date	Result of Toss (H or T)	Number of Heads So Far	Fraction of Heads So Far	Percent of Heads So Far
1				
2				
3				
4				
5				
6				
7				
8				
9				
10				
11				
12				
13				
14				
15				
16				
17				
18				
19				
20				
21				
22				
23				
24				
25				
26				
27				
28				
29				
30				

Labsheet 1.2   Cup-Toss Results

Trial Number	Result (End or Side)
1	
2	
3	
4	
5	
6	
7	
8	
9	
10	
11	
12	
13	
14	
15	
16	
17	
18	
19	
20	
21	
22	
23	
24	
25	
26	
27	
28	
29	
30	
31	
32	
32	
34	
35	
36	
37	
38	
39	
40	
41	
42	
43	
44	
45	
46	
47	
48	
49	
50	

Labsheet 1.3   Matching Coins

Trial Number	Result (Match or No-match)
1	
2	
3	
4	
5	
6	
7	
8	
9	
10	
11	
12	
13	
14	
15	
16	
17	
18	
19	
20	
21	
22	
23	
24	
25	
26	
27	
28	
29	
30	

Labsheet 1ACE   Exercise 2

1. Suppose Kalvin tosses a coin to determine his breakfast cereal every day. He starts on his 12th birthday and continues until his 18th birthday. About how many times would you expect him to eat Cocoa Blast cereal?

> **Hint:** Refer back to Problem 1.1. How many choices of cereal does Kalvin have?

What is the probability that Kalvin will get to eat Cocoa Blast on one day?

How many years are there between Kalvin's 12th birthday and his 18th birthday?

How many days are there in one year?

How many days are there between Kalvin's 12th birthday and his 18th birthday?

About how many times do you expect him to eat Cocoa Blast cereal?

Labsheet 2.4 Probability Vocabulary

Fill in the blanks using words from the box below.

number cube	theoretical probability	outcomes
tree diagram	experimental probability	equally likely
organized list	spinner	coin

1.

_____

2.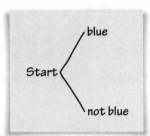

_____

3.

_____

4.

_____

5. Conducting experiments helps me find _____.

6. To identify possible combinations, I can use a(n) _____.

7. Results of an action or an event are also known as _____.

8. I need to count all possible outcomes to calculate the _____.

9. Events that have the same chance of occurring are _____.

Labsheet 2ACE   Exercise 11

11. Melissa is designing a birthday card for her sister. She has a blue, a yellow, a pink, and a green sheet of paper. She also has a black, a red, and a purple marker. Suppose Melissa chooses one sheet of paper and one marker at random.

Paper	Marker
Blue	Black
Yellow	Red
Pink	Purple
Green	

a. Make a tree diagram to find all of the possible color combinations. Use the one started below.

Paper   Markers

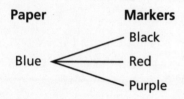

Yellow

Pink

Green

How many different combinations can Melissa make? _____

b. What is the probability that Melissa chooses pink paper and a red marker?

Labsheet 2ACE   Exercise 11

c. What is the probability that Melissa chooses blue paper?

What is the probability she does *not* choose blue paper?

d. What is the probability that she chooses a purple marker?

Labsheet 3.1   Kalvin's Spinner

Labsheet 3.2   Blank Spinner

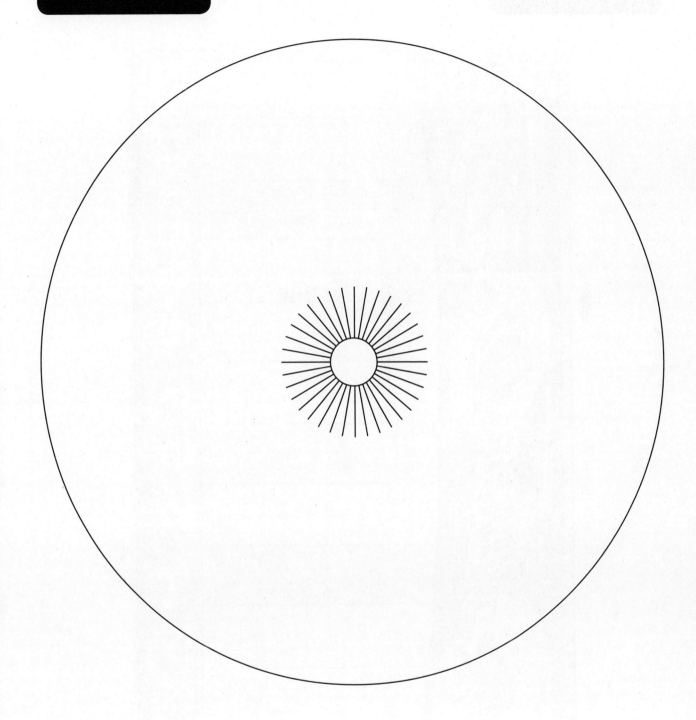

Labsheet 3.3   Roller Derby

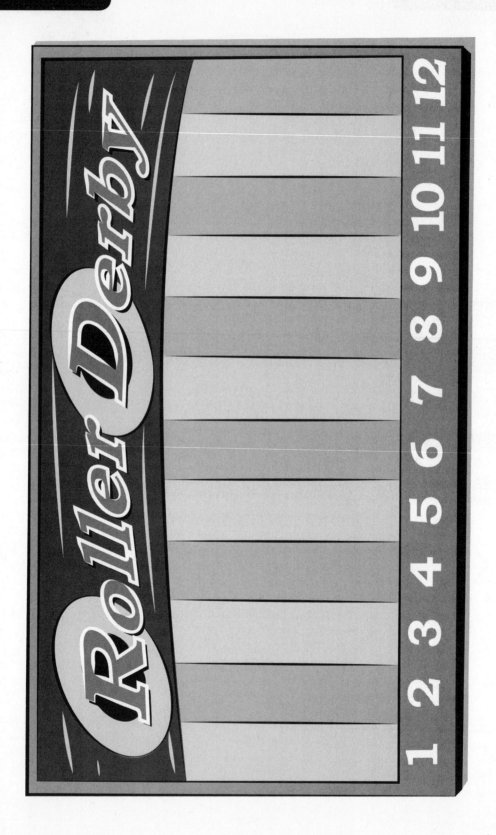

Labsheet 3ACE   Exercise 1

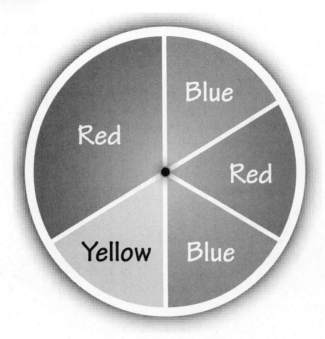

Labsheet 3ACE   Exercise 2

2. The cooks at Kyla's school make the spinners below to help them choose the lunch menu. They let the students take turns spinning. For parts (a)–(c), decide which spinner to choose. Explain your reasoning.

Spinner A

Spinner B

Hint: You may want to divide Spinner A and Spinner B into equal sections to answer the following questions. For example, Spinner A can be divided into 12 equal sections. Hot dogs would then be $\frac{2}{12}$ of the spinner. Spaghetti would be $\frac{2}{12}$. Lasagna would be _____, and Hamburger would be _____. Now you can do the same for Spinner B, if you want.

a. What spinner should you choose if your favorite lunch is pizza?

> **Hint:** What is the probability that Spinner A will land on the pizza section?

Labsheet 3ACE   Exercise 2

b. What spinner should you choose if your favorite lunch is lasagna?

> **Hint:** What is the probability that Spinner A will land on a lasagna section?

Explain why.

c. What spinner should you choose if your favorite lunch is hot dogs?

Explain why.

Labsheet 4.1   Area Model and Probabilities

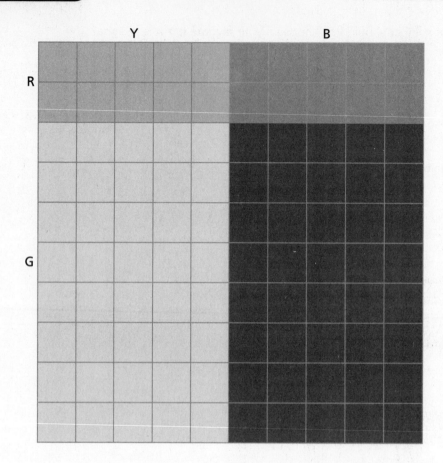

Labsheet 4.2   Making Purple

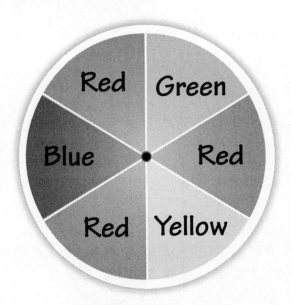

Spinner A

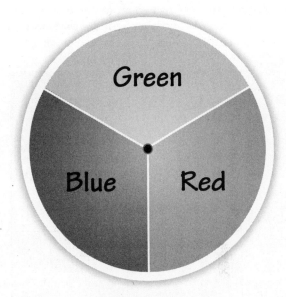

Spinner B

Labsheet 4ACE   Exercise 33

33. Fergus designs two more dartboards for the school carnival. A player plays
$1 to play and wins $2 if the dart lands in sections marked B. If the dart lands
in sections marked A, the player wins no money.

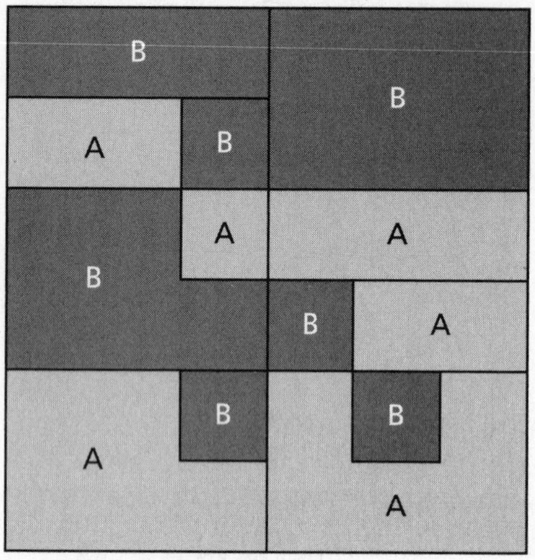

Dartboard 1

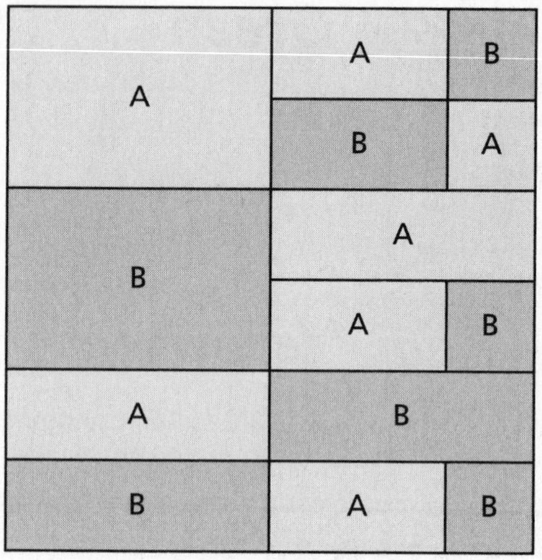

Dartboard 2

a. What is the probability of landing in sections marked **A** on Dartboard 1?
On Dartboard 2?

Dartboard 1:

Dartboard 2:

Explain.

b. How much money will the **player** expect to make (or lose) after 36 turns using **Dartboard 1?** Using Dartboard 2? (**Hint:** What is the probability of landing in a section marked B on Dartboard 1? On Dartboard 2? Remember that the cost to play 36 times must be subtracted from what each player makes.)

Dartboard 1:

Dartboard 2:

Explain.

c. How much money will the **carnival** expect to make (or lose) after 36 turns using **Dartboard 1?** Using **Dartboard 2?**

Dartboard 1:

Dartboard 2:

Explain.

d. Can the carnival expect to make a profit on this game with either board?

Explain.

Labsheet Choosing Paths Using Area Models

A. Carry out the experiment to simulate the 18 students playing the game and note the cave where each student ends.

B. What is the experimental probability of landing in Cave A? Of landing in Cave B?

C. Miguel draws this diagram to help him find the theoretical probabilities of ending in Cave A or in Cave B.

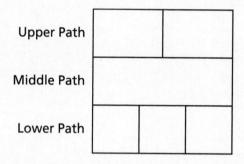

1. Explain what Miguel has done so far. Does this look reasonable?

2. Complete an area model to find the theoretical probabilities of ending in Cave A or Cave B. Show your work.

D. How are your experimental probabilities from Question A related to the theoretical probabilities?

E. Kenisha designs a new version of the game. It has a different arrangement of paths leading to Caves A and B. She makes the area model below to analyze the probabilities of ending in each cave.

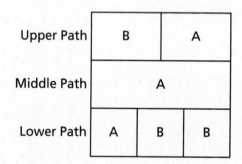

1. Create a path that fits the model.

2. Find the probability for each outcome.

Choosing Paths Using Area Models

This supplemental lesson is provided for teachers who need another opportunity to discuss area models with their students.

This supplemental lesson introduces a new probability context, that of analyzing paths in a game. At various places along the paths, students must choose a path at random until they end up in one of two caves. Students first simulate the game and assign probabilities using their simulation. An area model is then used to determine the theoretical probabilities.

Launch

Introduce the Choosing Paths game. Display the game screen, which is shown on Display Sheet 1: Choosing Paths Introduction. Discuss Kenisha's game to help the class focus on how the game is played and how to use a number cube to help make decisions at each split in the path.

Suggested Questions

- *Are you more likely to end in Cave A or in Cave B? Why?* (Some students may say Cave B because it is larger; some may say the caves have an equal chance of being entered because three paths lead into each room; some may say Cave A because the middle path leads directly into this cave.)

To help students better understand the paths, you could cover up all the diagram after the first split in the path, as below.

- *Suppose you are playing the game and have to make a random decision at the first split in the path about which part of the path (upper, middle, or lower) to follow. How can a number cube help?* (You could take the upper if 1 or 2 is rolled, the middle if 3 or 4 is rolled, and the lower if 5 or 6 is rolled.)

- *Does this give each of the paths the same chance of being chosen? Explain.* (Yes, since we have six equally outcomes on a number cube and want three equally likely outcomes for the paths, the previously described simulation will allow the same chance for each path to be chosen.)

- *What is the probability of selecting each one of these three paths?* $\left(\frac{1}{3}\right)$

Choosing Paths Using Area Models *(continued)*

Now move the paper to reveal the upper paths and again ask the question.

- *How can you use the number cube to help you decide which path to take if each is to have an equal chance?* (Let the upper path be selected if a 1, 2, or 3 is rolled and the lower path selected if a 4, 5, or 6 is rolled.)
- *What is the probability of selecting one of these paths?* $\left(\frac{1}{2}\right.$ for each fork of the path$\left.\right)$

Now focus on ways to simulate the maze. Explain to the class that a number cube is one way to simulate walking through the maze and choosing paths at random. Emphasize that choosing at random means that you can't choose paths by picking your favorite number or favorite direction. At each fork, every path must have exactly the same probability of being chosen. Play a version of the game with the class once or a couple of times to be sure students understand the rules. Provide students with number cubes so they can generate random choices.

Have students carry out the experiment 18 times and answer Questions A and B on the labsheet. Then move on to Questions C–E.

Explore

Play the game 18 times and record group results. As groups work, ask questions about what they are discovering.

Suggested Questions

- *Which cave seems to have the greater probability of the player entering it? What makes you think this?* (Cave A seems slightly more likely. If you take the upper path, there is a 50% chance of entering Cave A. If you take the lower path you will only have a $\frac{1}{3}$ chance of entering Cave A, but the middle path will go right into Cave A. The middle path seems to outweigh the other two paths.)
- *If you come to a fork that splits into three paths, what probability does each path have of being selected?* $\left(\frac{1}{3}\right)$
- *Suppose your first choice is to take one of three paths, each of which is followed by a choice of two paths. What is the probability that you will take any given second path?* $\left(\frac{1}{6}\right)$

Choosing Paths Using Area Models *(continued)*

When students move to the area model analysis to find a theoretical probability model, some students may try to label the top of the diagram. Here, labels do not work because each path may have different probabilities. The better way is to reallocate area allotted to a path into as many equal-sized parts as there are forks in the path (2, 0, or 3) as you read from the upper path to the middle path to the lower path. At this stage the diagram should look like the following.

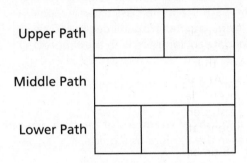

- *After the first division, what fraction of the total area of the square does each of the three paths represent?* $\left(\frac{1}{3}\right)$

Now students can make a diagram to show where you end for each of the options to get the following:

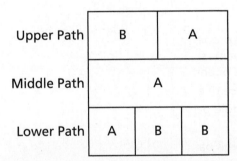

- *Now that we have divided a square to represent the different paths, what fraction would we assign to each part of the square?* $\left(\frac{1}{6}\right.$ *for each part of the upper path,* $\frac{1}{3}$ *for the middle path, and* $\frac{1}{9}$ *for each part of the lower path.* $\left.\right)$
- *What is the probability of landing in Cave A? In Cave B?* $\left(\frac{11}{18}\right.$ *for Cave A.* $\frac{7}{18}$ *for Cave B.* $\left.\right)$

As students work on Question E, have them put their path game on a large sheet of paper with the outcomes and probabilities for entering each cave.

Choosing Paths Using Area Models *(continued)*

Summarize

Collect groups' strategies for walking the maze and marking random path choices at each fork. Be sure to have the class confirm that these strategies make sense.

Have students share the experimental probabilities they found for each cave. Discuss reasons for variation in the data. Ask questions about other ways to make random choices at each split in the path. Help the class to pool their experimental data and to calculate the experimental probabilities based on all the groups' trials. Save the experimental data to compare with the theoretical data in Question C.

Ask students how their experimental prbability compared to their initial idea about the cave in which they would end.

Now move the students to Question C and look at examples of the area diagrams the students complete. Use the diagrams in the Explore as a guide.

Suggested Questions

- *How did you assign probabilities to ending in Cave A or Cave B?* (There were three different areas assigned to each cave.)

Cave A: $\frac{1}{6} + \frac{1}{3} + \frac{1}{9} = \frac{11}{18}$

Cave B: $\frac{1}{6} + \frac{1}{9} + \frac{1}{9} = \frac{7}{18}$

Some groups will partition the grid into equal-sized parts in order to find the probabilities. Partitioning into 18 parts is shown below.

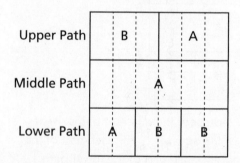

Another way to think about this is to write a number sentence for each probability and have the class connect the number sentence back to the area model. For example, the probability of landing in Cave B is:

$$\left(\frac{1}{3}\right)\left(\frac{1}{2}\right) + \left(\frac{1}{3}\right)\left(\frac{1}{3}\right) + \left(\frac{1}{3}\right)\left(\frac{1}{3}\right) = \frac{1}{6} + \frac{1}{9} + \frac{1}{9} = \frac{7}{18}$$

Choosing Paths Using Area Models (*continued*)

Choosing a way to simulate random events related to a particular problem is important. Discuss with the class other strategies that could have been used to simulate the path game.

- *Look back at the simulation we used to find the experimental probabilities of ending in Cave A or B. We used a number cube. Could we have used a spinner? If so, how?* (A six-section spinner can work just like a number cube. But we could also use several spinners depending on how many equally likely choices we have to make. In this game, we could use two spinners, one with three equal parts and one with two equal parts. Then you just spin the spinner that matches the number of choices.)

- *What are some other ideas about how to simulate the path game?* (Students might suggest colored cubes in buckets, pieces of paper labeled with choices, or other random devices.)

Note: Using the area model provides practice with writing equivalent fractions, adding, subtracting, and multiplying fractions. Subdividing the square twice is a model for multiplication of fractions that students studied in the Grade 6 Unit, *Let's Be Rational*. This is an opportunity to assess students' facility with fractions.

Check for Understanding

For a further check on whether students understand how to find the probabilities of successive events, use Display Sheet 2: More Paths.

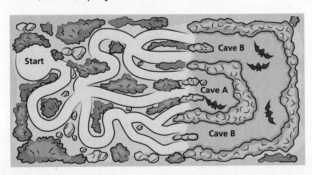

Give the class some time to think about the example. The associated area model for the example might look as follows:

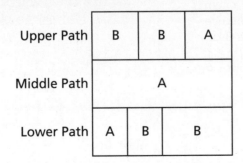

Adding the fractional parts of the drawing that represent ending in each cave gives

$\frac{1}{9} + \frac{1}{3} + \frac{1}{12} = \frac{19}{36}$ for Cave A and $\frac{1}{9} + \frac{1}{9} + \frac{1}{12} + \frac{1}{6} = \frac{17}{36}$ for Cave B.

Answers to Labsheet: Choosing Paths Using Area Models

A. Results will vary.

B. Answers may vary depending on the results in Question A. Combining all of the class data should bring the experimental probabilities close to the theoretical probabilities of $\frac{11}{18} \approx 61\%$ for Cave A and $\frac{7}{18} \approx 39\%$ for Cave B.

C. See diagrams in the Explore.

1. Miguel has recognized that each of the paths after the first split has a $\frac{1}{3}$ probability of being chosen. He has partitioned the square so that each of the three paths has the same probability.

2. See diagram and discussion in the Explore. $P(A) = \frac{11}{18}$ and $P(B) = \frac{7}{18}$.

D. If you combined the class's experimental data, their experimental probabilities should be close to the theoretical probabilities.

E. 1. Game screens will vary slightly, but should have a structure similar to the ones shown below. There are three main paths. The top path splits into two, the middle path does not split, and the bottom path splits into four. **Note:** Example C is a potential wrong answer. (The bottom path splits into four paths that are not each equally likely.)

Example a

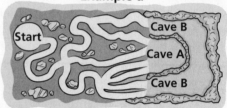

Example b

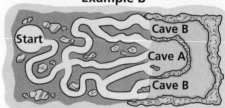

Example c: a wrong game

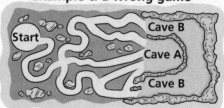

2. Cave A: $\frac{2}{3}$

$$\left(\frac{1}{3}\right)\left(\frac{1}{2}\right) + \left(\frac{1}{3}\right) + \left(\frac{1}{3}\right)\left(\frac{1}{4}\right) + \left(\frac{1}{3}\right)\left(\frac{1}{4}\right) =$$
$$\frac{1}{6} + \frac{1}{3} + \frac{1}{12} + \frac{1}{12} = \frac{2}{3}$$

Cave B: $\frac{1}{3}$

$$\left(\frac{1}{3}\right)\left(\frac{1}{2}\right) + \left(\frac{1}{3}\right)\left(\frac{1}{4}\right) + \left(\frac{1}{3}\right)\left(\frac{1}{4}\right) = \frac{1}{6} + \frac{1}{12} + \frac{1}{12} = \frac{1}{3}$$

Kenisha is designing a game involving paths that lead to caves. First, a player chooses either Cave A or Cave B. Next, the player starts at the beginning and chooses a path at random at each fork. Ending in the chosen cave wins.

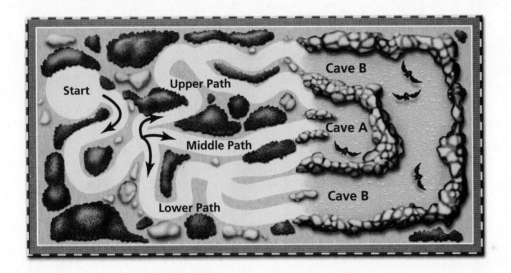

- Are you more likely to end in Cave A or in Cave B? Why?

The 18 students in Sarah's class design an experiment to play the game. For each trial, they trace the path and use a number cube to make the choice of direction at each fork.

- Is this a good way to find the experimental probability of the game? Why or why not?

- Are there other ways to make choices at a split in the path? Explain.

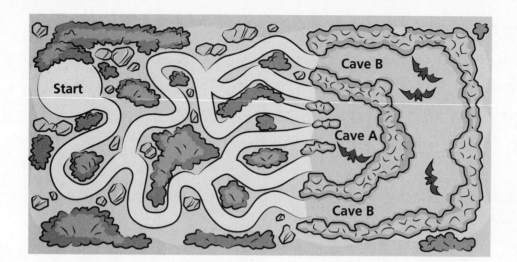

Labsheet 4.3 Nishi's One-and-One

Nishi's One-and-One

Nishi's One-and-One

Labsheet 4.4   One-and-One Free Throws

20% Free-Throw Percentage

P(0) _____
P(1) _____
P(2) _____

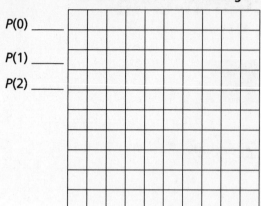

40% Free-Throw Percentage

P(0) _____
P(1) _____
P(2) _____

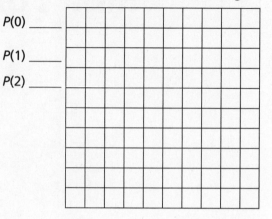

60% Free-Throw Percentage

P(0) _____
P(1) _____
P(2) _____

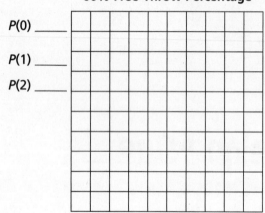

80% Free-Throw Percentage

P(0) _____
P(1) _____
P(2) _____

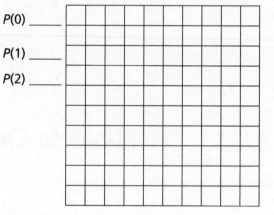

Labsheet 4.4 One-and-One Free Throws

Points Expected in 100 One-and-One Situations

Player's Free-Throw Percentage	Points			
	0	1	2	Expected Value, or Average
20%				
40%				
60%				
80%				

Points Expected in a One-and-One Situation

Labsheet 4ACE Exercise 20

Use the information in the table. It shows statistics for some of the players on a basketball team.

Free-Throw Statistics

Name	Free Throws Attempted	Free Throws Made	Percent Made
Gerrit	54	27	
David	49	39	
Ken	73	45	
Alex	60	42	

20. a. Which boy has the best chance of making his next free throw? (**Hint:** Doing part (b) could help you answer this question.)

Explain your reasoning.

b. What is the free-throw probability for each player?

Gerrit: Ken:

David: Alex:

Labsheet 5ACE   Exercise 1

1. It costs 6 tickets to play the Toss-a-Penny game at the school carnival. For each turn, a player tosses a penny **3 times**.

   If the penny lands heads up **2 or more times** in a turn, the player <u>wins 10 tickets</u> to spend on food and games.

   a. Suppose Benito plays the game 80 times. How many tickets can he **expect to win**?

   Either, complete a list of combinations that can occur if you flip a penny 3 times,

   H, H, T

   H, T, H

   or finish this tree diagram.

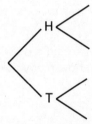

Labsheet 5ACE Exercise 1

b. What is the **average number of tickets** Benito can expect to win or lose per turn?

(**Hint:** Use your list or tree diagram from part (a) to find the probability that Benito will get 2 heads in his 3 flips of the penny.)

How many tickets would it cost Benito to play 80 times?
(**Hint:** Remember it costs 6 tickets to play once.)

Remember that Benito gets 10 tickets every time he wins. Based on the number of games he is expected to win, how many tickets will he win in total?

Based on the amount of tickets it costs Benito to play 80 games and the tickets he would receive if he won, how many tickets would he expect to have at the end of 80 games?

Labsheet 5.1   True/False Quiz

- Toss a penny to determine each quiz item.
- Write true (T) if a head shows and false (F) if a tail shows.
- After you have written your answers, your teacher will give you the correct answers.
- Mark your answers correct or incorrect. Record your score.

1. _____

2. _____

3. _____

4. _____

4 correct = 100, 3 correct = 75, 2 correct = 50, 1 correct = 25, 0 correct = 0

Score: _____

Name .... Date .... Class ....

What Do You Expect?

Check Up *for use after Investigation 2*

1. Rachel has tossed a fair coin ten times. It has landed heads up every time.

   a. Is this possible? Explain.

   b. Is this likely? Explain.

   c. Which of the following statements is true about what will happen when Rachel tosses the coin again? Why?

    i. The coin will land heads up.

    ii. The coin will land tails up.

    iii. The probabilities of the coin landing heads up or tails up are equal.

    iv. The coin is more likely to land heads up.

    v. The coin is more likely to land tails up.

Check Up (continued)

2. The probability of a particular event is $\frac{3}{8}$. What is the probability that the event will *not* happen? Explain.

3. Give an example of a situation with outcomes that are *not* equally likely.

4. Multiple Choice Which of the following numbers could *not* be a probability? Explain.

A. $\frac{1}{3}$ **B.** 0 **C.** $\frac{8}{9}$ **D.** 1 **E.** $\frac{5}{4}$

Check Up (continued)

5. Mandy has a bag containing one green block (G), one brown block (B), and one yellow block (Y). She conducted 20 trials in which she drew one block from the bag and then flipped a fair coin. Here are the results of her experiment.

Color	G	Y	G	G	Y	Y	B	Y	G	Y	B	Y	B	Y	Y	B	G	G	Y	Y
Coin	T	T	H	T	H	T	T	H	T	T	T	H	T	T	T	T	H	T	H	T

a. What is the experimental probability of drawing the brown block and flipping heads? What is the theoretical probability?

b. What is the experimental probability of drawing the yellow block and flipping tails? What is the theoretical probability?

c. How would you explain the differences you found between the experimental and theoretical probabilities?

6. a. Give an example of an event that has a 100% chance of happening.

b. Give an example of an outcome that is impossible.

c. If an event is impossible, what is the probability that it will occur?

Name .... Date .... Class ....

What Do You Expect?

Partner Quiz *for use after Investigation 4*

1. The Alphabet Game costs $.25 to play. Before the game, 26 slips of paper, each with a different letter of the alphabet on it, are put into a bag. A player draws one slip from the bag. If the player draws a vowel (A, E, I, O, or U), he or she wins $1.

   a. What is the probability of winning the game?

   b. What is the probability of losing the game?

   c. If a player plays the Alphabet Game 26 times, how much money would you expect the player to win or lose? Explain your reasoning.

2. Matt has three pairs of dark socks and six pairs of white socks. Each pair is rolled together. First, he will close his eyes to select a pair of socks. If the socks are dark, Matt will choose an outfit that includes dress pants. If the socks are white, Matt will toss a coin. If he gets heads, he will wear jeans. If he gets tails, he will wear shorts.

   a. What is the probability that Matt will wear white socks to school?

   b. What is the probability that Matt will wear shorts to school?

   c. What is the probability that Matt will wear dress pants to school?

   d. What is the probability that Matt will wear jeans with dark socks?

   e. Is Matt equally likely to wear dress pants, shorts, or jeans today? Explain your answer.

Partner Quiz (continued)

3. The diagram below shows the dartboard in Holly's basement. What is the probability that a dart thrown will land in section C?

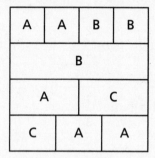

4. Ann Marie has a spinner that is divided into four regions. She spins the spinner several times and records the results in a table. Based on her results, make a drawing of what the spinner might look like.

Region	1	2	3	4
Number of Times Spinner Lands in That Region	9	4	12	11

Unit Test Correlation

Unit Test Item	Problem
Item 1, parts (a)–(d)	Problem 2.4
Item 2, parts (a) and (b)	Problem 2.1
Item 3, part (a)	Problem 3.2
Item 3, part (b)	Problem 4.4
Item 4, part (a)	Problem 4.2
Item 4, part (b)	Problem 5.1
Item 5, parts (a)–(c)	Problem 2.3
Item 6, parts (a) and (b)	Problem 4.1

Unit Test *for use after Investigation 5*

1. A bag contains one green marble, two yellow marbles, four blue marbles, and five red marbles.

    a. What is the theoretical probability of randomly drawing a blue marble from the bag?

    b. If you triple the number of green, yellow, blue, and red marbles in the bag, what will be the theoretical probability of drawing a blue marble?

    c. Compare your answers for part (a) and (b). Are they the same or different? Explain.

    d. How many blue marbles would you need to add to the *original* bag of marbles to make the probability of drawing a blue marble $\frac{1}{2}$? Explain.

Unit Test (continued)

2. A gumball machine contains orange, yellow, and purple gumballs. The probability of getting an orange gumball is $\frac{3}{4}$. The probability of getting a yellow gumball is $\frac{1}{6}$.

a. What is the probability of getting a purple gumball? Explain how you determined your answer.

b. If there are 36 gumballs in the machine, how many are purple? Yellow? Orange?

3. Use the spinner below to answer the following questions.

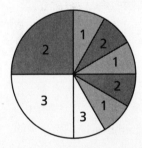

a. You spin the spinner. Are the possible outcomes 1, 2, and 3 equally likely? Explain.

b. If you spin the spinner 120 times, how many times would you expect to land on 2?

Unit Test (continued)

4. To pay you for mowing the lawn, your grandmother puts money in a bag. The bag has one $10 bill and four $1 bills. You get to draw out two bills.

   a. What is the theoretical probability of getting $11? What is the probability of getting $2? Explain.

   b. Would you rather that your grandmother give you $6 per job or use the bills in the bag? Explain.

5. Let's Make a Meal is a restaurant that lets customers design their own meals. Customers choose items from two categories: one entree and one drink.

Let's Make a Meal Menu

Entrees	Drinks
Hamburger	Milk
Hot Dog	Juice
Pizza	
Chicken	

   a. How many different meals can be designed?

   b. If meals are made randomly, what is the theoretical probability that a meal will include a hamburger?

   c. If meals are made randomly, what is the theoretical probability of a meal having chicken and juice?

Unit Test (continued)

6. Tua has created a new game called Making Green. To play the game, a player spins twice. If the player gets blue in one section and yellow in the other, the player wins, because blue and yellow together make green. The player can choose either spinner for either of their two spins.

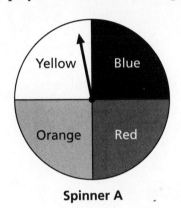

Spinner A

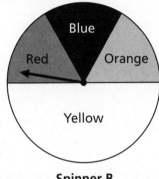

Spinner B

a. Tua spins Spinner A once and Spinner B once. What is the probability she will get green? Show how you got your answer.

b. Is there a different choice of selecting the spinners to make the probability of making green greater than that in part (a)? Explain.

Self Assessment

Mathematical Ideas

After studying the mathematics in this Unit:

1. a. I learned these things about mathematics:

b. Here are page numbers of notebook entries that give evidence of what I have learned, along with descriptions of what each entry shows:

2. a. These are the mathematical ideas that I am still struggling with:

b. This is why I think these ideas are difficult for me:

c. Here are page numbers of notebook entries that give evidence of what I am struggling with, and descriptions of what each entry shows:

Class Participation

I contributed to the classroom **discussion** and understanding of the mathematics in this Unit when I ... (Give examples.)

Self Assessment (continued)

Learning Environment

Rate each learning activity listed below using this scale:

1. I consistently struggled to understand the mathematics and I'm still not sure that I understand it.

2. I struggled somewhat but now I understand more than I did.

3. I had to work, but I feel confident that I understand now.

4. I understood everything pretty easily and I feel confident that I know the mathematics in these problems.

5. Everything came easily. I knew most of the mathematics before we did this.

Learning Activities

____ Problems from the Investigations

____ ACE Homework Assignments

____ Mathematical Reflections

____ Check Ups

____ Partner Quiz

____ Looking Back

____ Unit Test

Check any of the following that you feel are the most helpful in adding to the success of your learning.

☐ Working on my own in class

☐ Discussing a problem with a partner

☐ Working in a small group of 3 or 4 people

☐ Discussing a problem as a whole class

☐ Hearing how other people solved the problem

☐ Summarizing the mathematics as a class and taking notes

☐ Completing homework assignments

Notebook Checklist

Place a ✔ next to each item you have completed.

Notebook Organization

_____ Problems and Mathematical Reflections are labeled and dated.

_____ Work is neat and easy to find and follow.

Vocabulary

_____ All words are listed.   _____ All words are defined or described.

Assessments

_____ Check Up   _____ _____

_____ Partner Quiz   _____ _____

_____ Unit Test   _____ _____

Assignments

_____ _____   _____ _____

_____ _____   _____ _____

_____ _____   _____ _____

_____ _____   _____ _____

_____ _____   _____ _____

_____ _____   _____ _____

_____ _____   _____ _____

_____ _____   _____ _____

_____ _____   _____ _____

_____ _____

Assessment Answers

Check Up

1. a. Yes. Each time Rachel tosses the coin, it has a 50% possibility of landing heads up.

b. It is not very likely that a coin will land the same way ten times in a row. There are many ways a coin can land in ten tosses; ten heads is only one possibility.

Note: The number of different results of tossing a fair coin 10 times is 1,024, or 2^{10}. For example, TTTTTTTTTH or TTTTTTTTHT. Therefore, the probability of getting 10 heads is exactly $\frac{1}{1,024}$.

c. Statement (iii) is true, because the coin is fair. Every time she tosses the coin, the probability of landing heads up is exactly 50%.

2. Either the event will happen or it won't. In other words, the probability that the event will happen plus the probability that the event will not happen is 1. Therefore, the probability of the event not happening is $1-\frac{3}{8}=\frac{5}{8}$.

3. Possible answers: From a bag with 3 red blocks, 1 blue block, and 1 yellow block, the events *drawing a blue block* and *drawing a red block* are not equally likely since $P(\text{red})=\frac{3}{5}$ and $P(\text{blue})=\frac{1}{5}$. OR *Rolling a prime number* on a standard number cube and *rolling a 2* are not equally likely since $P(\text{prime})=\frac{3}{6}$ and $P(2)=\frac{1}{6}$.

4. $\frac{5}{4}$ cannot be a probability because probabilities are always greater than or equal to zero and less than or equal to 1.

5. a. The experimental probability is 0, since it never happened. The theoretical probability is $\frac{1}{6}$.

b. The experimental probability is $\frac{6}{20}$, but the theoretical probability is $\frac{1}{6}$.

c. With so many possible outcomes, Mandy did not do enough trials to get a good estimate for the theoretical probability from the experiment.

6. a. Possible answers: Pulling a red block out of a bag containing only red blocks; flipping a coin and getting either heads or tails.

b. Possible answer: Pulling a black block out of a bag containing only red blocks.

c. 0

Partner Quiz

1. a. $\frac{5}{26}$

b. $\frac{21}{26}$

c. You lose $1.50 because it costs $6.50 to play 26 times and you are only likely to win 5 times, which means you would win $5, but that does not make up for what it costs to play.

Assessment Answers *(continued)*

2. a. P(white socks) $= \frac{2}{3}$. This part does
not require the area model. For
parts (b)–(e), students might draw
an area model for this problem,
such as the one below. Because the
probabilities of pants, shorts, and
jeans are not equally likely, a tree
or a list is not as useful.

dark socks with pants	
white socks with jeans	white socks with shorts

b. P(shorts) $= \frac{1}{2}$ of $\frac{2}{3} = \frac{1}{3}$

c. P(dress pants) $= \frac{1}{3}$

d. P(jeans with dark socks) $= 0$

e. Yes, the three are equally likely to be
worn. In the area model, each region
is $\frac{1}{3}$ of the square, so each choice is
equally likely.

3. $\frac{5}{24}$

4. Region 1 is 90°, Region 2 is 40°, Region
3 is 120°, and Region 4 is 110°. Below
are three possible drawings.

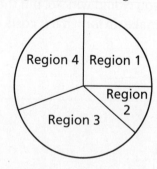

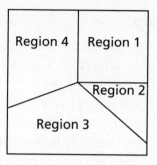

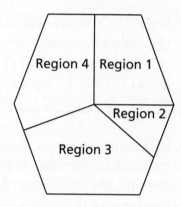

Unit Test

1. a. P(blue) $= \frac{4}{12} = \frac{1}{3}$

b. P(blue) $= \frac{12}{36} = \frac{1}{3}$

c. They are the same because tripling
the amount of each marble color
does not change the part-to-whole
relationship. In both situations,
there is 1 blue for every 3 marbles.

d. Add 4 blue marbles. In the original
bag, P(blue) $= \frac{4}{12}$. If you add 4 blue
marbles, P(blue) $= \frac{8}{16}$ or $\frac{1}{2}$.

Assessment Answers (continued)

2. a. $P(\text{purple}) = \frac{1}{12}$ because $P(\text{purple})$

$= 1 - [P(\text{orange}) + P(\text{yellow})]$

$= 1 - \left(\frac{3}{4} + \frac{1}{6}\right)$

$= 1 - \left(\frac{9}{12} + \frac{2}{12}\right)$

$= 1 - \frac{11}{12}$

$= \frac{1}{12}$

b. Number of Purple: $\frac{1}{12} \cdot 36 = 3$;

Number of Yellow: $\frac{1}{6} \cdot 36 = 6$;

Number of Orange: $\frac{3}{4} \cdot 36 = 27$

3. a. No, they are not equally likely.
Region 1 is $\frac{3}{12}$ of the circle.

Region 2 is $\frac{5}{12}$ of the circle.

Region 3 is $\frac{4}{12}$ of the circle.

b. 50 times

4. a. $P(\$11) = \frac{8}{20}$ and $P(\$2) = \frac{12}{20}$. Since you are not putting the first bill back into the bag before you choose the second bill, there are 5 options for the first draw and 4 options for the second draw, or 20 possible options (See Figure 1).

b. If you choose the original plan, the expected value is:
$\frac{8}{20}(11) + \frac{12}{20}(2) = \frac{56}{10} = \$5.60$ per job.
The $6 per job is the better plan over the long run.

5. a. From four entrees and two drinks, $4 \cdot 2 = 8$ different meals can be designed. Students will probably construct a list or tree to determine this. Let H stand for hamburger, D for hot dog, P for pizza, C for chicken, M for milk, and J for Juice:

Meal Combinations

HM	DM	PM	CM
HJ	DJ	PJ	CJ

b. Of the 8 possible meals, 2 have a hamburger, a probability of $\frac{2}{8} = \frac{1}{4}$. Or, as one of the four entrees is a hamburger, and as every meal has an entree, there is a $\frac{1}{4}$ probability that a lunch will have a hamburger.

c. This is one of the 8 possible meals, and since they are chosen at random, each is equally likely, so the probability of any particular meal is $\frac{1}{8}$.

Figure 1

First Draw

Second Draw		$10	$1	$1	$1	$1
	$10	NA	$11	$11	$11	$11
	$1	$11	$2	$2	$2	$2
	$1	$11	$2	$2	$2	$2
	$1	$11	$2	$2	$2	$2
	$1	$11	NA	NA	NA	NA

Assessment Answers (continued)

6. a. $\frac{4}{24} = \frac{1}{6}$. For a possible answer for an area model if spinning A and B each once, see Figure 2.

b. No. If you choose just Spinner A, the probability is $\frac{2}{16} = \frac{1}{8}$. If you choose Spinner B only, the probability is $\frac{6}{36} = \frac{1}{6}$. For a possible answer for an area model if spinning only Spinner A, see Figure 3.

Figure 2

Spinner B

Spinner A	Red	Blue	Orange	Yellow	Yellow	Yellow
Yellow	Orange	Green	Orange-Yellow	Yellow	Yellow	Yellow
Blue	Purple	Blue	Orange-Blue	Green	Green	Green
Orange	Red-Orange	Blue-Orange	Orange	Yellow-Orange	Yellow-Orange	Yellow-Orange
Red	Red	Purple	Orange-Red	Orange	Orange	Orange

Figure 3

Spinner A

Spinner A	Yellow	Blue	Orange	Red
Yellow	Yellow	Green	Orange-Yellow	Orange
Blue	Green	Blue	Orange-Blue	Purple
Orange	Yellow-Orange	Blue-Orange	Orange	Red-Orange
Red	Orange	Purple	Orange-Red	Red

Looking Back Answers

1. a. Possible answer:

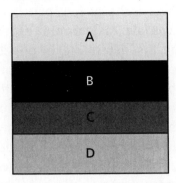

b. $\frac{1}{4}$

c. $\frac{3}{4}$

d. $\frac{7}{10}$

2. a.

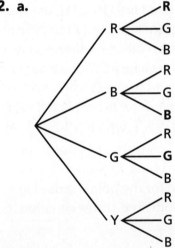

b. $\frac{1}{4}$

c. $\frac{3}{4}$

d. Each player does not have an equally likely chance of winning. Nick has a 75% chance of getting a match, and Gabrielle has only a 25% chance of getting a match.

e. This is not a fair game. See Nick's and Gabrielle's chances from part (d). It could be made fair by readjusting the point scheme. For example, 3 points for a match and 1 point for a no-match is fair.

3. a. He should expect 3 wins for a total of 12 points, 9 losses for a total loss of 18 points. Altogether, he should expect to lose 6 points.

b. $-\frac{1}{2}$ (a loss of $\frac{1}{2}$ point)

c. This game is not fair because the player loses a little bit on an average turn. One way to make it fair is to award 3 points for a win and take away 1 point for a loss.

4. The fractions tell us that over a large number of trials, the desired outcome will occur about 1 out of 2 times or 2 out of 3 times or 5 out of 8 times. Generally, these fractions can be converted to percents, and thus the event will occur about 50% or $66\frac{2}{3}$% or 62.5% of the time. These are mathematical predictions based upon the available information about a situation. The actual outcomes will be close to these predictions if the number of trials is large enough.

5. As the number of trials increases, the experimental probability approaches the theoretical probability. For a small number of trials, the experimental and theoretical probabilities for a given event are likely to differ.

Looking Back Answers (continued)

6. If one or some events have a greater probability of occurring, then they are not equally likely. For example, if a bag has five red marbles, two blue marbles, two yellow marbles, and one white marble, the chance of selecting a red marble is 50%, a blue marble is 20%, a yellow marble is 20%, and a white marble is 10%. If the chance of selecting any of the four colors were equally likely, there would be the same number of each color and each would have a 25% chance.

7. a. Tree diagrams offer a method to find all the possible outcomes of a situation. Student examples will vary. One example of using a tree diagram is to find out the outcomes of spinning two spinners, as in the Making Purple game in Problem 2.1.

b. Area models are useful in making a visual representation of the likelihood of each of the possible outcomes. They show what part of the whole each possible outcome represents. Student examples will vary. One example of using an area model was in Problem 4.2, when students were trying to figure out how many times Nicky would score 0, 1, or 2 points in a one-and-one free-throw situation.

8. The expected value, or long-term average, is the average payoff over many trials. To determine expected value, first determine the possible outcomes and the related theoretical probabilities. Once the theoretical probabilities are known, multiply the number of trials to be completed by each of these probabilities to determine the expected values for the given situation. For example, suppose you are playing a game with two coins in which you score 2 points if the toss is at least one head and 1 point if the toss is two tails. The theoretical probability of getting a head is $\frac{3}{4}$ (HH, TH, or HT) and of getting two tails is $\frac{1}{4}$ (TT). If you toss the two coins 36 times, then you would expect to get a head 27 times out of the 36 tosses and two tails 9 times out of 36 tosses. Therefore, the expected value is $\frac{3}{4} \times 2 + \frac{1}{4} \times 1$, which is $\frac{7}{4}$ or $1\frac{3}{4}$. You expect to score about $1\frac{3}{4}$ points per toss of the coins. Expected value was computed for the points scored in a one-and-one free-throw situation in Problem 4.2.

Parent Letters

Labsheets

Assessments

Dear Family,

The next Unit in your child's mathematics class this year is **Filling and Wrapping: Three-Dimensional Measurement**. Its focus is volume (filling) and surface area (wrapping) of objects such as prisms, cylinders, cones, and spheres. In addition, students will understand, find, and use area and circumference of circles. They will also extend their understanding of similarity and scale factors to three-dimensional figures.

Unit Goals

Students develop strategies for measuring surface area and volume. Their strategies are discussed and used to formulate rules for finding the surface areas and volumes of prisms and cylinders. Students also investigate other solids—including cones and spheres—to develop volume relationships.

In this Unit, students will revisit and extend ideas from previous Units. For example, students will build on what they learned in *Stretching and Shrinking* to study the connection of how changing the scale of a box affects its surface area and volume.

Homework and Conversations About The Mathematics

In your child's notebook, you can find worked-out examples, notes on the mathematics of the Unit, and descriptions of the vocabulary words.

You can help with homework and encourage sound mathematical habits as your child studies this Unit by asking questions such as:

- *What quantities are involved in the problem?*
- *Which measure of an object is involved—volume or surface area?*
- *What method should I use to determine this measure?*
- *What strategies or formulas might help?*

You can help your child with his or her work for this Unit in several ways:

- *Talk with your child about the size and shape of boxes in your home, and ask why they may be shaped as they are.*
- *Ask your child about the different strategies the class has explored for finding the surface areas and volumes of various shapes.*
- *Look at your child's mathematics notebook. You may want to review the section where your child is recording definitions for new words that he or she is encountering in the Unit.*
- *Have your child pick a question that was interesting to him or her and explain it to you.*

Common Core State Standards

While all of the Standards for Mathematical Practice are developed and used by students throughout the curriculum, particular attention is paid to reasoning abstractly and quantitatively as students develop meaning and algorithms for volume and surface area. *Filling and Wrapping* focuses on the Geometry domain.

A few important mathematical ideas that your child will learn in *Filling and Wrapping* are given on the next page.

As always, if you have any questions or concerns about this Unit or your child's progress in the class, please feel free to call. We are interested in your child and want this year's mathematics experiences to be enjoyable and to promote a firm understanding of mathematics.

Sincerely,

Important Concepts	Examples

Surface Area of Rectangular Prisms

Surface area is the sum of the areas of the faces.

Surface Area = (area of the front $\times$ 2) + (area of the side $\times$ 2) + (area of the top $\times$ 2)

   or

Surface Area = (area of the front + area of the side + area of the top) $\times$ 2 = $(w \times h + w \times \ell + \ell \times h) \times 2$.

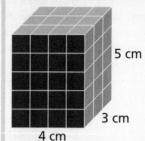

5 cm

3 cm

4 cm

There are three sets of two congruent faces:

4 cm by 3 cm (area is 12 cm²);
4 cm by 5 cm (area is 20 cm²);
3 cm by 5 cm (area is 15 cm²).
Surface area = 94 cm²

Volume of Rectangular Prisms

The volume (the total number of unit cubes) of a rectangular prism is the area of its base (the number of unit cubes in the first layer) multiplied by its height (the total number of layers).

Volume = Area of the base $\times$ height = $Bh = \ell wh$

$3 \times 2 = 6$ cubes on the base

5 layers of cubes (height);

Volume = $6 \times 5 = 30$ cubic units

Volume of Prisms

The same layering strategy is used to generalize the method for finding the volume of any prism. The volume of any prism is the area of its base multiplied by its height.

Volume = Area of the base $\times$ height = Bh

Rectangular Triangular Hexagonal
Prism   Prism   Prism

Area of Circles

Students begin by finding the number of "radius squares" with side lengths that are equal to the radius, that cover the circle. It is a little more than 3, or pi.

The area of a circle is pi $\times$ a "radius square" or pi $\times$ radius $\times$ radius
$= \pi \times r \times r$
$= \pi r^2$

Perimeter of Circles (Circumference)

Students count the number of diameter lengths needed to surround the circle. It is a little more than 3, or pi.

The circumference of a circle is pi $\times$ diameter, or πd.

Surface Area of Cylinders

By folding a flat pattern to form a cylinder, students discover that the surface area of the cylinder is the area of the rectangle that forms the lateral surface ($2\pi rh$) plus the areas of the two circular ends ($2\pi r^2$).
Surface Area = $2\pi r^2 + 2\pi rh$

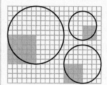

Use 3.14 for π.
$r = 4$ $h = 5$

$2\pi \cdot 4^2 + 2\pi \cdot 4(5)$
$\approx 100.48 + 125.6$
$= 226.08$ square units

Volume of Cylinders

The volume of a cylinder is the number of unit cubes in one layer (the area of the circular base, πr^2) multiplied by the number of layers (the height h) needed to fill the cylinder. Volume = $Bh = \pi r^2 h$

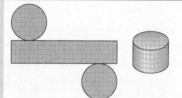

Estimate the number of unit cubes in one layer.

Multiply by the number of layers.

Area of base $B = \pi r^2$
$\approx 3.14 \times 2.5^2$
$= 19.625$ square units

$V = Bh$
$= 19.625 \times 7$
$= 137.375$ cubic units

Volumes of Cones and Spheres

If a cylinder, a cone, and a sphere all have the same radius and the same height (the height being equal to two radii), then it takes 3 cones to fill the cylinder, and $1\frac{1}{2}$ spheres to fill the cylinder.

Volume$_{cone} = \frac{1}{3} \cdot$ Volume$_{cylinder} = \frac{1}{3}\pi r^2 h$
Volume$_{sphere} = \frac{2}{3} \cdot$ Volume$_{cylinder} = \frac{2}{3}\pi r^2 h$

 =
 =

Volume$_{cylinder} = 628$ cm³
Volume$_{cone} \approx 209$ cm³
Volume$_{sphere} \approx 419$ cm³

Estimada familia:

La siguiente Unidad de la clase de Matemáticas de su hijo(a) este año es ***Llenar y envolver: Medición tridimensional***. Esta Unidad se enfoca en el volumen (llenar) y el área (envolver) de objetos como prismas, cilindros, conos y esferas. Además, los estudiantes comprenderán, hallarán y usarán el área y la circunferencia de círculos. También ampliarán su comprensión de la semejanza y los factores de escala de figuras tridimensionales.

▷ Objetivos de la unidad

Los estudiantes desarrollan estrategias para medir el área y el volumen. Sus estrategias se analizan y se usan para formular reglas para hallar las áreas totales y los volúmenes de prismas y cilindros. Los estudiantes también investigan otros sólidos, incluyendo conos y esferas, para desarrollar relaciones de volumen.

En esta Unidad, los estudiantes retomarán y ampliarán ideas de Unidades previas. Por ejemplo, los estudiantes desarrollarán lo que aprendieron en *Estirar y encoger* para estudiar la conexión de cómo el cambio en la escala de una caja influye en su área total y su volumen.

▷ Ayudar con la tarea y tener conversaciones acerca de las matemáticas

Usted puede ayudar a su hijo(a) con la tarea y fomentarle hábitos matemáticos sólidos a medida que estudia esta Unidad haciéndole preguntas como:

- *¿Qué cantidades incluye el problema?*
- *¿Qué medida de un objeto se incluye: el volumen o el área total?*
- *¿Qué método debo usar para determinar esta medida?*
- *¿Qué estrategias o fórmulas me podrían ayudar?*

Usted puede ayudar a su hijo(a) con la tarea para esta Unidad de varias maneras:

- *Hable con su hijo(a) acerca del tamaño y la forma de cajas que haya en su casa y pregúntele por qué podrían tener la forma que tienen.*
- *Pregúntele acerca de las distintas estrategias que la clase ha explorado para hallar las áreas totales y los volúmenes de varias figuras.*
- *Revise el cuaderno de matemáticas de su hijo(a). Puede revisar la sección donde anota las definiciones de nuevas palabras que ha encontrado en la Unidad.*
- *Pídale que escoja una pregunta que le haya interesado para que se la explique.*

▷ Estándares estatales comunes

Aunque los estudiantes desarrollan y usan todos los Estándares de prácticas matemáticas a lo largo del curso, en esta Unidad se presta especial atención al razonamiento abstracto y cuantitativo a medida que los estudiantes encuentran el sentido y desarrollan algoritmos para hallar el volumen y el área total. *Llenar y envolver* se enfoca en la rama de la Geometría.

Algunas importantes ideas matemáticas que su hijo(a) aprenderá en *Llenar y envolver* se presentan en la página siguiente.

Como siempre, si usted tiene cualquier pregunta o preocupación acerca de esta Unidad o con respecto al progreso de su hijo(a) en clase, por favor no dude en llamar. Estamos interesados en su hijo(a) y queremos que él o ella disfrute las experiencias matemáticas de este año, además de promover un entendimiento firme de las matemáticas.

Sinceramente,

Conceptos importantes	Ejemplos
Área total de prismas rectangulares El área total de un prisma es la suma de las áreas de sus caras. Área total = (área de la parte frontal × 2) + (área del lado × 2) + (área de la parte superior × 2) o Área total = (área de la parte frontal + área del lado + área de la parte superior) × 2 = $(a \times h + a \times \ell + \ell \times h) \times 2$.	 5 cm 3 cm 4 cm Hay tres conjuntos de dos caras congruentes: 4 cm por 3 cm (el área es de 12 cm²); 4 cm por 5 cm (el área es de 20 cm²); 3 cm por 5 cm (el área es de 15 cm²). Área total = 94 cm²
Volumen de prismas rectangulares El volumen (el número total de bloques de unidades) de una prisma rectangular es el área de su base (el número de bloques de unidades de la primera capa) multiplicada por su altura (el número total de capas). Volumen = Área de la base × altura = $Bh = \ell ah$	$3 \times 2 = 6$ cubos en la base 5 capas de cubos (altura); Volumen = $6 \times 5 = 30$ unidades cúbicas
Volumen de prismas La misma estrategia de usar capas se usa para generalizar el método para hallar el volumen de cualquier prisma. El volumen de cualquier prisma es el área de su base multiplicada por su altura. Volumen = Área de la base × altura = Bh	 Prisma Prisma Prisma rectangular triangular hexagonal
Área total de círculos Los estudiantes comienzan por hallar el número de "cuadrados de radio", que tienen longitudes de lado iguales al radio, que cubren el círculo. Es un poco más que 3, o pi.	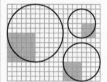 El área de un círculo es pi × un "cuadrado de radio" o pi × radio × radio $= \pi \times r \times r$ $= \pi r^2$
Perímetro de círculos (circunferencia) Los estudiantes cuentan el número de longitudes de diámetro necesarias para rodear al círculo. Es un poco más que 3, o pi.	La circunferencia de un círculo es pi × diámetro, o πd.
Área total de cilindros Al doblar un modelo plano para formar un cilindro, los estudiantes descubren que el área total del cilindro es el área del rectángulo que forma la superficie lateral ($2\pi rh$) más las áreas de los dos extremos circulares ($2\pi r^2$). Área = $2\pi r^2 + 2\pi rh$	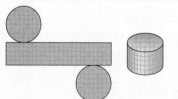 Usa 3.14 para π. $r = 4 \quad h = 5$ $2\pi \cdot 4^2 + 2\pi \cdot 4(5)$ $\approx 100.48 + 125.6$ $= 226.08$ unidades cuadradas
Volumen de cilindros El volumen de un cilindro es el número de bloques de unidades de una capa (el área de la base circular, πr^2) multiplicada por el número de capas (la altura h) necesarias para llenar el cilindro. Volumen = $Bh = \pi r^2 h$	 Estima el número de bloques de unidades en una capa. Multiplica por el número de capas. Área de la base $B = \pi r^2$ $\approx 3.14 \times 2.5^2$ $= 19.625$ unidades cuadradas $V = Bh$ $= 19.625 \times 7$ $= 137.375$ unidades cúbicas
Volúmenes de conos y esferas Si un cilindro, un cono y una esfera tienen el mismo radio y la misma altura (una altura igual a dos radios), entonces se requieren 3 conos para llenar el cilindro y $1\frac{1}{2}$ esferas para llenar el cilindro. Volumen$_{cono} = \frac{1}{3} \cdot$ Volumen$_{cilindro} = \frac{1}{3}\pi r^2 h$ Volumen$_{esfera} = \frac{2}{3} \cdot$ Volumen$_{cilindro} = \frac{2}{3}\pi r^2 h$	  Volumen$_{cilindro} = 628$ cm³ Volumen$_{cono} = 209$ cm³ Volumen$_{esfera} = 419$ cm³

Labsheet 1.2   Packing Cubes in a Rectangular Prism

Possible Arrangements of 24 Cubes

Length (in.)	Width (in.)	Height (in.)	Volume (in.^{3})	Surface Area (in.^{2})	Sketch

Labsheet 1.2   Packing Cubes in a Rectangular Prism

Possible Arrangements of 24 Cubes

Length (in.)	Width (in.)	Height (in.)	Volume (in.³)	Surface Area (in.²)	Sketch

Labsheet 1ACE   Exercise 4

4. Each of these boxes holds 36 table tennis balls.

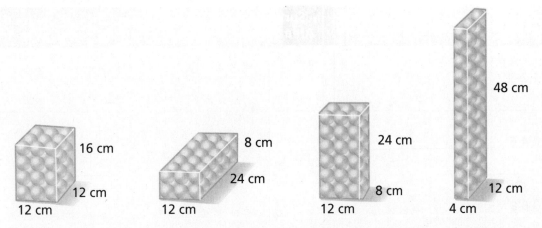

16 cm
12 cm
12 cm

8 cm
24 cm
12 cm

24 cm
8 cm
12 cm

48 cm
12 cm
4 cm

a. Without any calculations, how can you tell which box has the **least surface area**?

> **Hint** Remember that surface area of a box is the total area of all its faces.

Why does it have the least surface area?

b. Check your guess by finding the **surface area** of each box.

First box:

Second box:

Third box:

Fourth box:

Labsheet 1.4   Similar Compost Boxes

Compost Box Project

Open Box (h-w-ℓ)	Scale Factor	Surface Area (ft²)	Volume (ft³)	Amount of Garbage Decomposed in a Day (lb)	Number of Worms Needed
1-2-3					
2-4-6					
3-6-9					
4-8-12					
⋮					
		1,024			
⋮					
			6,000		
⋮					
	f				

Labsheet 2.1A   Lateral Surface on a Grid (index card)

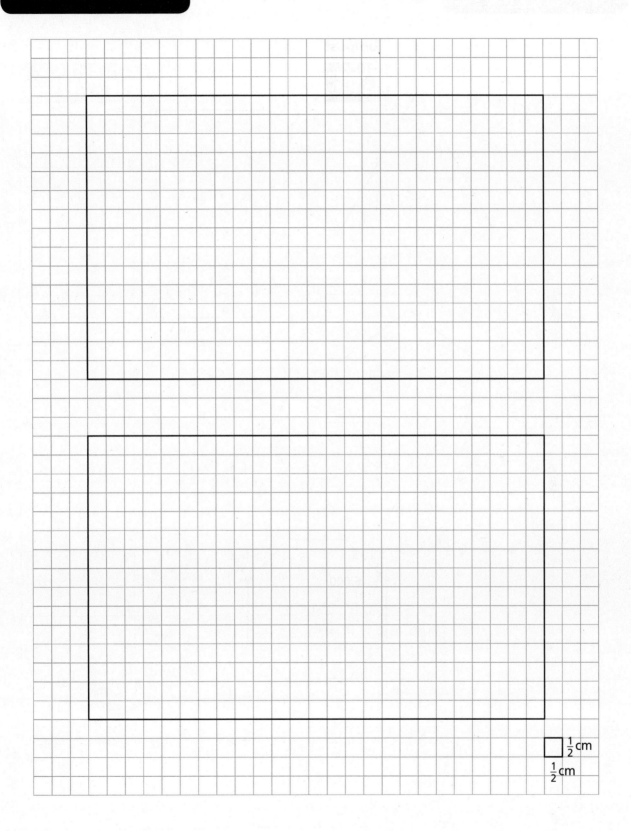

$\frac{1}{2}$ cm
$\frac{1}{2}$ cm

Labsheet 2.1B — Prism Bases on a Grid (index card)

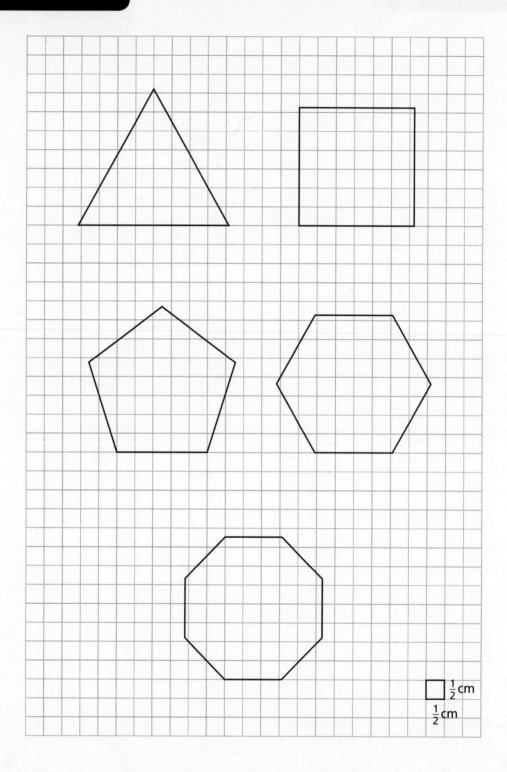

$\frac{1}{2}$ cm

$\frac{1}{2}$ cm

Labsheet 2.1C Prism Bases on a Grid (sheet of paper)

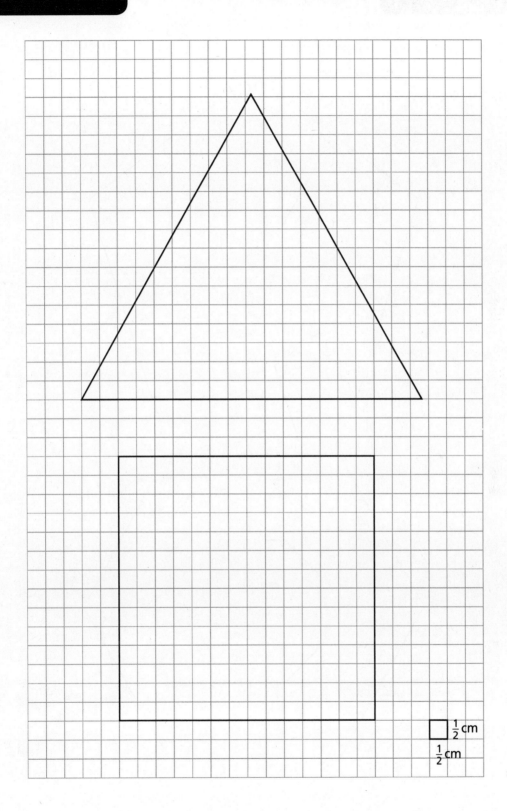

$\frac{1}{2}$ cm

$\frac{1}{2}$ cm

Labsheet 2.1C

Prism Bases on a Grid (sheet of paper)

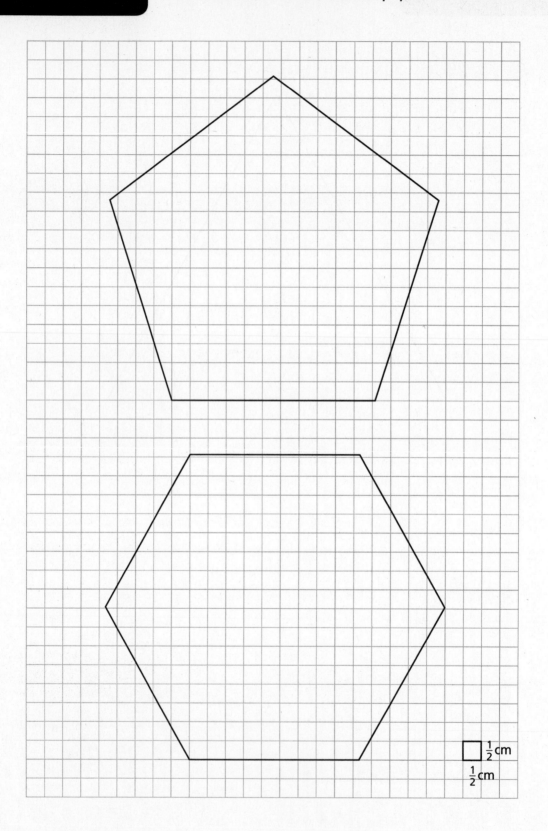

$\square$ $\frac{1}{2}$ cm

$\frac{1}{2}$ cm

Labsheet 2.1C

Prism Bases on a Grid (sheet of paper)

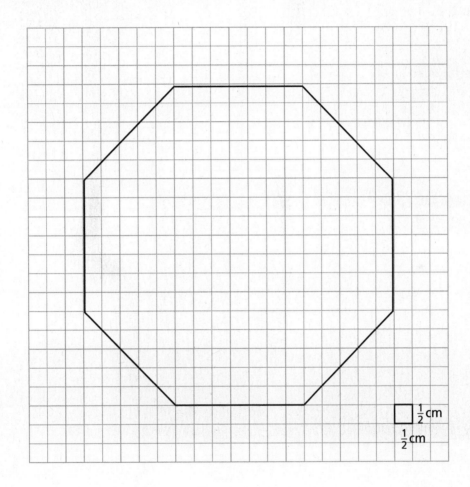

$\frac{1}{2}$ cm

$\frac{1}{2}$ cm

Labsheet 2.1D   Surface Area Table

Surface Areas of Prisms

Prism Type	Area of Sides	Area of Top and Bottom	Total Surface Area
Triangular			
Square			
Pentagonal			
Hexagonal			
Octagonal			

Labsheet 2ACE   Exercise 1

1. a.

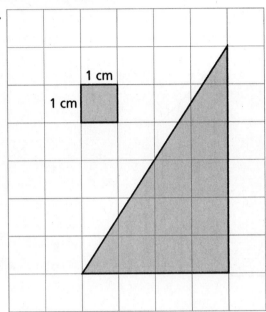

b.

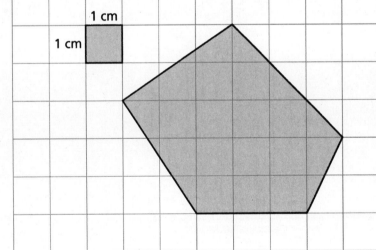

Labsheet 2ACE Exercise 1

c.

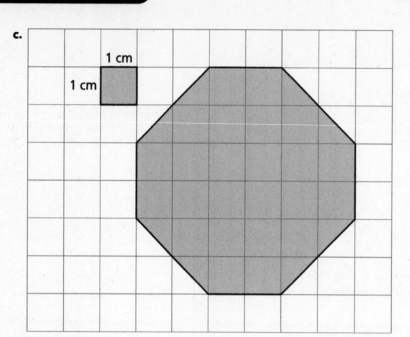

1 cm

1 cm

Labsheet 2ACE   Exercises 3–5

3.

Labsheet 2ACE | Exercises 3–5

4.

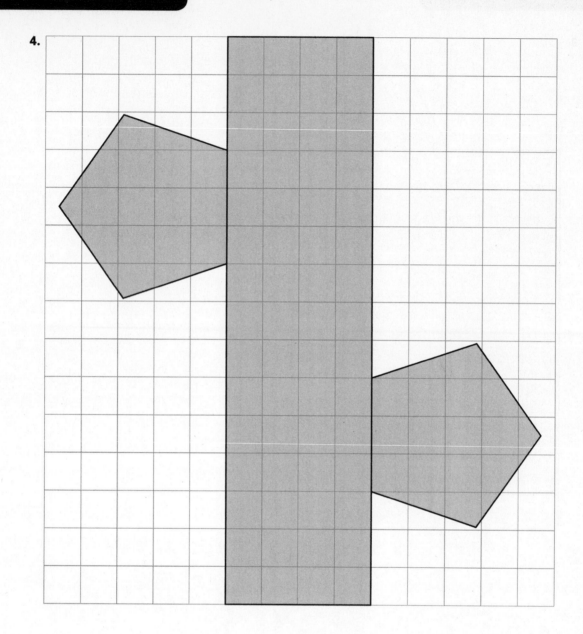

Labsheet 2ACE   Exercises 3–5

5.

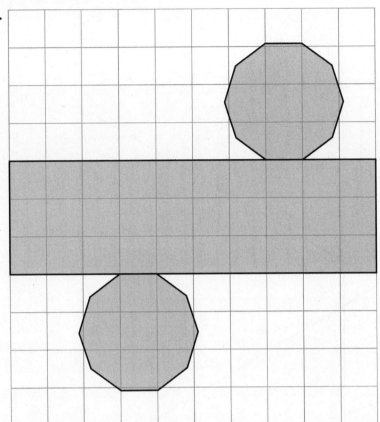

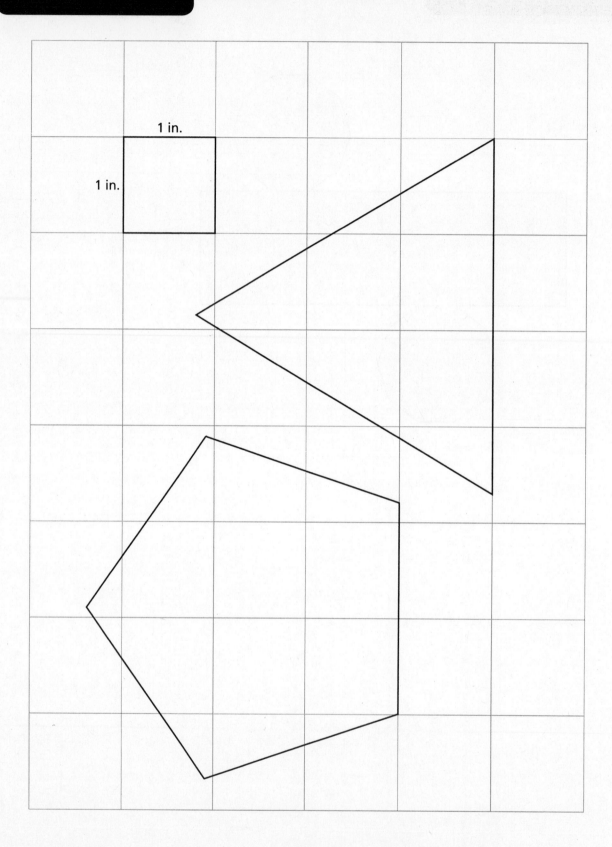

1 in.

1 in.

Labsheet 2ACE   Exercise 12

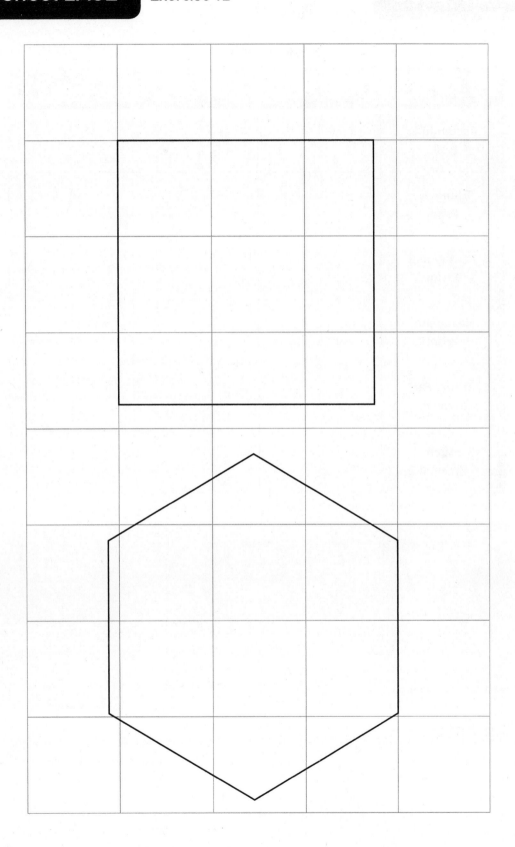

Labsheet 2ACE Exercise 31

Euler's Formula

Figure	Vertices	Edges	Faces
Rectangular Prism			
Triangular Prism			
Pentagonal Prism			
Hexagonal Prism			
Triangular Pyramid			
Square Pyramid			

Labsheet 3.1 — Diameter and Circumference Data

Measurements of Circular Objects

Object Name	Diameter	Circumference	Ratio of $\dfrac{\text{Circumference}}{\text{Diameter}}$

Labsheet 3ACE   Exercises 1–7

For Exercises 1–4, identify the part of the circle drawn in gray as its circumference, diameter, or radius. Then, measure that part in centimeters.

1.

2.

3.
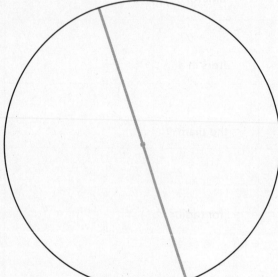

4.
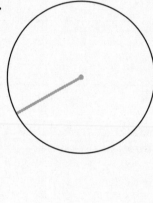

5. Use your measurements from Exercises 1–4 to find the measure of the part of each circle in black.

Labsheet 3ACE   Exercises 1–7

6. Draw three different diameters on the circle below.

   a. What is the measure, in centimeters, of each diameter?

   b. What can you say about the measures of diameters in a circle?

   c. Estimate the circumference of this circle using the diameter
   measurements you found.

7. Draw three different radii (RAY dee eye, the plural for radius) on the
   circle below.

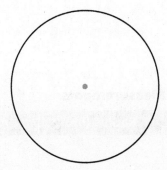

   a. What is the measure, in centimeters, of each radius?

   b. What can you say about the measures of the radii in the same
   circle?

   c. Estimate the circumference of this circle using the radius
   measurements you found.

Labsheet 3.2   Measuring Pizzas

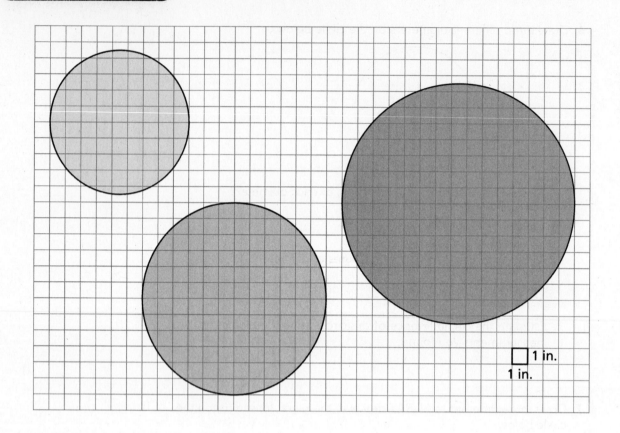

1 in. □ 1 in.

Pizza Measurements

Size	Diameter (in.)	Radius (in.)	Area (in.²)
Small			
Medium			
Large			

Labsheet 3.3   Circles and Radius Squares

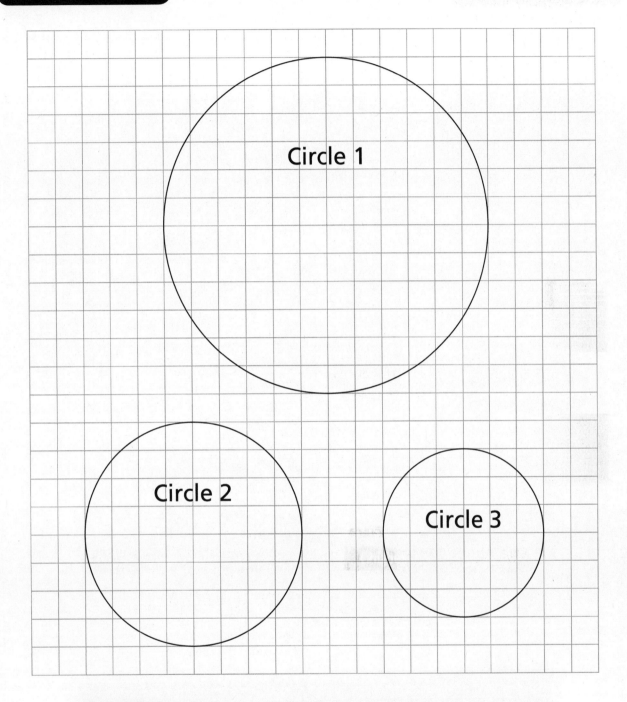

Circle	Radius of Circle (units)	Area of Radius Square (square units)	Area of Circle (square units)	Number of Radius Squares Needed
1				
2				
3				

Labsheet 3.3

Circles and Radius Squares

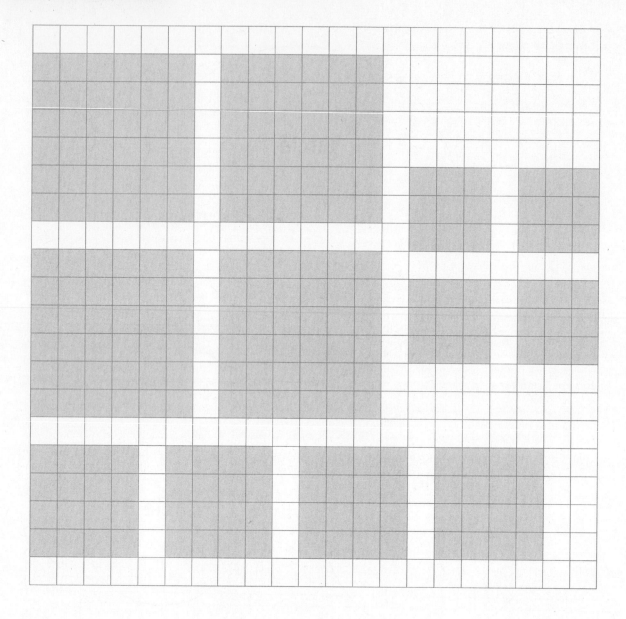

Labsheet 3ACE   Exercises 24–29

For Exercises 24–29, estimate the area in square centimeters and the perimeter or circumference in centimeters.

24.

25.

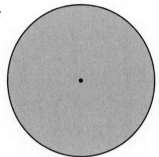

26.

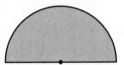

27.

28.

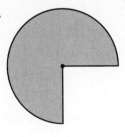

29.

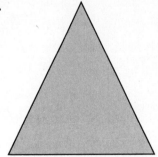

Labsheet 3.4   Circle and Parallelogram

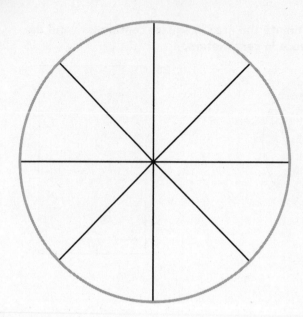

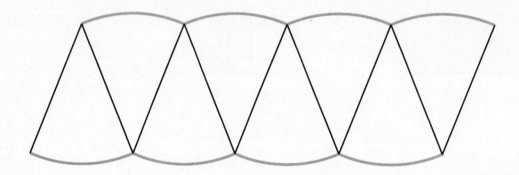

Labsheet 4.1 Net of a Cylinder

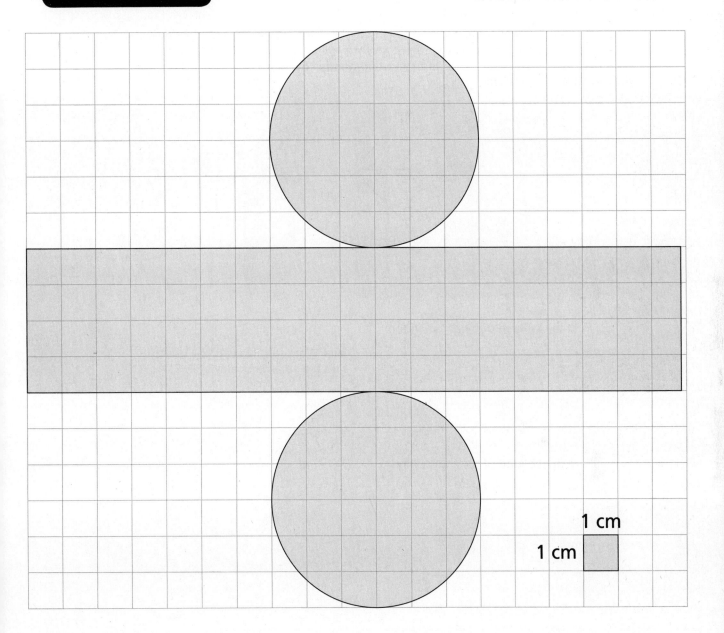

1 cm

1 cm

Labsheet 4ACE   Exercise 1

1. Cut a sheet of paper in half so you have two identical half-sheets of paper. Tape the long sides of one sheet together to form a cylinder. Tape the short sides of the second sheet together to form another cylinder. Suppose that each cylinder has a top and bottom.

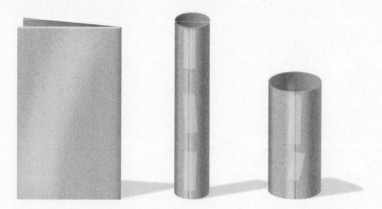

    a. Find the **volume** of the tall cylinder.

                          Hint What formula can you use to find the volume of a cylinder?

    Find the **volume** of the short cylinder.

    Which cylinder has a **greater** volume? Explain.

Labsheet 4ACE Exercise 1

b. Find the **surface area** of the tall cylinder.

> **Hint** Remember to include a top and bottom for each cylinder.

Find the **surface area** of the short cylinder.

Which cylinder has a **greater** surface area? Explain.

Labsheet 4.2A   Filling Cylinders (index card)

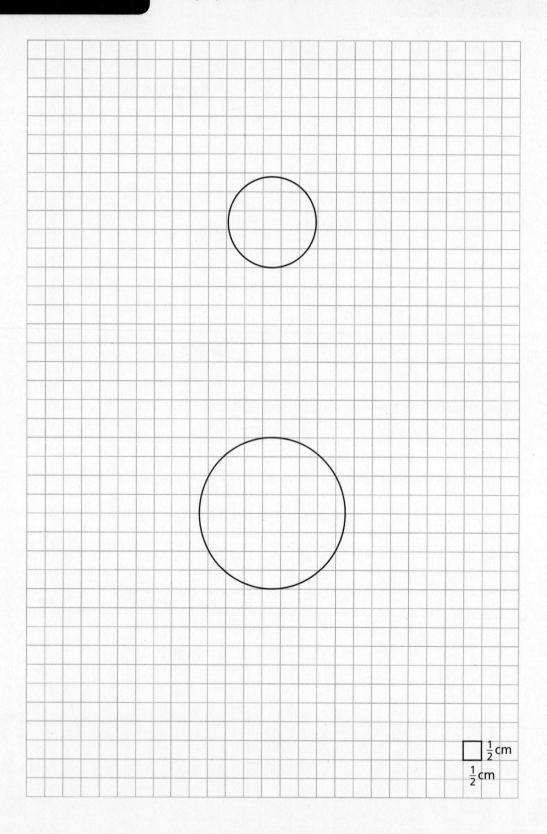

$\frac{1}{2}$ cm

$\frac{1}{2}$ cm

Labsheet 4.2B   Filling Cylinders (sheet of paper)

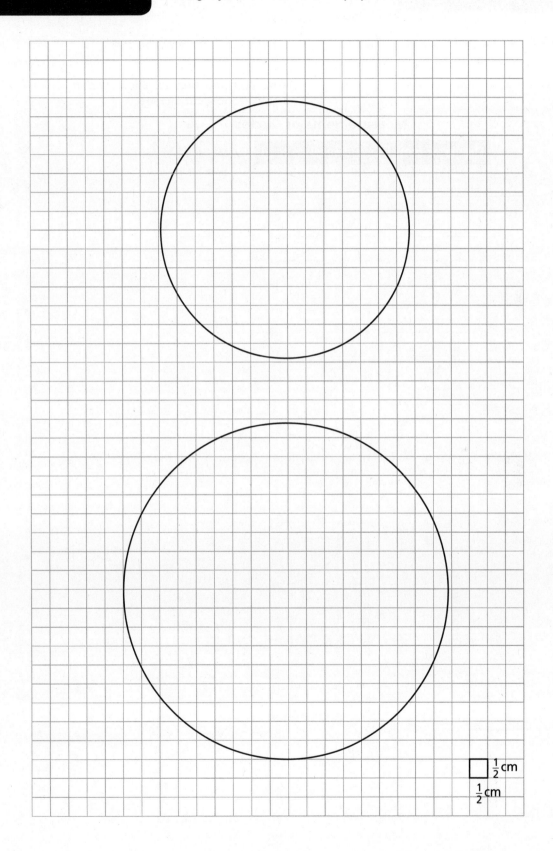

$\frac{1}{2}$ cm

$\frac{1}{2}$ cm

Labsheet 4ACE   Exercise 36

36. a. Make a table showing the relationship between the diameter and the circumference of a circle.

> **Hint** What is the relationship between circumference and diameter?

Measurements of Circles

Diameter (cm)	Circumference (cm)	
1		
2		
3		
4		
5		
6		
7		
8		
9		
10		

b. Make a graph of the (*diameter, circumference*) data in your table.

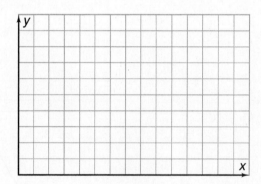

Diameter

Labsheet 4ACE   Exercise 36

c. Suppose that each of the circles represented in your table is the base of a cylinder with a height of 2 cm. Some of these cylinders are shown below. Add a column to your table in part (a) to show the relationship between the diameter of the base and the volume of the cylinder.

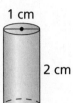
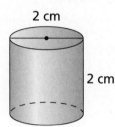
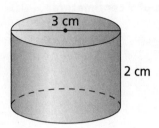

d. Make a graph of the (*diameter, volume*) data in your table.

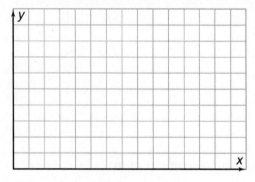

Diameter (cm)

e. Compare the graphs for part (b) and part (d).

How are they **alike**?

How are they **different**?

Labsheet 4ACE   Exercise 9

9. A popcorn vender needs to order popcorn boxes. The vendor must decide between a cylindrical box and a rectangular box (both without tops).

- The cylindrical box has a **height of 20 centimeters** and a **radius of 7 centimeters.**

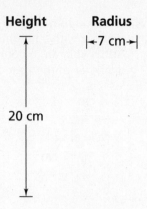

Height   **Radius**
|◄7 cm►|

20 cm

- The rectangular box has a **height of 20 centimeters** and a **square base with 12-centimeter sides.**

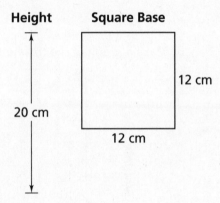

Height   **Square Base**

20 cm

12 cm

12 cm

- The **cost** of each box is based on the **amount of material** needed to make the box.

- The vendor plans to charge $2.75 for popcorn, regardless of the shape of the box.

a. Make a sketch of each box. **Label the dimensions.**

cylindrical box   **rectangular box**

Labsheet 4ACE   Exercise 9

b. Find the **volume** and **surface area** of each box.

Volume of cylindrical box:

Surface area of cylindrical box:

Volume of rectangular box:

Surface area of rectangular box:

c. Which box would you choose?

Give the reasons for your choice.

Reason 1:

Reason 2:

Other reasons?

What additional information might help you make a better decision?

Labsheet 4ACE   Exercise 48

48. A cylindrical can is packed securely in a box as shown
at the right.

   a. Find the **radius** of the can.

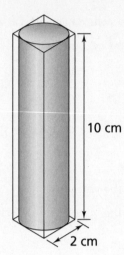

10 cm

2 cm

   Find the **height** of the can.

   b. What is the volume of the **empty space** between the can and the box?

   Hint What is the volume of the box?
   What is the volume of the can?

   c. Find the **ratio** of the volume of the can to the volume of the box.

   Hint Remember that a ratio can be
   written as a fraction.

Labsheet 4ACE Exercise 48

d. Make up a **similar example** with a can and a box of different sizes.
Sketch the can and the box.

What is the **ratio** of the volume of your can to the volume of your box?
What is the volume of the box?

What is the volume of the can?

Ratio:

How does the ratio **compare** with the ratio you found in part (c)?

Labsheet 4.4A Nets of Cones

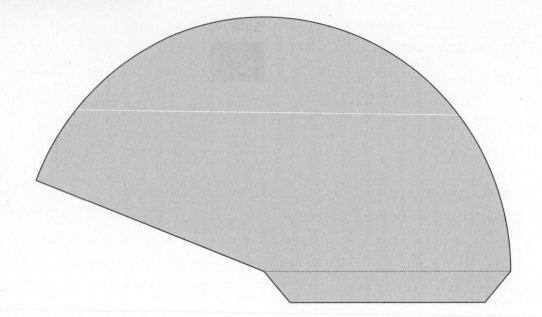

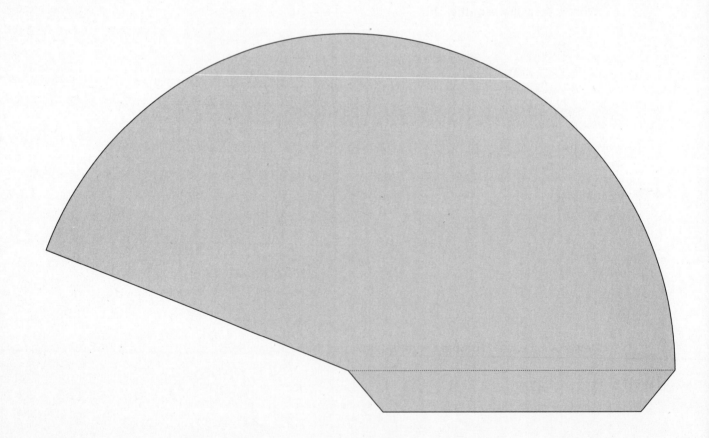

Labsheet 4.4B   Sphere Radius and Volume

Volumes of Spheres

Radius	Volume
1	
2	
3	
4	
5	
⋮	
10	

Labsheet 4ACE   Exercise 15

15. The prices and dimensions of several movie theater popcorn containers are shown below.

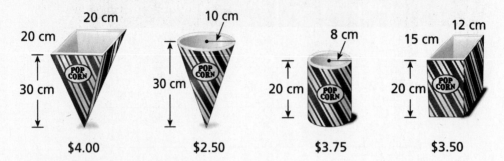

Find the **volume** of each container.

Pyramid:

> **Hint** Remember that a pyramid has one-third the volume of the related prism with the same dimensions.

Cone:

Cylinder:

Prism:

Labsheet 4ACE   Exercise 15

Find the amount of popcorn per dollar for each container.

Hint You can first write a ratio that compares the volume of popcorn to the number of dollars. Find the unit rate for each container.

Pyramid:

Cone:

Cylinder:

Prism:

Which container gives the most popcorn per dollar?

Name .... Date .... Class ....

Filling and Wrapping

Check Up 1 *for use after Investigation 1*

....

1. Tyler asks for a fish tank for his birthday. The tank he wants is a rectangular prism 20.25 inches long, 10.5 inches wide, and 12.5 inches tall.

    a. How much water will the fish tank hold? Show how you found your answer.

    b. How much wrapping paper will his father need to wrap the fish tank? Show how you found your answer.

2. Tyler enjoys the fish so much that, after his birthday, his family decides to take him to a famous aquarium. A tank at the aquarium is similar to his tank with a scale factor of 8.

    a. How many times greater is the volume of the tank at the aquarium than the volume of Tyler's tank?

    b. How many times greater is the surface area of the tank at the aquarium than the surface area of Tyler's tank?

Check Up 1 (continued)

3. A pool table supply company is making a cardboard box to package new cubes of pool cue chalk. Each cube of chalk is 1 cubic inch. The company considers all the ways to arrange 16 cubes of the chalk.

- 16 inches by 1 inch by 1 inch
- 8 inches by 2 inches by 1 inch
- 4 inches by 4 inches by 1 inch
- 4 inches by 2 inches by 2 inches

a. Which arrangement of chalk would require the most cardboard for the box? How do you know?

b. Which arrangement of chalk would require the least cardboard for the box? How do you know?

Partner Quiz *for use after Investigation 2*

1. A chocolate company sells chocolates in different sizes and packaging shapes. The packages below are in the shape of triangular prisms, where the bases are equilateral triangles.

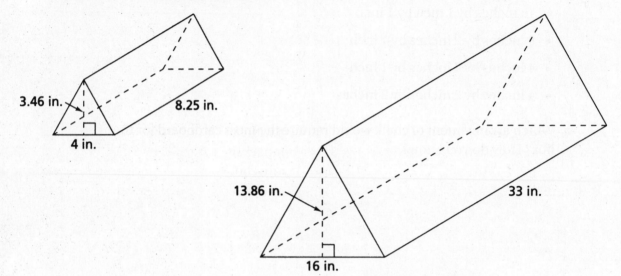

3.46 in.

8.25 in.

4 in.

13.86 in.

33 in.

16 in.

Not drawn to scale

a. How many square inches of cardboard are needed to make the smaller package?

b. How many square inches of cardboard are needed to make the larger package?

c. How many cubic inches of chocolate will the smaller package hold?

d. How many cubic inches of chocolate will the larger package hold?

Partner Quiz (continued)

e. Suppose the smaller package sells for $2. What should be the price of the larger package if the company wants to base the price on the amount of chocolate the package will hold?

f. Suppose other possible packages are prisms with lateral faces that are the same size as those of the original smaller package (4 inches by 8.25 inches). What package shape would hold more chocolate than the original smaller package?

2. In Japan, growers have developed ways of growing watermelon cubes that fit into small refrigerators.

Suppose you cut one of these watermelon cubes open using only one cut. Which two-dimensional shapes would you see on the cut faces? Explain your answer.

Check Up 2 *for use after Investigation 3*

1. a. A children's pony ride at a zoo has ponies attached to a carousel pole in the center of a circle that the ponies walk around as children ride. Suppose the diameter of the circle is 25 feet. How many feet does a pony walk to complete one trip around the circle? Show how you found your answer.

b. The zoo also has a merry-go-round. To set up the merry-go-round, the zoo manager has to clear some land. The diameter of the merry-go-round is 18 feet. How much land does the manager need to clear in order to build the merry-go-round? Show how you found your answer.

2. A circular cookie cutter has a 2.5-inch radius. What is the area of a cookie cut from this cutter?

Check Up 2 (continued)

3. The circumference of a circle is 113 feet. What is its diameter?

4. Suppose a circle has diameter 10 centimeters and a square has side length 10 centimeters. Which shape has the greater area? Explain.

Unit Test Correlation

Unit Test Item	Problem
Item 1	Problem 2.2
Item 2	Problem 2.2
Item 3, parts (a), (b), and (c)	Problem 1.4
Item 4, parts (a) and (b)	Problem 1.1
Item 5, parts (a) and (b)	Problem 2.3
Item 6, part (a)	Problem 3.3
Item 6, part (b)	Problem 3.1
Item 7	Problem 2.2
Item 8, part (a)	Problem 4.2
Item 8, part (b)	Problem 4.1
Item 9	Problem 4.4

Unit Test

Use the following information to answer Exercises 1–3. Remember to show your work.

A movie theater sells two sizes of popcorn. One box has the shape of a triangular prism (Popcorn T). The other box has the shape of a rectangular prism (Popcorn R). The boxes do not have tops.

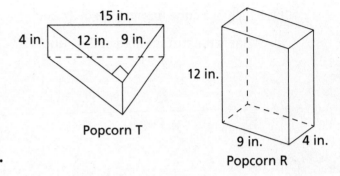

15 in.

4 in. 12 in. 9 in.

12 in.

Popcorn T

9 in. 4 in.

Popcorn R

1. How many square inches of cardboard are needed to make each box? Which box needs more cardboard? Explain your reasoning.

2. How many cubic inches of popcorn will fit in each box if the top of the popcorn is level with the top of the box? Which box holds more? Explain your reasoning.

3. Suppose the theater decides to sell a third popcorn size, the family-size box. The family-size box is a rectangular prism without a top. The scale factor from the rectangular box (Popcorn R) to the family-size box is 1.5.

   a. Suppose the Popcorn R box sells for $1.50. What should be the price of the family-size box if it is based on the amount of popcorn the box holds?

   b. What is the surface area of the family-size box?

   c. What is the volume of the family-size box?

Name .... Date .... Class ....

Filling and Wrapping

Unit Test (continued)

4. One face of a cube has an area of 25 cm^2.

   a. What is the surface area of the cube?

   b. What is the volume of the cube?

5. **a.** Describe the two solid figures that will result from a cut in the direction shown.

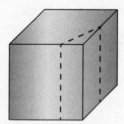

   b. Describe the two-dimensional shape of the face formed by the cut.

Unit Test (continued)

6. A pizzeria sells a round pizza with diameter 16 inches. Another pizzeria sells a large square pizza with side length 15 inches.

   a. Which of the two shapes gives you more pizza? How much more?

   b. Which has more crust along the outside edge of the pizza, the square pizza or the round pizza? Show how you found your answer.

7. Find the surface area and volume of the regular hexagonal prism shown below. The base has an area of 30.6 square centimeters.

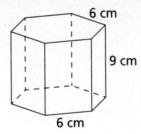

6 cm

9 cm

6 cm

Unit Test (continued)

8. At the right are scale drawings of two cylinders. One cylinder has a diameter of 6 cm and a height of 10 cm. The other cylinder has a diameter of 10 cm and a height of 6 cm.

6 cm

10 cm

10 cm

6 cm

   a. Do the cylinders have the same volume? Explain your reasoning.

   b. Do the cylinders have the same surface area? Explain your reasoning.

9. The figure below is a sketch of the nose cone of a delivery system for a new satellite. Find the volume of the nose cone.

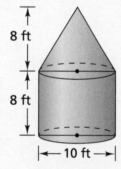

8 ft

8 ft

|← 10 ft →|

Self Assessment

Mathematical Ideas

After studying the mathematics in this Unit:

    1. a. I learned these things about mathematics:

        b. Here are page numbers of notebook entries that give evidence of what
            I have learned, along with descriptions of what each entry shows:

    2. a. These are the mathematical ideas that I am still struggling with:

        b. This is why I think these ideas are difficult for me:

        c. Here are page numbers of notebook entries that give evidence of what
            I am struggling with, and descriptions of what each entry shows:

Class Participation

I contributed to the classroom **discussion** and understanding of the
mathematics in this Unit when I ... (Give examples.)

Self Assessment (continued)

Learning Environment

Rate each learning activity listed below using this scale:

1. I consistently struggled to understand the mathematics and I'm still not sure that I understand it.

2. I struggled somewhat but now I understand more than I did.

3. I had to work, but I feel confident that I understand now.

4. I understood everything pretty easily and I feel confident that I know the mathematics in these problems.

5. Everything came easily. I knew most of the mathematics before we did this.

Learning Activities

_____ Problems from the Investigations

_____ ACE Homework Assignments

_____ Mathematical Reflections

_____ Check Ups

_____ Partner Quiz

_____ Looking Back

_____ Unit Test

Check any of the following that you feel are the most helpful in adding to the success of your learning.

☐ Working on my own in class

☐ Discussing a problem with a partner

☐ Working in a small group of 3 or 4 people

☐ Discussing a problem as a whole class

☐ Hearing how other people solved the problem

☐ Summarizing the mathematics as a class and taking notes

☐ Completing homework assignments

Notebook Checklist

Place a ✔ next to each item you have completed.

Notebook Organization

_____ Problems and Mathematical Reflections are labeled and dated.

_____ Work is neat and easy to find and follow.

Vocabulary

_____ All words are listed.   _____ All words are defined or described.

Assessments

_____ Check Up   _____ _____

_____ Partner Quiz   _____ _____

_____ Unit Test   _____ _____

Assignments

_____ _____   _____ _____

_____ _____   _____ _____

_____ _____   _____ _____

_____ _____   _____ _____

_____ _____   _____ _____

_____ _____   _____ _____

_____ _____   _____ _____

_____ _____   _____ _____

_____ _____   _____ _____

_____ _____   _____ _____

Assessment Answers

Check Up 1

1. **a.** 20.25 in. • 10.5 in. • 12.5 in. = 2,657.8125 in.^{3}

   b. 2[(20.25 in. • 10.5 in.) + (20.25 in. • 12.5 in.) + (10.5 in. • 12.5 in.)] = 1,194 in.^{2}

2. **a.** 8 • 8 • 8 = 512 times greater

   b. 8 • 8 = 64 times greater

3. **a.** 16 inches by 1 inch by 1 inch, because it is least close to a cube, or it shows the most surfaces of the interior chalk cubes, or it has the greatest surface area (66 in.^{2}).

   b. 4 inches by 2 inches by 2 inches, because it is closest in shape to a cube, or it shows the fewest surfaces of the interior chalk cubes, or it has the least surface area (40 in.^{2}).

Partner Quiz

1. **a.** about $3(4 \cdot 8.25) + 2\left(\frac{1}{2}\right)(4)(3.46) = 112.84$ in.^{2}

   b. about $3(16 \cdot 33) + 2\left(\frac{1}{2}\right)(16)(13.86) = 1,805.76$ in.^{2}

   c. about $\left(\frac{1}{2}\right)(4)(3.46)(8.25) = 57.09$ in.^{3}

   d. about $\left(\frac{1}{2}\right)(16)(13.86)(33) = 3,659.04$ in.^{3}

   e. $\$2 \cdot 4^3 = \$128$

   f. Any prism with lateral faces that are the same size as the smaller package and with bases that are polygons with more than three sides would hold more chocolate than the smaller package.

2. Answers will vary. Samples: a square from cutting vertically or horizontally, a triangle from cutting off a corner at a slant, or a rectangle from cutting through a diagonal of one face. (**Note:** A rectangle, a parallelogram, a pentagon, and a hexagon are also possible, but it is unlikely that students will come up with these.)

Check Up 2

1. **a.** 25 ft • 3.14 = 78.5 ft

   b. 9 ft • 9 ft • 3.14 = 254.34 ft^2

2. 2.5 in. • 2.5 in. • 3.14 = 19.625 in.^{2}

3. The diameter is 113 ft ÷ 3.14, which is approximately equal to 36 ft.

4. The area of a circle with a diameter of 10 cm is approximately 78.5 cm^2. The area of a square with side lengths of 10 cm is 100 cm^2. Therefore, the square has the greater area.

Unit Test

1. Surface Area for Popcorn R:
   2(9 in. • 12 in. + 4 in. • 12 in.) + (4 in. • 9 in.) = 2(108 in.^{2} + 48 in.^{2}) + 36 in.^{2} = 2(156 in.^{2}) + 36 in.^{2} = 312 in.^{2} + 36 in.^{2} = 348 in.^{2}
   Surface Area for Popcorn T:
   $(\frac{1}{2}$ • 9 in. • 12 in.) + (4 in. • 9 in.) + (4 in. • 12 in.) + (4 in. • 15 in.) = 54 in.^{2} + 36 in.^{2} + 48 in.^{2} + 60 in.^{2} = 198 in.^{2}
   Popcorn R requires more cardboard because it has the greater surface area.

2. Volume for Popcorn R: 4 in. • 9 in. • 12 in. = 432 in.^{3}
   Volume for Popcorn T: $\frac{1}{2}$ • 9 in. • 12 in. • 4 in. = 216 in.^{3}
   Popcorn R holds more popcorn because it has the greater volume.

3. **a.** about $5.06 ($1.5^3$ or 3.375 times the price of Popcorn R)

   b. 1.5^2 • 348 in.^{2} = 783 in.^{2}

   c. 1.5^3 • 432 in.^{3} = 1,458 in.^{3}

4. **a.** 25 cm^2 • 6 = 150 cm^2

   b. 5 cm • 5 cm • 5 cm = 125 cm^3

Assessment Answers (continued)

5. a. One piece will be a pentagonal prism, the other a triangular prism. The pentagonal prism will have 15 edges, and the triangular prism will have 9 edges. The lateral faces of both solids will be rectangles.

b. A rectangle is formed by the cut.

6. a. The square pizza has more area: 225 in.^{2} versus the round pizza's area of 201.06 in.^{2}, for 23.94 in.^{2} more.

b. The crust of a pizza is measured by its perimeter or circumference. The square pizza has a larger perimeter (and therefore more crust), 60 inches versus the 50.27 inches of crust on the round pizza.

7. Surface Area: $6 \cdot 9 \text{ cm} \cdot 6 \text{ cm} = 324 \text{ cm}^2$ (for the sides) $+ 30.6 \text{ cm}^2 \cdot 2$ (for the top and bottom) $= 385.2 \text{ cm}^2$

Volume: $30.6 \text{ cm}^2 \cdot 9 \text{ cm} = 275.4 \text{ cm}^3$

8. a. No, the cylinders have different volumes.

Volume of the shorter cylinder: $\pi \cdot (5 \text{ cm})^2 \cdot 6 \text{ cm}$, which is $150\pi \text{ cm}^3$.

Volume of the taller cylinder: $\pi \cdot (3 \text{ cm})^2 \cdot 10 \text{ cm}$, which is $90\pi \text{ cm}^3$.

b. No, the cylinders do not have the same surface area.

Surface area of the shorter cylinder: $2 \cdot \pi (5 \text{ cm})^2 + \pi \cdot 2(5 \text{ cm})(6 \text{ cm}) = 110\pi \text{ cm}^2$, or about 345.58 cm^2.

Surface area of the taller cylinder: $2 \cdot \pi (3 \text{ cm})^2 + \pi \cdot 2(3)(10) \text{ cm} = 78\pi \text{ cm}^2$, or about 245.04 cm^2.

9. The volume of the cylinder section is $\pi \cdot (5 \text{ ft})^2 \cdot 8 \text{ ft}$, which is $200\pi \text{ ft}^3$, or about 628.32 ft^3. The volume of the cone section is $\frac{1}{3} \cdot \pi \cdot (5 \text{ ft})^2 \cdot 8 \text{ ft}$, which is $\frac{200}{3} \cdot \pi$, or about 209.44 ft^3. So, the total volume of the figure is $628.32 \text{ ft}^3 + 209.44 \text{ ft}^3$, or 837.76 ft^3.

Looking Back Answers

1. **a.** The dimensions of the box are 32 cm by 16 cm by 8 cm.
   b. The surface area is 1,792 cm².
   c. The volume is 4,096 cm³.

2. **a.** The box that requires the most cardboard has dimensions 1 in. × 1 in. × 40 in.
   b. The box that requires the least cardboard has dimensions 2 in. × 4 in. × 5 in.
   c. See Figure 1.

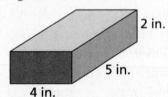

2 in.

5 in.

4 in.

   d. If the dimensions of the box are doubled, there will be 280 more caramels, for a total of 320 caramels. This is 8 times as many caramels as in the original box.

3. **a.** The volume of the cylinder is 90π cubic inches, or about 282.74 in.³.
   b. The volume of the square prism is 179.776 in.³. So, the difference is $282.74 - 179.776$, or about 102.964 in.³.
   c. The cost per cubic inch for each container is about $.008 ($2.19 ÷ 90\pi$). So, the new square prism should cost $.008 × 179.776, or about $1.44.

   d. There are many possibilities. A cone with the same volume as the cylinder could have a height of 10 in. and a radius approximately equal to 5.2 in. or a height of 9 in. and a radius approximately equal to 5.5 in. Each of these is close in height and radius to the original cylinder. **Note:** Due to the approximation of π or square roots, the volumes are not exactly equal. The simplest and most exact way to get a cone with equal volume would be to leave the base radius alone and triple the height to 30 in.

4. The volume of a solid figure tells you the number of unit cubes that will completely fill it. The surface area is the total area of the faces of the solid figure. It tells you how much wrapping is needed to exactly cover the solid figure.

5. **a.** The volume of the rectangular prism can be found by the calculation $\ell \times w \times h$. The surface area can be found by the calculation $2(\ell \times w + \ell \times h + w \times h)$.
   b. The volume of the cylinder can be found by the calculation $\pi \times r \times r \times h$, or $\pi r^2 h$. The surface area can be found by the calculation $2\pi r^2 + 2\pi rh$.

Figure 1

1 in.

1 in.

40 in.

Looking Back Answers *(continued)*

6. The volume of the rectangular prism can be found by the calculation $\ell \times w \times h$. The calculation $\ell \times w$ yields the number of unit cubes that will fit on the first layer of the prism, and h is the number of layers needed to fill the prism. The surface area can be found by finding the sum of the areas of each of the six faces, which is the calculation $2(\ell \times w + \ell \times h + w \times h)$.
The volume of the cylinder can be found by the calculation $\pi \times r \times r \times h$, or $\pi r^2 h$. The area of the base is πr^2. This calculation gives the number of unit cubes that will fit on the first layer of the cylinder, and h is the number of layers needed to fill the cylinder. The surface area can be found by finding the sum of the areas of the two circular bases and the lateral surface area. The combined area of the bases is $2\pi r^2$, and the lateral surface area is the area of a rectangle whose height is h and whose width is the circumference of the circular base. So, the surface area is $2\pi r^2 + 2\pi rh$.

7. If the sphere, cone, and cylinder have the same radius, and if the heights of both the cylinder and the cone are equal to the diameter of the sphere, then the volume of the sphere is two thirds that of the cylinder, and the volume of the cone is one third that of the cylinder.

8. If two solid figures are similar and the scale factor is f, then the volume of the larger solid is f times the dimensions of the smaller solid, or $f\ell \times fw \times fh$. In other words, the volume of the larger solid is f^3 times the volume of the smaller solid. The surface area of the larger solid is f^2 times the surface area of the smaller solid.

Parent Letters

Labsheets

Assessments

Dear Family,

The next Unit in your child's mathematics class this year is *Samples and Populations: Making Comparisons and Predictions*. In this Unit, your child will work within the process of statistical investigation, paying special attention to the ways that data are collected and analyzed.

▶ Unit Goals

In this Unit, students pose questions, collect and analyze data, and interpret the data to answer the questions. Students write and use simple surveys as a method of collecting data.

This Unit uses statistical concepts that were introduced in Grade 6. *Samples and Populations* reinforces and extends these concepts in Grade 7. Students will organize data using tables, dot plots, line plots, bar graphs, histograms, and box-and-whisker plots. Students will then explore measures of center (mean, median, and mode), and measures of spread (range, mean absolute deviation, and interquartile range).

Students extend their previous work by applying these concepts to samples, or subsets of populations. Students decide whether or not samples are representative of the population. They also compare samples to draw conclusions about those samples and the populations from which they come.

▶ Homework and Conversations About the Mathematics

In your child's notebook, you can find worked-out examples, notes on the mathematics of the Unit, and descriptions of the vocabulary words. You can help with homework and encourage sound mathematical habits as your child studies this Unit by asking questions such as:

- *Describe the sample. From what population was the sample collected?*
- *What relationships can you describe among the data?*
- *Can you interpret the data to draw conclusions about the sample? About the population?*
- *Can you compare the data with another data set to identify relationships between them?*
- *Can you use the results from the analyses to answer the original question(s)?*

You can help your child with his or her work for this Unit in several ways:

- Help your child identify statistics in newspapers, magazines, television, or radio reports, paying particular attention to who or what was sampled.
- Discuss graphical displays of data and ask your child questions about the information shown.
- Ask your child about the data studied in class. What were the typical (mode, median, or mean) values for these data?
- Review your child's work. Be sure that all questions are answered and clearly explained.

▶ Common Core State Standards

While all of the Standards of Mathematical Practice are developed and used by students throughout the curriculum, in this unit particular attention is paid to constructing viable arguments and critiquing the reasoning of others as students make conjectures about relationships they see in data sets. *Samples and Populations* focuses largely on the Statistics and Probability domain of the CCSSM.

A few important mathematical ideas that your child will learn in *Samples and Populations* are given on the back.

As always, if you have any questions or concerns about this Unit or your child's progress in class, please feel free to call. All of us here are interested in your child's progress and want to be sure that this year's mathematics experiences are enjoyable and promote a firm understanding of mathematics.

Sincerely,

Important Concepts	Examples
The Process of Statistical Investigation This process involves posing questions, collecting data, analyzing distributions, and interpreting analyses in light of the questions. It also involves considering whether to collect new data or use existing data. Finally, the results are communicated.	Students refine their ideas about asking questions and collecting data. The questions must be clear, and the samples of data must be unbiased. For example, if a survey asks about the number of movies watched during a particular time frame, the definition of "movie" must be clarified. Also, if the sample is intended to be representative of a greater population, it must be free of bias. The method of collecting data, therefore, is important.
Exploring the Concept of Sampling Sampling is used to draw conclusions about a whole population by analyzing only a part of it. Collecting data on the entire population may be difficult because of cost or the size of the population. Statisticians try to obtain a representative sample by selecting the sample at random. Sample size is also important.	A *random sample* is one in which every member of a population is equally likely to be chosen. A *representative sample* is one whose characteristics accurately reflect those of the larger population. For example, when determining the typical number of movies students watch, you can number each student in the population and then choose numbers at random. Sampling methods that are not random, such as surveying a movie club, are less likely to be representative.

Making Sense of Data With Data Displays
Statisticians use representations or statistics to analyze data. This involves displaying data, reading graphs, and calculating measures of central tendency and measures of spread.

Line Plots (Dot Plots): Each item is represented by an "*X*" (or a dot) above a number line.

Histogram: The size of the bar over each interval shows the frequency of data values in that interval; frequencies may be displayed as counts or percentages.

Ordered-Value Bar Graph: Each case is represented by a separate bar. The length of each bar corresponds to the magnitude or value of the case. The bars are ordered from least to greatest or greatest to least.

Frequency Bar Graph: A bar's height is not the value of an individual case, but rather the number (frequency) of cases that have that value.

Box-and-Whisker Plot: Box plots group data into quartiles to make the data easier to analyze or to compare with other sets of data. They display symmetry or skewness of data.

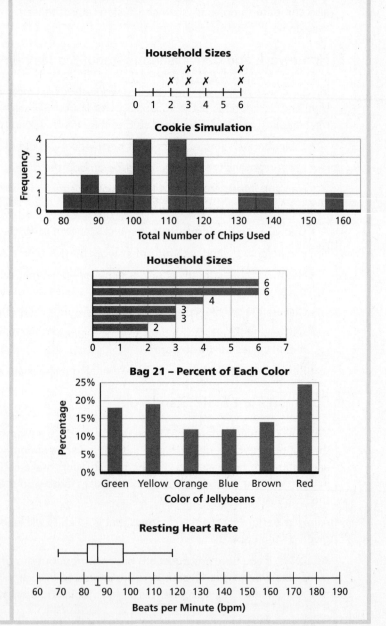

Estimada familia:

La siguiente Unidad de la clase de Matemáticas de su hijo(a) este año es **Muestras y poblaciones: Datos**. En esta Unidad, su hijo(a) trabajará con los procesos de investigación estadística, poniendo especial atención en las maneras en que se recopilan y analizan los datos

▶ Objetivos de la unidad

En esta Unidad, los estudiantes plantean preguntas y recopilan, analizan e interpretan los datos para responder a las preguntas. Ellos escriben y usan encuestas simples para recopilar datos.

Esta Unidad usa los conceptos estadísticos presentados en el Grado 6. *Muestras y poblaciones* refuerza y amplía estos conceptos en el Grado 7. Los estudiantes organizarán datos usando tablas, diagramas de puntos, gráficas de barras, histogramas y gráficas de caja y bigotes. Los estudiantes explorarán luego medidas de tendencia central (media, mediana y moda) y medidas de dispersión (rango, desviación absoluta media y rango entre cuartiles).

Los estudiantes amplían su trabajo previo aplicando estos conceptos a muestras, o subconjuntos de poblaciones. Ellos deciden si las muestras son representativas o no de la población. También comparan muestras para sacar conclusiones sobre ellas y las poblaciones de las que provienen.

▶ Tareas y conversaciones acerca de las matemáticas

En el cuaderno de su hijo(a) puede hallar ejemplos resueltos, notas sobre las matemáticas de la Unidad y descripciones del vocabulario. Usted puede ayudar a su hijo(a) con la tarea y fomentarle hábitos matemáticos a medida que estudia esta Unidad haciéndole preguntas como:

- *Describe la muestra. ¿De qué población se recopiló la muestra?*
- *Qué relaciones puedes describir entre los datos?*
- *¿Puedes interpretar los datos para sacar conclusiones sobre la muestra? ¿Y sobre la población?*
- *¿Puedes comparar los datos con los de otro conjunto para identificar relaciones entre ellos?*
- *¿Puedes usar los resultados de los análisis para responder a las preguntas originales?*

Usted puede ayudar a su hijo(a) con la tarea para esta Unidad de varias maneras:

- Ayude a su hijo(a) a identificar estadísticas en informes de periódicos, revistas, televisión o radio, prestando especial atención a cómo se formaron las muestras.
- Comente gráficas de datos y hágale preguntas sobre la información que se muestra.
- Pregunte a su hijo(a) sobre los datos estudiados en clase. ¿Cuáles fueron los valores típicos (moda, mediana o media) de esos datos?
- Revise la tarea y asegúrese de que esté completa y de que sus explicaciones son claras.

▶ Estándares estatales comunes

Aunque los estudiantes desarrollan y usan todos los Estándares de prácticas matemáticas a lo largo del curso en esta Unidad se presta especial atención a construir argumentos viables y evaluar el razonamiento de otros a medida que los estudiantes hacen conjeturas sobre las relaciones que ven en los conjuntos de datos. *Muestras y poblaciones* se enfoca sobre todo en la rama de Estadística y probabilidad de los Estándares estatales comunes.

Algunas importantes ideas matemáticas que su hijo(a) aprenderá en *Muestras y poblaciones* se presentan en la página siguiente.

Como siempre, si usted tiene cualquier pregunta o preocupación acerca de esta Unidad, o con respecto al progreso de su hijo(a) en clase, por favor no dude en llamar. Estamos interesados en su hijo(a) y queremos que él o ella disfrute las experiencias matemáticas de este año, además de promover un entendimiento firme de las matemáticas.

Sinceramente,

Conceptos importantes	Ejemplos
El proceso de investigación estadística Este proceso incluye plantear preguntas, recopilar datos, analizar distribuciones e interpretar análisis a la luz de las preguntas. También incluye considerar si es necesario recopilar nuevos datos o usar los existentes. Finalmente, se comunican los resultados.	Los estudiantes refinan sus ideas acerca de hacer preguntas y recopilar datos. Las preguntas deben ser claras y las muestras de datos no deben estar sesgadas. Por ejemplo, si una encuesta pregunta sobre el número de películas vistas durante un periodo específico, se debe aclarar la definición de "película". Además, si se tiene la intención de que la muestra sea representativa de una población mayor, debe estar libre de sesgo. Por tanto, el método de recopilación de datos es muy importante.
Explorar el concepto de muestreo Se usa el muestreo para sacar conclusiones sobre toda una población analizando solo parte de ella. Recopilar datos de la población entera puede ser difícil por el costo o el tamaño de la misma. Los estadísticos intentan obtener una muestra representativa seleccionando la muestra al azar El tamaño de la muestra también es importante.	Una *muestra aleatoria* es aquella para la que cada miembro de una población tiene la misma probabilidad de ser elegido. Una *muestra representativa* es aquella cuyas características reflejan con precisión las de la población mayor. Por ejemplo, al determinar el número típico de películas que los estudiantes ven, se puede numerar a cada estudiante de la población y después elegir números al azar. Los métodos de muestreo que no son aleatorios, como las encuestas en un cineclub, tienen menores probabilidades de ser representativas.

Entender los datos con representaciones
Los estadísticos usan representaciones o estadísticas para analizar los datos. Esto incluye representar los datos, leer gráficas y calcular medidas de tendencia central y de dispersión.

Diagramas de puntos: Cada elemento está representado con una "**X**" (o un punto) sobre una recta numérica.

Tamaños de los hogares

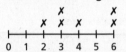

Histogramas: El tamaño de la barra sobre cada intervalo muestra la frecuencia de valores de datos en ese intervalo; las frecuencias pueden representarse como conteos o porcentajes.

Simulación de galletas

Gráfica de barras de valores ordenados: Cada caso está representado por una barra separada. La longitud de cada barra corresponde a la magnitud o valor del caso. Las barras están ordenadas de menor a mayor o de mayor a menor.

Tamaños de los hogares

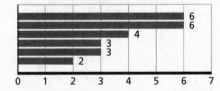

Gráfica de barras de frecuencia: La longitud de una barra no representa el valor de un caso individual, sino el número de casos (la frecuencia) que tienen ese valor.

Bolsa 21 – Porcentaje de cada color

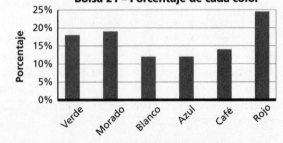

Gráfica de caja y bigotes: Agrupa datos en cuartiles para facilitar el análisis o la comparación con otros conjuntos de datos. Muestra la simetría o la inclinación de los datos.

Frecuencia cardiaca en reposo

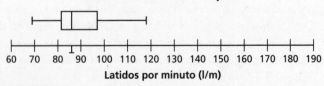

372

Labsheet 1.2 Fundraising Money Collected

Money Collected During Fundraiser
(dollars)

Team 1	Team 2	Team 3	Team 4	Team 5	Team 6
45	50	100	70	64	50
43	50	45	63	50	35
35	35	20	50	42	35
33	25	20	17	30	35
29	25	15	10	24	35
25	25	10	0		20

Labsheet 1.3   Roller Coaster Survey Responses

Roller Coaster Seating Preferences

Preference	Votes From Internet	Votes From 7th Graders	Votes From Your Class
Front	97	27	
Middle	50	22	
Back	18	14	
Total Votes	**165**	**63**	

Other Roller Coaster Preferences

Preference	Votes From Internet	Votes From 7th Graders	Votes From Your Class
Airtime	88	31	
Height	36	24	
Inversions	59	29	
Smoothness	39	12	
Speed	105	57	
Total Votes	**327**	**153**	

Labsheet 1.4A   Sample of 30 Steel-Frame Roller Coasters

Name	Year Opened	Maximum Drop (feet)	Maximum Height (feet)	Track Length (feet)	Top Speed (mi/h)	Duration (minutes)
Steel-Frame Coaster 1	1998	20	28	679	22	0.73
Steel-Frame Coaster 2	1995	—	46	1,217	22	1.50
Steel-Frame Coaster 3	1991	35	59	1,427	35	1.43
Steel-Frame Coaster 4	1999	40	45	1,772	35	1.50
Steel-Frame Coaster 5	1998	—	65	1,650	35	1.67
Steel-Frame Coaster 6	1995	45	65	2,602	35	2.00
Steel-Frame Coaster 7	1970	45	50	1,837	40	1.53
Steel-Frame Coaster 8	1976	64	70	3,100	42	2.00
Steel-Frame Coaster 9	1980	47	47	502	45	1.10
Steel-Frame Coaster 10	1976	90	95	2,130	45	1.75
Steel-Frame Coaster 11	1999	125	125	875	48	1.80
Steel-Frame Coaster 12	1999	125	125	875	48	1.80
Steel-Frame Coaster 13	1993	87	100	2,693	50	2.00
Steel-Frame Coaster 14	1994	87	105	2,700	50	2.00
Steel-Frame Coaster 15	1996	—	78	2,705	54	2.40
Steel-Frame Coaster 16	1978	138	138	849	55	0.50
Steel-Frame Coaster 17	1998	138	138	985	55	1.50
Steel-Frame Coaster 18	1978	114	130	3,240	60	2.17
Steel-Frame Coaster 19	2012	135	210	3,127	61	2.37
Steel-Frame Coaster 20	1997	144	154	4,155	63	3.00
Steel-Frame Coaster 21	2012	174	192	1,204	66	1.50
Steel-Frame Coaster 22	2008	177	192	1,204	66	1.53
Steel-Frame Coaster 23	1998	218	218	1,300	70	0.55
Steel-Frame Coaster 24	1999	205	208	5,400	70	2.50
Steel-Frame Coaster 25	1999	210	170	4,882	73	2.25
Steel-Frame Coaster 26	2010	211	232	5,316	75	3.30
Steel-Frame Coaster 27	1987	65	76	2,800	76	2.00
Steel-Frame Coaster 28	1991	225	225	3,500	80	2.07
Steel-Frame Coaster 29	2000	235	255	4,500	85	3.00
Steel-Frame Coaster 30	2010	300	305	5,100	90	3.00

— means data not available

Labsheet 1.4B   Sample of 30 Wood-Frame Roller Coasters

Name	Year Opened	Maximum Drop (feet)	Maximum Height (feet)	Track Length (feet)	Top Speed (mi/h)	Duration (min)
Wood-Frame Coaster 1	1951	25	37	1,300	25	1.50
Wood-Frame Coaster 2	2011	—	40	1,365	32	0.83
Wood-Frame Coaster 3	1976	35	40	1,356	35	1.67
Wood-Frame Coaster 4	1927	78	85	2,746	44	1.25
Wood-Frame Coaster 5	1923	65	80	2,767	45	1.30
Wood-Frame Coaster 6	1989	95	100	4,230	45	2.22
Wood-Frame Coaster 7	2002	75	80	2,750	47	1.25
Wood-Frame Coaster 8	1935	52	55	2,650	50	1.75
Wood-Frame Coaster 9	1946	78	84	3,360	50	1.75
Wood-Frame Coaster 10	1991	78	95	2,970	50	1.83
Wood-Frame Coaster 11	1995	80	100	3,458	50	1.75
Wood-Frame Coaster 12	2000	85	90	3,400	51	2.33
Wood-Frame Coaster 13	2007	91.5	97.5	3,113	51	2.00
Wood-Frame Coaster 14	2009	87.3	95	2,877	51	3.00
Wood-Frame Coaster 15	2009	85	102	3,074	51	2.50
Wood-Frame Coaster 16	1924	95	70	2,887	55	1.50
Wood-Frame Coaster 17	1975	85	86	3,368	55	2.25
Wood-Frame Coaster 18	2000	100	102	3,800	55	2.00
Wood-Frame Coaster 19	1998	102	120	3,500	56	1.65
Wood-Frame Coaster 20	2004	105	110	2,602	56	1.50
Wood-Frame Coaster 21	1927	85	85	2,640	60	1.83
Wood-Frame Coaster 22	1997	85	90	2,900	60	1.42
Wood-Frame Coaster 23	1999	103	100	3,000	60	1.67
Wood-Frame Coaster 24	1976	92	110	3,872	62	2.50
Wood-Frame Coaster 25	1978	115	125	4,325	62	3.08
Wood-Frame Coaster 26	1990	137	143	4,920	62	2.50
Wood-Frame Coaster 27	2001	91	86	3,120	62	1.63
Wood-Frame Coaster 28	1992	124	180	5,080	65	2.41
Wood-Frame Coaster 29	2000	115	145	4,752	65	2.50
Wood-Frame Coaster 30	1981	147	127	4,650	66	2.38

— means data not available

Labsheet 1.4C   Dot Plots of Top-Speed Data

Steel-Frame Roller Coaster Speeds

Mean speed = 55.03 mi/h
MAD = 14.64 mi/h

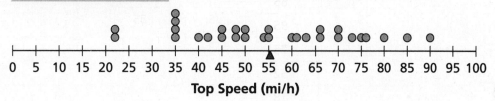

Top Speed (mi/h)

Wood-Frame Roller Coaster Speeds

Mean speed = 52.6 mi/h
MAD = 7.47 mi/h

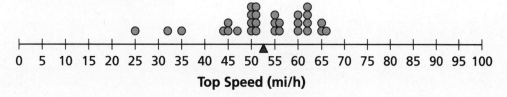

Top Speed (mi/h)

Labsheet 1ACE   Exercises 3–7

**Money Collected During Fundraiser
(dollars)**

Team 1	Team 2	Team 3	Team 4
55	56	100	80
53	53	50	73
44	50	40	44
44	38	40	38
39	37	25	35
35	36	15	

Labsheet 1ACE   Exercises 3–7

Money Collected During Fundraiser

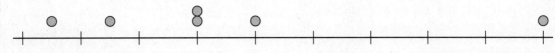

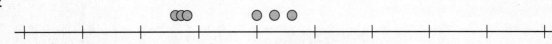

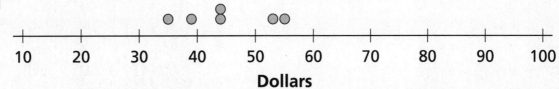

Dollars

Labsheet 2.3A — Responses to Grade 7 Movie and Sleep Survey

Student	Gender	Sleep Last Night (h)	Movies Last Week (no. of)
01	boy	11.5	14
02	boy	2.0	8
03	girl	7.7	3
04	boy	9.3	1
05	boy	7.1	16
06	boy	7.5	1
07	boy	8.0	4
08	girl	7.8	1
09	girl	8.0	13
10	girl	8.0	15
11	boy	9.0	1
12	boy	9.2	10
13	boy	8.5	5
14	girl	6.0	15
15	boy	6.5	10
16	boy	8.3	2
17	girl	7.4	2
18	boy	11.2	3
19	girl	7.3	1
20	boy	8.0	0
21	girl	7.8	1
22	girl	7.8	1
23	boy	9.2	2
24	girl	7.5	0
25	boy	8.8	1
26	girl	8.5	0
27	girl	9.0	0
28	girl	8.5	0
29	boy	8.2	2
30	girl	7.8	2
31	girl	8.0	2
32	girl	7.3	8
33	boy	6.0	5
34	girl	7.5	5

Student	Gender	Sleep Last Night (h)	Movies Last Week (no. of)
35	boy	6.5	5
36	boy	9.3	1
37	girl	8.2	3
38	boy	7.3	3
39	girl	7.4	6
40	girl	8.5	7
41	boy	5.5	17
42	boy	6.5	3
43	boy	7.0	5
44	girl	8.5	2
45	girl	9.3	4
46	girl	8.0	15
47	boy	8.5	10
48	girl	6.2	11
49	girl	11.8	10
50	girl	9.0	4
51	boy	5.0	4
52	boy	6.5	5
53	girl	8.5	2
54	boy	9.1	15
55	girl	7.5	2
56	girl	8.5	1
57	girl	8.0	2
58	girl	7.0	7
59	girl	8.4	10
60	girl	9.5	1
61	girl	7.3	5
62	girl	7.3	4
63	boy	8.5	3
64	boy	9.0	3
65	boy	9.0	4
66	girl	7.3	5
67	girl	5.7	0

Student	Gender	Sleep Last Night (h)	Movies Last Week (no. of)
68	girl	5.5	0
69	boy	10.5	7
70	girl	7.5	1
71	boy	7.8	0
72	girl	7.3	1
73	boy	9.3	2
74	boy	9.0	1
75	boy	8.7	1
76	boy	8.5	3
77	girl	9.0	1
78	boy	8.0	1
79	boy	8.0	4
80	boy	6.5	0
81	boy	8.0	0
82	girl	9.0	8
83	girl	8.0	0
84	boy	7.0	0
85	boy	9.0	6
86	boy	7.3	0
87	girl	9.0	3
88	girl	7.5	5
89	boy	8.0	0
90	girl	7.5	6
91	boy	8.0	4
92	boy	9.0	4
93	boy	7.0	0
94	boy	8.0	3
95	boy	8.3	3
96	boy	8.3	14
97	girl	7.8	5
98	girl	8.5	1
99	girl	8.3	3
100	boy	7.5	2

Labsheet 2.3B   Blank Number Lines for Movies Watched Line Plots

Your Sample of 30

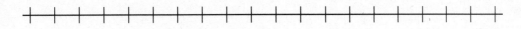

Number of Movies Watched Last Week

A Classmate's Sample of 30

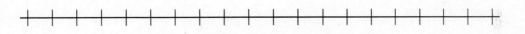

Number of Movies Watched Last Week

Another Classmate's Sample of 30

Number of Movies Watched Last Week

Labsheet 2.3C   Blank Number Lines for Hours Slept Box Plots

Your Sample of 30

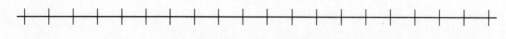

Number of Hours Slept Last Night

A Classmate's Sample of 30

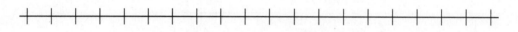

Number of Hours Slept Last Night

Another Classmate's Sample of 30

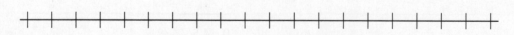

Number of Hours Slept Last Night

Labsheet 2.4A   Blank Number Lines for Movies Watched Last Week (Means)

Samples of Size 5

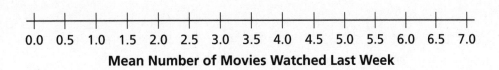

Samples of Size 10

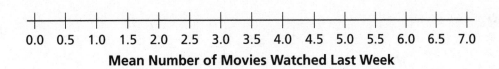

Samples of Size 30

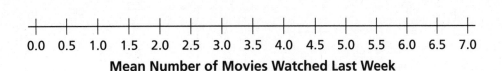

Labsheet 2.4B Blank Number Lines for Movies Watched Last Week (Medians)

Samples of Size 5

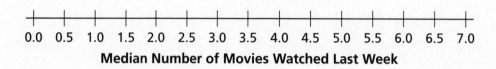

Median Number of Movies Watched Last Week

Samples of Size 10

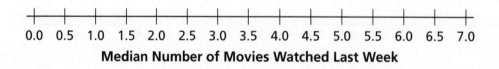

Median Number of Movies Watched Last Week

Samples of Size 30

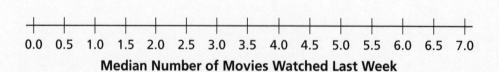

Median Number of Movies Watched Last Week

Labsheet 2.4C   Blank Number Lines for Hours of Sleep Last Night (Means)

Samples of Size 5

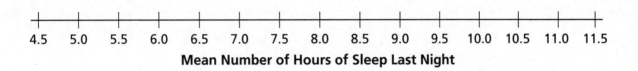

Mean Number of Hours of Sleep Last Night

Samples of Size 10

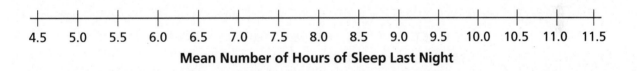

Mean Number of Hours of Sleep Last Night

Samples of Size 30

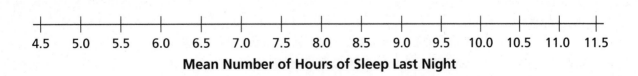

Mean Number of Hours of Sleep Last Night

Labsheet 2.4D — Blank Number Lines for Hours of Sleep Last Night (Medians)

Samples of Size 5

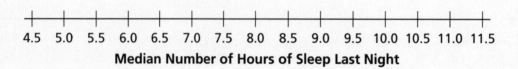

Median Number of Hours of Sleep Last Night

Samples of Size 10

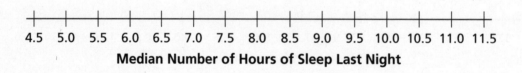

Median Number of Hours of Sleep Last Night

Samples of Size 30

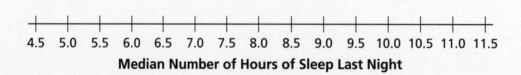

Median Number of Hours of Sleep Last Night

Labsheet 2.4E — Group Organizer for Sample-Size Statistics

Student 1 Movies Watched

Sample	Mean	Median	MAD	IQR
Size 5				
Size 10				
Size 30				

Student 1 Hours Slept

Sample	Mean	Median	MAD	IQR
Size 5				
Size 10				
Size 30				

Student 2 Movies Watched

Sample	Mean	Median	MAD	IQR
Size 5				
Size 10				
Size 30				

Student 2 Hours Slept

Sample	Mean	Median	MAD	IQR
Size 5				
Size 10				
Size 30				

Student 3 Movies Watched

Sample	Mean	Median	MAD	IQR
Size 5				
Size 10				
Size 30				

Student 3 Hours Slept

Sample	Mean	Median	MAD	IQR
Size 5				
Size 10				
Size 30				

Labsheet 2.4F   **Class Organizer for Sample-Size Statistics**

Class Sample-Size Statistics for _____

Student	Sample Size 5				Sample Size 10				Sample Size 30			
	Mean	Median	MAD	IQR	Mean	Median	MAD	IQR	Mean	Median	MAD	IQR

Labsheet 2ACE   Exercises 20–22

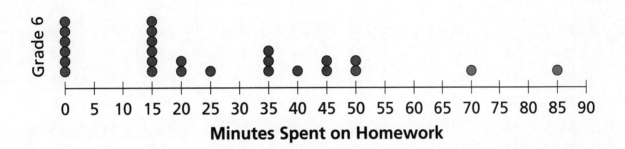

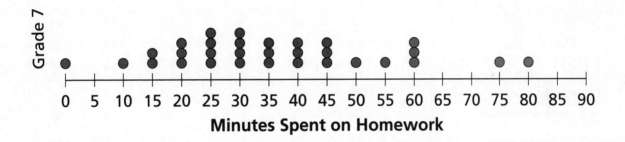

Time Spent on Homework (minutes)

Grade	Mean	Median	MAD
6	25.8		18.56
7	36.13		14.53

Labsheet 3.1A Arrowhead Data

Site I: 15 Arrowheads

Length (mm)	Width (mm)	Neck Width (mm)
24	19	8
27	19	10
29	19	11
29	22	12
31	16	12
31	32	16
37	23	11
38	22	12
38	26	14
40	25	16
45	22	11
45	28	15
55	22	13
62	26	14
63	29	18

SOURCE: *Plains Anthropologist*

Site II: 37 Arrowheads

Length (mm)	Width (mm)	Neck Width (mm)
13	10	6
15	11	7
16	12	8
16	13	7
17	15	9
18	12	10
19	12	8
19	13	9
20	12	7
20	12	9
21	11	7
22	13	9
22	13	9
22	13	8
22	14	10
23	14	9
23	15	9
24	11	8
24	12	7

Length (mm)	Width (mm)	Neck Width (mm)
24	13	8
24	13	8
24	14	10
24	15	9
24	15	8
25	13	7
25	13	7
25	15	10
25	24	7
26	14	10
26	14	11
26	15	11
27	14	8
28	11	6
28	13	9
32	12	8
42	16	11
43	14	9

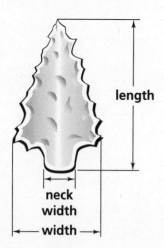

length

neck
width

width

Labsheet 3.1A Arrowhead Data

Big Goose Creek: 52 Arrowheads

Length (mm)	Width (mm)	Neck Width (mm)	Length (mm)	Width (mm)	Neck Width (mm)
16	13	9	26	12	12
16	14	10	26	14	9
17	13	8	26	16	10
17	13	10	27	13	9
18	12	7	27	13	9
18	12	8	27	14	9
18	13	7	27	14	9
18	15	11	27	17	13
19	11	8	28	10	5
20	11	6	28	13	7
20	12	8	28	13	8
21	11	7	28	15	9
21	12	7	29	15	8
21	12	9	30	11	7
22	12	9	30	13	8
22	13	8	30	14	8
22	13	10	30	14	8
23	13	8	30	14	9
23	13	9	30	15	11
23	14	9	31	12	8
24	14	9	33	13	7
24	14	11	33	15	9
25	13	7	34	15	9
25	13	8	35	14	10
25	14	8	39	18	12
26	11	8	40	14	8

SOURCE: *Plains Anthropologist*

Wortham Shelter: 45 Arrowheads

Length (mm)	Width (mm)	Neck Width (mm)	Length (mm)	Width (mm)	Neck Width (mm)
18	11	8	27	14	8
19	12	9	27	14	10
19	14	10	27	15	11
19	14	10	28	13	11
19	16	14	28	14	10
20	13	8	28	16	12
20	14	10	29	13	10
20	15	11	29	14	9
22	12	9	29	14	9
22	14	8	29	17	12
23	13	11	30	14	11
23	14	11	30	16	9
23	15	11	30	17	11
24	12	9	31	13	10
24	13	10	31	14	10
25	14	8	31	14	11
25	14	10	31	16	12
25	15	10	31	17	12
25	15	10	32	14	7
25	15	12	32	15	10
26	13	9	35	18	14
26	13	10	42	18	7
26	15	12			

Labsheet 3.1A Arrowhead Data

Kobold/Buffalo Creek: 52 arrowheads

Length (mm)	Width (mm)	Neck Width (mm)	Length (mm)	Width (mm)	Neck Width (mm)
25	18	15	45	22	13
30	17	12	46	17	13
30	19	15	46	20	14
31	16	13	46	23	14
31	17	12	47	19	13
32	20	13	47	20	12
32	22	17	47	22	13
32	23	18	49	20	14
35	19	11	50	21	13
35	22	14	50	23	15
37	18	12	50	23	16
37	21	11	51	18	10
38	18	9	52	17	12
38	24	15	52	22	15
39	21	14	52	24	16
40	19	15	54	24	13
40	20	12	56	19	12
40	20	13	56	21	15
40	21	12	56	25	13
41	21	13	57	21	15
42	22	14	61	19	12
42	22	15	64	21	13
44	20	11	66	20	15
44	20	12	67	21	13
44	25	14	71	24	13
45	20	13	78	26	12

Laddie Creek/Dead Indian Creek: 18 Arrowheads

Length (mm)	Width (mm)	Neck Width (mm)
25	18	13
27	20	13
27	20	14
29	14	11
29	20	13
30	23	13
31	18	11
32	16	10
32	19	10
35	20	15
37	17	13
38	17	14
39	18	15
40	18	11
41	15	11
42	22	12
44	18	13
52	21	16

Labsheet 3.1B   Blank Tables for Arrowhead Summary Statistics

Arrowhead Lengths (mm)

Statistics	Kobold/ Buffalo Creek	Laddie Creek/ Dead Indian Creek	Site I	Site II	Big Goose Creek	Wortham Shelter
Minimum						
Q1						
Median						
Q3						
Maximum						
Range						
Mean (nearest tenth)						
MAD (nearest tenth)						

Arrowhead Widths (mm)

Statistics	Kobold/ Buffalo Creek	Laddie Creek/ Dead Indian Creek	Site I	Site II	Big Goose Creek	Wortham Shelter
Minimum						
Q1						
Median						
Q3						
Maximum						
Range						
Mean (nearest tenth)						
MAD (nearest tenth)						

Labsheet 3.1B   Blank Tables for Arrowhead Summary Statistics

Arrowhead Neck Widths (mm)

Statistics	Kobold/ Buffalo Creek	Laddie Creek/ Dead Indian Creek	Site I	Site II	Big Goose Creek	Wortham Shelter
Minimum						
Q1						
Median						
Q3						
Maximum						
Range						
Mean (nearest tenth)						
MAD (nearest tenth)						

Labsheet 3.1C   Arrowhead Summary Statistics

Arrowhead Lengths (mm)

Statistics	Kobold/ Buffalo Creek	Laddie Creek/ Dead Indian Creek	Site I	Site II	Big Goose Creek	Wortham Shelter
Minimum	25	25			16	18
Q1	38	29			21	23
Median	45	33.5			26	26
Q3	52	40			29.5	30
Maximum	78	52			40	42
Range	53	27			24	24
Mean (nearest tenth)	45.9	35			25.4	26.3
MAD (nearest tenth)	8.7	5.9			4.5	3.9

Arrowhead Widths (mm)

Statistics	Kobold/ Buffalo Creek	Laddie Creek/ Dead Indian Creek	Site I	Site II	Big Goose Creek	Wortham Shelter
Minimum	16	14			10	11
Q1	19	17			12	13
Median	21	18			13	14
Q3	22	20			14	15
Maximum	26	23			18	18
Range	10	9			8	7
Mean (nearest tenth)	20.7	18.6			13.3	14.4
MAD (nearest tenth)	1.8	1.8			1.2	1.2

Labsheet 3.1C   Arrowhead Summary Statistics

Arrowhead Neck Widths (mm)

Statistics	Kobold/ Buffalo Creek	Laddie Creek/ Dead Indian Creek	Site I	Site II	Big Goose Creek	Wortham Shelter
Minimum	9	10			5	7
Q1	12	11			8	9
Median	13	13			8.5	10
Q3	15	14			9	11
Maximum	18	16			13	14
Range	9	6			8	7
Mean (nearest tenth)	13.3	12.7			8.7	10.1
MAD (nearest tenth)	1.3	1.4			1.2	1.2

Labsheet 3.1D   Box Plots for Arrowhead Data

Arrowhead Lengths

Site

Kobold/Buffalo Creek

Laddie Creek/Dead Indian Creek

Site I

Site II

Big Goose Creek

Wortham Shelter

```
  10  15  20  25  30  35  40  45  50  55  60  65  70  75  80
```

Length (mm)

Arrowhead Widths

Site

Kobold/Buffalo Creek

Laddie Creek/Dead Indian Creek

Site I

Site II

Big Goose Creek

Wortham Shelter

```
  10  12  14  16  18  20  22  24  26  28  30  32
```

Width (mm)

Labsheet 3.1D   Box Plots for Arrowhead Data

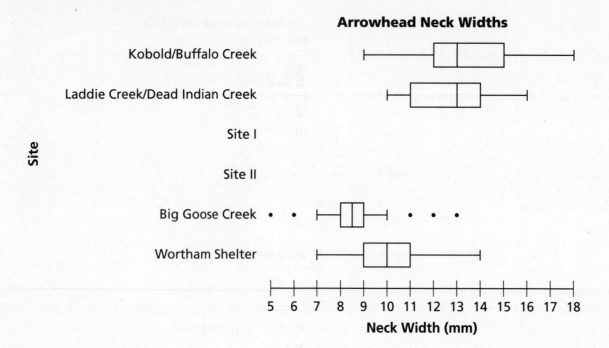

Arrowhead Neck Widths

398

Investigation 3

Labsheet 3.2   Heights of Basketball Players

Heights of Male Professional Basketball Players

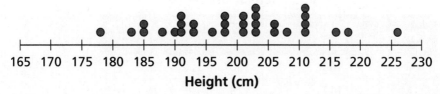

Heights of Female Professional Basketball Players

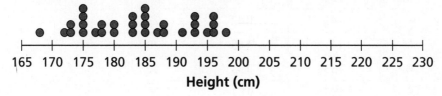

Heights of Mystery Players

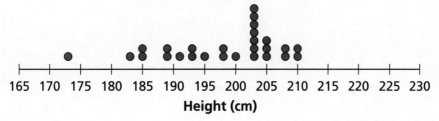

Labsheet 3ACE   Exercises 3–6

A sample of students measured their heights, arm spans, and foot lengths.
Use the table below for Exercises 3–6.

Student Measurement Data

Gender	Height (cm)	Arm Span (cm)	Foot Length (cm)
F	160	158	25
M	111	113	15
F	160	160	23
F	152	155	23.5
F	146	144	24
F	157	156	24
M	136	135	21
F	143	142	23
M	147	145	20
M	133	133	20
F	153	151	25
M	148	149	23
M	125	123	20
F	150	149	20

3. a. Make a **line plot** displaying the foot lengths of **female** students.

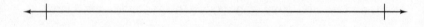

b. What is the **mean** of the data? The **MAD**?

c. On your line plot, **mark** the locations of **one MAD** and **two MADs** less than and greater than the mean.

Labsheet 3ACE   Exercises 3–6

4. **a.** Make a **line plot** displaying the foot lengths of **male** students.

   b. What is the **mean** of the data? The **MAD**?

   c. On your line plot, **mark** the locations of **one MAD** and **two MADs** less than and greater than the mean.

5. Use your answers from Exercises 3 and 4. Mark the **mean male foot length** on the **line plot of female foot lengths**. Is the mean male foot length an **unexpected** data value for the female line plot? Explain?

> **Hint:** Is the mean male foot length within one MAD of the female mean foot length? Within two MADs? More than two MADs away?

6. Use your answers from Exercises 3 and 4. Mark the **mean female foot length** on the **line plot of male foot lengths**. Is the mean female foot length an unexpected data value for the male line plot? Explain?

> **Hint:** Is the mean female foot length within one MAD of the male mean foot length? Within two MADs? More than two MADs away?

Labsheet 3ACE Exercise 7

7. The line plots below display the name lengths of a sample of 30 U.S. students and a sample of 30 Chinese students.

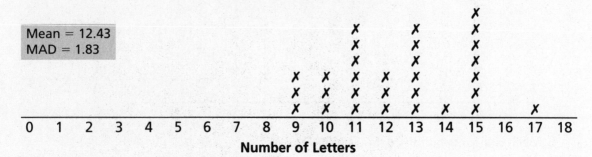

Lengths of U.S. Names

Mean = 12.43
MAD = 1.83

Number of Letters

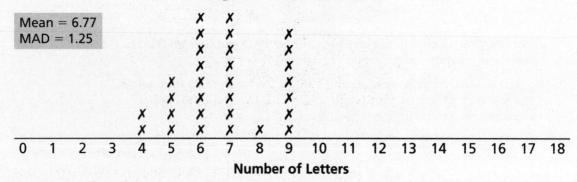

Lengths of Chinese Names

Mean = 6.77
MAD = 1.25

Number of Letters

Keron and Ethan notice that the U.S. names are **longer than** the Chinese names.

Keron thinks this is **due to naturally occurring variability**.

Ethan thinks the differences are **too great to be explained only by naturally occuring variability**.

Do you agree with Keron or with Ethan? Explain.

Hint: Mark up the line plots above.

Within **how many MADs** of the mean of the U.S. data is the mean of the Chinese data?

Within **how many MADs** of the mean of the Chinese data is the mean of the U.S. data?

Labsheet 3.3 Cookie Simulation Tables

Cookie Simulation

Cookie Number	Number of Chips in the Cookie
1	
2	
3	
4	
5	
6	
7	
8	
9	
10	
11	
12	

Labsheet 3.3   Cookie Simulation Tables

Trials for Recommended Number of Chips

Simulation Trial Number	Does Each Cookie Have at Least Five Chips?
1	
2	
3	
4	
5	
6	
7	
8	
9	
10	
11	
12	
13	
14	
15	
16	
17	
18	
19	
20	
21	
22	
23	
24	
25	
26	
27	
28	
29	
30	

Labsheet 3.4   Capture–Tag–Recapture Table

Capture–Tag–Recapture Sampling Data

Sample Size	Number of Marked Beans	Number of Unmarked Beans	Estimate of Total Number of Beans
25			
50			
75			
100			
125			
150			

Labsheet 3ACE   Exercises 8 and 9

Keisha opens a bag containing 60 chocolate chip cookies. She selects a sample of 20 cookies and counts the chips in each cookie. Use Keisha's data below to answer the questions.

Cookie Sample

Cookie Number	Number of Chips	Cookie Number	Number of Chips
1	6	11	8
2	8	12	7
3	8	13	9
4	11	14	9
5	7	15	8
6	6	16	6
7	6	17	8
8	7	18	10
9	11	19	10
10	7	20	8

8. Estimate the number of total chips in the bag. Explain your answer.

9. Copy and complete each statement with the most appropriate fraction: $\frac{1}{4}, \frac{1}{6},$ or $\frac{1}{2}$.

More than _____ of the cookies have at least 8 chips.

More than _____ of the cookies have at least 9 chips.

More than _____ of the cookies have at least 10 chips.

Labsheet 3ACE Exercise 11

11. Yung-nan wants to **estimate** the numer of beans in a large jar. She takes out 150 beans and marks each with a red dot. She returns the beans to the jar and mixes them with the unmarked beans. She then takes four samples from the jar. The table shows Yung-nan's data.

Bean Samples

Sample	Total Number of Beans	Number of Beans With Red Dots
1	25	3
2	150	23
3	75	15
4	250	25

a. For each sample, find the **relative frequency** of total beans that are marked with red dots.

> **Hint:** To find the **relative frequency**, find the **ratio** of red beans to total beans. Then, write this ratio as a **percent**.

b. Which sample has the **greatest** percent of marked beans? Use this sample to estimate the number of beans in the jar. Be sure to show your work.

> **Hint:** Use your answers from part (a).

c. Which sample has the **least** percent of marked beans? Use this sample to estimate the number of beans in the jar. Show your work.

> **Hint:** Use your answers from part (a).

d. Diya used the shaded bars below to make an **estimate** from **Sample 3**.

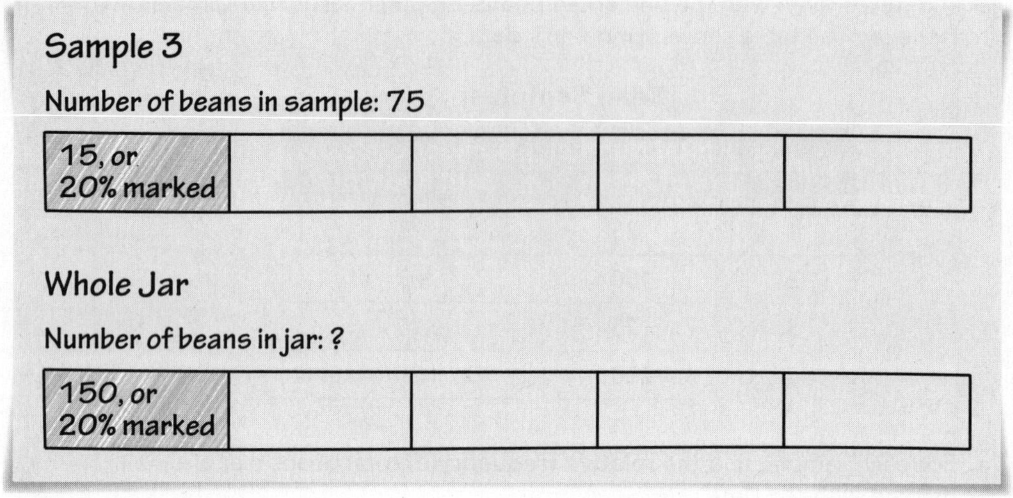

Sample 3

Number of beans in sample: 75

15, or 20% marked				

Whole Jar

Number of beans in jar: ?

150, or 20% marked				

Explain what the bars show.

Explain how the bars can be used to estimate the number of beans in the whole jar.

e. Use your answers from **parts (a)–(d)**. What is your **best guess** for the **total number of beans** in the jar? Explain your reasoning.

Labsheet   Looking Back

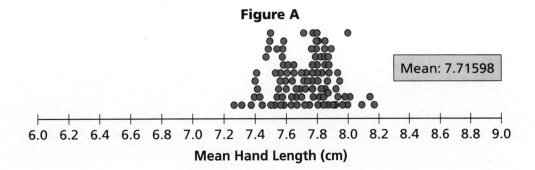

Figure A

Mean: 7.71598

Mean Hand Length (cm)

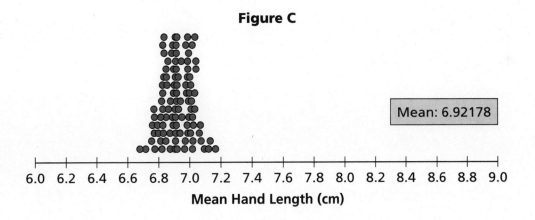

Figure B

Mean: 6.90999

Mean Hand Length (cm)

Figure C

Mean: 6.92178

Mean Hand Length (cm)

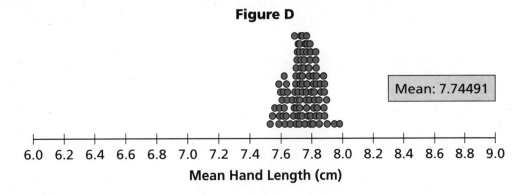

Figure D

Mean: 7.74491

Mean Hand Length (cm)

Labsheet   Looking Back

Figure E

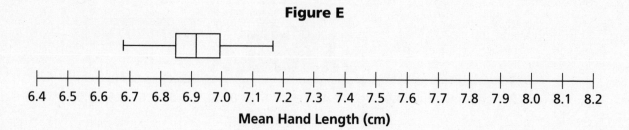

Mean Hand Length (cm)

Figure F

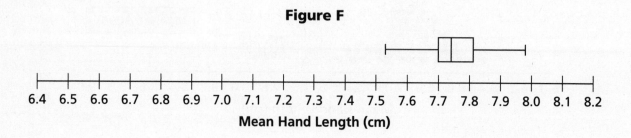

Mean Hand Length (cm)

Check Up *for use after Investigation 1*

1. Below are the ages of 20 players from each of two baseball teams.

Splashing Orcas

30	30	24	21	27	35	31	26	26	31
32	32	27	25	26	31	32	29	28	25

Fighting Narwhals

30	29	40	26	28	32	29	29	29	31
38	36	31	34	25	29	35	38	30	34

a. Fill in the table below to compare the ages of the teams.

	Splashing Orcas	Fighting Narwhals
Mean		
MAD		
Median		
IQR		
Range		

b. Use the table from part (a). Which team is older? Justify your answer.

Check Up (continued)

2. The table below shows boys' and girls' preferences for each sport.

	Football	Baseball	Track	Basketball	Hockey	Soccer	Total
Boys	8	10	8	10	9	9	54
Girls	5	9	7	7	6	11	45

a. Make a double bar graph to display the data from the table. Use one color for the boys' data and a different color for the girls' data. Show the relative frequency of student preference for each sport.

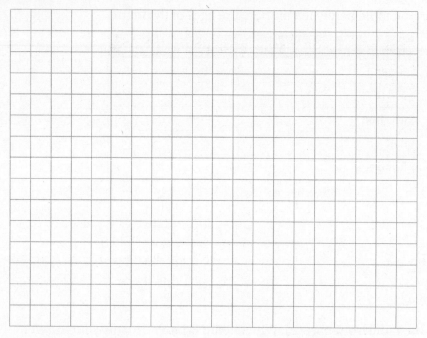

b. Use the double bar graph to write two different statements comparing the data.

Partner Quiz *for use after Investigation 2*

1. **a.** The principal wants to send ten students to represent the school at a state conference. She makes an announcement about the conference. She decides to send the first ten students who contact her after the announcement. Which sampling method did the principal use? Explain your answer.

   i. convenience sampling

   ii. voluntary-response sampling

   iii. systematic sampling

   iv. random sampling

   b. The principal wants the group to be representative of the school population. Is the principal's method of selecting students a good method? Explain your reasoning. If you think the principal's method is not adequate, explain how you think the principal should select students.

Partner Quiz (continued)

2. Use the table below to answer parts (a)–(d).

Data From 100 Bags of Jellybeans

Bag	Green	Yellow	Orange	Blue	Brown	Red	Total
1	3	10	9	5	10	18	55
2	5	12	4	6	19	11	57
3	7	10	9	4	16	12	58
4	4	14	2	1	14	19	56
5	12	7	8	7	14	13	61
6	10	9	6	5	15	8	55
7	11	11	6	6	12	12	58
8	8	15	5	3	16	10	57
9	2	11	4	4	24	12	57
10	5	7	4	1	26	13	56
11	6	13	4	4	15	18	60
12	5	8	4	2	23	16	58
13	9	13	4	4	14	11	55
14	9	10	5	5	14	14	57
15	5	19	5	2	13	14	58
16	3	15	5	2	19	11	55
17	3	10	4	3	23	14	57
18	6	7	5	5	15	22	60
19	5	7	3	4	21	14	54
20	8	7	8	2	20	16	61
21	10	11	7	7	8	14	57
22	7	10	3	5	20	12	57
23	3	8	6	3	25	10	55
24	6	11	9	3	10	17	56
25	10	12	1	2	15	17	57
26	4	12	4	7	14	16	57
27	6	9	6	7	15	13	56
28	5	11	6	7	17	7	53
29	1	10	6	5	22	14	58

Bag	Green	Yellow	Orange	Blue	Brown	Red	Total
30	10	4	8	0	26	9	57
31	4	14	6	4	18	12	58
32	6	18	2	4	19	14	58
33	6	7	8	4	20	11	56
34	12	11	6	4	11	11	55
35	5	10	6	2	12	16	51
36	8	9	4	4	16	17	58
37	2	12	2	6	11	21	54
38	5	7	3	4	21	19	59
39	8	7	8	2	20	16	61
40	10	11	7	7	8	14	57
41	7	10	3	5	20	12	57
42	3	8	6	3	23	10	50
43	6	11	9	3	10	17	56
44	10	12	1	2	15	17	57
45	5	13	2	4	22	11	57
46	6	10	9	5	14	13	57
47	6	16	7	3	16	9	57
48	6	10	4	5	23	10	58
49	10	7	2	6	19	9	53
50	4	12	8	6	10	15	55
51	9	9	6	6	17	10	57
52	4	13	4	6	17	13	57
53	6	12	3	8	13	12	54
54	11	8	8	12	9	8	56
55	1	16	7	3	22	10	59
56	6	11	6	4	19	11	57
57	7	7	7	3	10	21	55
58	7	2	8	10	15	13	55

continued on the next page

Partner Quiz (continued)

Data From 100 Bags of Jellybeans (continued)

Bag	Green	Yellow	Orange	Blue	Brown	Red	Total
59	6	10	6	7	12	15	56
60	6	16	7	3	16	9	57
61	6	10	4	5	23	10	58
62	10	7	2	6	19	9	53
63	4	12	8	6	10	15	55
64	9	12	8	6	8	15	58
65	10	6	5	4	12	16	53
66	4	11	3	2	21	15	56
67	6	15	4	8	10	10	53
68	6	8	7	1	19	14	55
69	6	8	8	6	10	16	54
70	9	11	7	4	15	10	56
71	6	9	8	2	19	14	58
72	3	10	9	5	10	18	55
73	5	12	4	6	19	11	57
74	7	10	9	4	16	12	58
75	4	14	2	1	16	19	56
76	1	8	10	1	22	14	56
77	5	15	4	9	11	11	57
78	3	11	6	3	24	10	57
79	10	9	4	1	23	10	57

Bag	Green	Yellow	Orange	Blue	Brown	Red	Total
80	5	10	7	1	21	13	57
81	6	14	7	7	14	5	53
82	9	11	2	6	13	16	57
83	7	7	9	0	13	20	56
84	8	10	4	5	13	10	50
85	4	11	2	1	24	15	57
86	4	12	6	3	21	12	58
87	5	8	7	4	20	13	57
88	7	11	7	7	13	10	55
89	9	11	4	2	12	18	56
90	4	15	8	4	16	10	57
91	7	11	6	4	18	11	58
92	5	8	8	3	20	12	56
93	7	3	2	6	26	11	55
94	9	6	3	1	28	12	59
95	12	11	9	2	18	5	58
96	9	11	3	3	17	12	55
97	5	12	6	5	17	13	58
98	4	11	9	3	21	10	58
99	11	12	5	3	17	9	57
100	6	16	6	6	16	4	54

Partner Quiz (continued)

a. Select a random sample from the table of data about jellybeans on the previous pages. Fill in the table below with data from your sample. Select as many bags as you think are needed to give a reasonable sample size (you may not need to fill in the entire table).

Samples of Jellybeans

Bag Number	Number of Blue Jellybeans	Total Number in Bag	Percent of Blue Jellybeans

Partner Quiz (continued)

b. Explain how you made sure that your samples were chosen at random.

c. What is your sample size? Explain how you chose a sample size. Why is the sample size reasonable?

d. Use your sample from part (a). Estimate the percent of blue jellybeans in a typical bag of jellybeans. Explain how you found your answer.

Unit Test Correlation

Unit Test Item	Problem
Item 1, part a	Problem 1.4
Item 1, part b	Problem 1.4
Item 2, part a	Problem 1.3
Item 2, part b	Problem 2.3
Item 2, part c	Problem 3.3
Item 2, part d	Problem 3.2
Item 2, part e	Problem 3.3
Item 2, part f	Problem 2.4
Item 2, part g	Problem 3.4

Unit Test *for use after Investigation 3*

1. Ms. Zhu wants to analyze the performance of her seventh-grade classes. She thinks that students perform better in the morning than in the afternoon. The box plots below show the scores of Ms. Zhu's first-period, second-period, and sixth-period classes for one quiz.

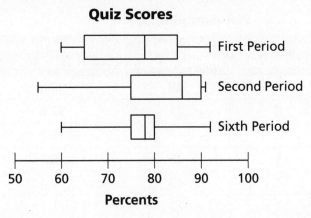

Quiz Scores

a. Compare the box plots. Use statistics to support your answer.

b. Use the box plots above. Is there any evidence that Ms. Zhu's students perform differently in the morning than in the afternoon? Explain.

Unit Test (continued)

2. A biologist studies a system of rivers and lakes. He takes samples by catching fish at different places and studying the fish. Some of the fish are diseased because of water pollution.

a. The biologist's samples are shown below. Complete the table.

Fish-Sampling Data

Sample	Diseased Fish in Sample	Total Number of Fish Caught	Percent of Diseased Fish in Total
1	5	15	33.3
2	8	25	32.0
3	2	12	16.7
4	3	28	10.7
5	2	40	5.0
6	2	22	
7	5	33	
8	3	27	
9	4	29	
10	4	31	
11	3	35	
12	5	40	
13	4	22	
14	1	11	
15	2	21	

b. The biologist will recommend intervention if he thinks that the percent of diseased fish in the whole system is above 15%. Should the biologist call for intervention immediately after he sees the results of Samples 1 and 2? Explain.

Name .... Date .... Class ....

Samples and Populations

Unit Test (continued)

c. Make a box plot or a histogram to show the percent of diseased fish in the samples.

d. Is Sample 1 typical of all the samples? Explain your answer.

e. Should the biologist call for intervention after he sees the results from all of the samples? Explain.

f. Suppose the biologist takes a new sample of two fish. Both of the fish are diseased. How might this change your answer to part (e)? Explain.

g. Use the data in the table. What percent of fish in this entire system do you think are diseased? Explain.

Self Assessment

Mathematical Ideas

After studying the mathematics in this Unit:

1. a. I learned these things about mathematics:

    b. Here are page numbers of notebook entries that give evidence of what I have learned, along with descriptions of what each entry shows:

2. a. These are the mathematical ideas that I am still struggling with:

    b. This is why I think these ideas are difficult for me:

    c. Here are page numbers of notebook entries that give evidence of what I am struggling with, and descriptions of what each entry shows:

Class Participation

I contributed to the classroom **discussion** and understanding of the mathematics in this Unit when I ... (Give examples.)

Self Assessment (continued)

Learning Environment

Rate each learning activity listed below using this scale:

1. I consistently struggled to understand the mathematics and I'm still not sure that I understand it.

2. I struggled somewhat but now I understand more than I did.

3. I had to work, but I feel confident that I understand now.

4. I understood everything pretty easily and I feel confident that I know the mathematics in these problems.

5. Everything came easily. I knew most of the mathematics before we did this.

Learning Activities

____ Problems from the Investigations

____ ACE Homework Assignments

____ Mathematical Reflections

____ Check Ups

____ Partner Quiz

____ Looking Back

____ Unit Test

Check any of the following that you feel are the most helpful in adding to the success of your learning.

☐ Working on my own in class

☐ Discussing a problem with a partner

☐ Working in a small group of 3 or 4 people

☐ Discussing a problem as a whole class

☐ Hearing how other people solved the problem

☐ Summarizing the mathematics as a class and taking notes

☐ Completing homework assignments

Notebook Checklist

Place a ✔ next to each item you have completed.

Notebook Organization

_____ Problems and Mathematical Reflections are labeled and dated.

_____ Work is neat and easy to find and follow.

Vocabulary

_____ All words are listed.   _____ All words are defined or described.

Assessments

_____ Check Up   _____ _____

_____ Partner Quiz   _____ _____

_____ Unit Test   _____ _____

Assignments

_____ _____   _____ _____

_____ _____   _____ _____

_____ _____   _____ _____

_____ _____   _____ _____

_____ _____   _____ _____

_____ _____   _____ _____

_____ _____   _____ _____

_____ _____   _____ _____

_____ _____   _____ _____

_____ _____   _____ _____

Assessment Answers

Check Up

1. a.

	Splashing Orcas	Fighting Narwhals
Mean	28.4	31.65
MAD	2.9	3.38
Median	28.5	30.5
IQR	5	5.5
Range	14	15

b. The Fighting Narwhals are older because their mean and median are greater than the mean and median for the Splashing Orcas. Also, the Fighting Narwhals have more diversity in their ages because the range, IQR, and MAD are greater for the Fighting Narwhals than for the Splashing Orcas.

2. a. (See Figure 1.)

b. Answers will vary. Possible answers: Even though there are more boys than girls who prefer baseball, the girls' relative frequency of preference is higher than the boys' $\left(\frac{9}{45} > \frac{10}{54}, \text{ or } 20\% > \approx 19\%\right)$. There are only two more girls than boys who prefer soccer, but the difference in the graphs looks larger because the relative frequency for girls is much greater than for boys $\left(\frac{11}{45} > \frac{9}{54}, \text{ or } \approx 24\% > \approx 17\%\right)$.

Partner Quiz

1. a. ii; This is a voluntary-response sample because the students choose to contact the principal.
Note: Students might also say this is a convenience sample. These ten students might all be in the only class whose teacher allowed them out of class to see the principal. Or, they might all be in the classroom that is closest to the principal's office.

Figure 1

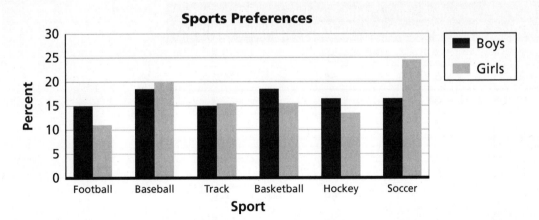

Sports Preferences

Boys / Girls

Assessment Answers (continued)

b. This sample would not likely be representative because it only contains students who are interested in representing the school at the conference. Students will have various ideas about how the principal might select a representative group of students. Students should give answers that indicate a random sampling process.

2. a. Samples will vary. See part (d) for an example of the samples selected by one student using a calculator's random-number generator.

b. Answers will vary. Students might roll a numbered deltohedron (a 10-sided solid with faces that are congruent kites) twice or spin a 10-section spinner twice, once for the first digit and once for the second digit (counting a roll or spin of 00 as 100). They could also use the random-number generator on their calculators to choose integers from 1 to 100. Students need to account for eliminating repeated bag numbers if they decide to have a sample size greater than 1.

c. Sample sizes should be small enough to be less cumbersome than working with all 100 values, yet large enough to not be influenced by data that are not representative of the population. Typical sizes might be between 15 and 20 bags.

d. The actual proportion of blue jellybeans in the table is approximately 7.5%. Answers will vary. One student's data are shown below. This student calculated the percent of blue jellybeans in each bag. This student reported that, in his sample, he had a total of 44 blue jellybeans out of a total of 566 jellybeans, which is 7.8%. He found that the mean of the ten percentages in his table is also about 7.8%. (See Figure 2.)

Figure 2

Sample of Jellybean Bags

Bag Number	Number of Blue Jellybeans	Total Number in Bag	Percent of Blue Jellybeans
86	3	58	5.2
100	6	54	11.1
13	4	55	7.3
26	7	57	12.3
72	5	55	9.1
48	5	58	8.6
38	4	59	6.8
59	7	56	12.5
10	1	56	1.8
15	2	58	3.4

Assessment Answers (continued)

Unit Test

1. **a.** Answers will vary. The range and median for the first- and sixth-period classes are the same, but the middle 50% of the data is much more spread out in the first period. The sixth-period class has a concentration of grades in the 75 percent to 80 percent range and it shows the least variability. Fewer students did poorly in the sixth-period class, but fewer students also did very well in this period. The second-period class has the students with the lowest grades of all three classes and does not have anyone who scored as highly as the top students in the other two classes. On the other hand, the middle 50% did better in the second-period class than in either of the other two classes.

   b. The scores of the morning classes show more variability than the scores of the afternoon class. But the median of the afternoon class is similar to the median of the first-period class and within the middle 50% of the scores for the second-period class. So, using the median as a comparison, these classes are not different enough for Ms. Zhu to conclude that morning classes do better.

2. **a.** (See Figure 3.)

Figure 3

Fish-Sampling Data

Sample	Diseased Fish in Sample	Total Number of Fish Caught	Percent of Diseased Fish in Total
1	5	15	33.3
2	8	25	32.0
3	2	12	16.7
4	3	28	10.7
5	2	40	5.0
6	2	22	9.1
7	5	33	15.2
8	3	27	11.1
9	4	29	13.8
10	4	31	12.9
11	3	35	8.6
12	5	40	12.5
13	4	22	18.2
14	1	11	9.1
15	2	21	9.5

Assessment Answers (continued)

b. Sample answer: No; samples vary. Large samples are more likely to be similar to the underlying population. So, making a decision on the basis of two fairly small samples is probably not going to give very reliable predictions about the whole population. In fact, the percentages of diseased fish in the first two samples are quite unlike the percentages from other samples. These unusual outcomes are the result of natural variation in samples. There is nothing wrong with the samples; they are just not a good representation of how most samples turned out.

c.

Fish Sampling

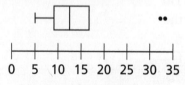

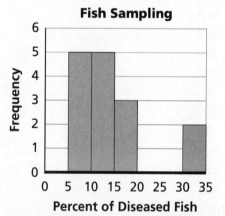

d. No; Sample 1 is one of two samples that are quite different from the others. The median of the percent of diseased fish for the samples is 12.5%; 33.3% is the maximum value and far from the median.

e. Answers will vary. Using the histogram, most of the samples lie in the 5% to 15% range, and using the box plot, most lie in the 9.1% to 16.7% range, so the percent of diseased fish in the entire population is probably in this range. Some students may also calculate the mean (14.5%) or the median (12.5%) and point out that while neither of these is at the official "action" level, these percents are approaching that level, so some action may be warranted—perhaps sampling more often or putting a readiness plan into place.

f. This sample size is so small that it is probably of no use in making predictions. The biologist could, however, include this sample in the calculations of measures of center and in the data displays. Including more samples of this type may change the recommendation of intervention.

g. According to the histogram, the diseased percentage of most of the samples lie in the 5% to 15% range; using the box plot, most lie in the 9.1% to 16.7% range. Using the mean or the median, students may decide that the level is actually on the upper end of this range.

Looking Back Answers

1. a. $\frac{1}{10} = \frac{20}{x}$, so $x = 200$

b. $\frac{9}{10} = \frac{20}{x}$, so, scaling both the numerator and the denominator of $\frac{9}{10}$ by $\frac{20}{9}$, we get $\dfrac{\left(9 \times \frac{20}{9}\right)}{\left(10 \times \frac{20}{9}\right)} = \frac{20}{x}$,

so $x = 10 \times \frac{20}{9} \approx 22$.

c. $\frac{25}{50} = \frac{100}{x}$, so, scaling both the numerator and the denominator of $\frac{25}{50}$ by $\frac{100}{25}$, we get $\dfrac{\left(25 \times \frac{100}{25}\right)}{\left(50 \times \frac{100}{25}\right)} = \frac{100}{x}$,

so $x = 50 \times \frac{100}{25} = 200$

d. In each case, taking some more samples from the population would be valuable. Also, if multiple samples are taken, as is done in this Exercise, you can use information from all the iterations of the experiment to tailor your answer. Note that the estimates from parts (a) and (c) are identical. Because of this, you may give these estimates more weight than the estimate from part (b). You shouldn't, however, completely discount the answer from part (b). It indicates that you may want to choose an estimate less than 200 for your final estimate.

2. a. Males: Figures A and D; Females: Figures B and C; Figures A and D show hand lengths that are greater than those in Figures B and C. We know that male hand lengths are longer than female hand lengths.

b. Samples of 10: Figure A; Samples of 30: Figure D; In Figure D, the sample means are more tightly packed around the mean of the distribution than in Figure A. Sample sizes of 30 are more likely to give more similar distributions and have less variability between the means.

c. Samples of 10: Figure B; Samples of 30: Figure C; Again, in Figure C, the sample means are more tightly packed around the mean of the distribution than in Figure B. Sample sizes of 30 are more likely to give more similar distributions and have less variability between the means.

d. There is little variability among the 100 samples of 30 for each; the means are tightly packed around the distribution mean in each case. The mean for males is greater than the mean for females; it appears that male hand lengths are longer than female hand lengths.

e. The female MAD is greater than the male MAD, so you can conclude that female hands differ more from each other than male hands do.

3. a. Figure E: females; Figure F: males

b. The IQRs for each are similar; the IQR for females is a bit larger.

c. The two distributions look quite similar; the box plots almost mirror each other; however, the box plot for males is shifted further right than the box plot for females.

4. The related measure of spread when using the mean is the mean absolute deviation (MAD). The MAD describes how much the data values differ, on average, from the mean. Most data values in a distribution are located within two MADs of the mean.

Looking Back Answers *(continued)*

5. The related measure of spread when using the median is the interquartile range (IQR). The IQR spans the location of the middle 50% of the data and uses the median as the middle marker.

6. A voluntary sample, such as those done in magazines asking readers to write in, may not produce a good sample. The sample will include people who encounter the survey (for example, by reading a particular magazine), people who may have time to submit answers, or people who may be more interested in giving feedback. It therefore eliminates large groups of people. This method, however, makes it easy on the data collector to track data and receive data.

A random sampling method gives a sample where each individual in the population is equally likely to be chosen for the sample. There is no large subset of individuals that is discounted. It requires, however, that the data collector come up with a method for sampling that is completely random. An example of a random sampling method is assigning each individual a number, then choosing the sample using a spinner, a random-number generator on a calculator, or a number cube.

A convenience sample does not give a representative sample, but it is very easy to collect the data. An example would be a student surveying his class to find out which type of pizza is preferred school-wide. The class can be easily surveyed, but it does not represent the entire school.

A systematic sample, such as choosing every other name alphabetically, does not give each individual an equally likely chance to be chosen. Once the pattern is set, each person is either determined to be in the sample or determined to be discounted. It is, however, an easy way to avoid taking a cluster of like individuals (such as individuals with their last names beginning with B).

7. You can choose a random sample by setting up some kind of probability arrangement. Use number cubes, a random number generator on a calculator, or some other way of choosing numbers that simulates a random situation.

8. If a sample is a random sample selected from the population in question and is of a size of 30 or more cases, this sample can be used to study a population. Samples are used to study populations when it would be difficult to get information from each population member, either because of the population size or accessibility to the population members.

430

Labsheets

Polystrips

Note: A Polystrip set contains six strips of each length.

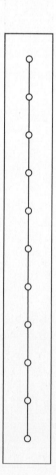

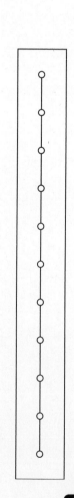

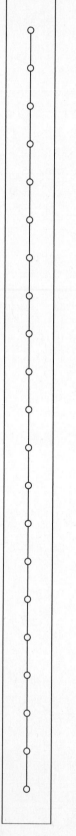

Polystrips

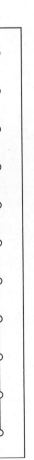
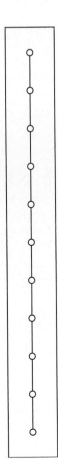
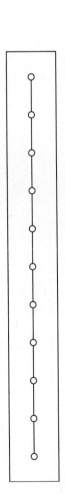
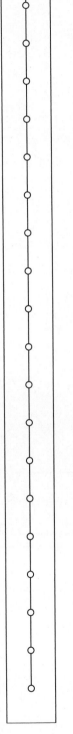
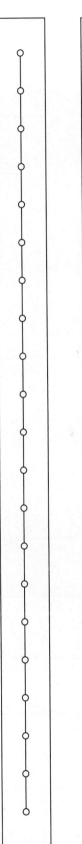
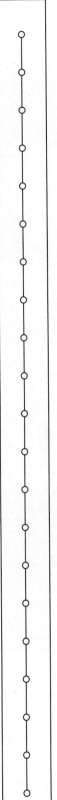

Name .... Date .... Class ....

Shapes Set

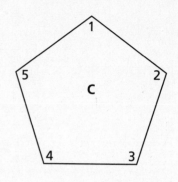

B

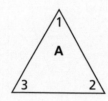

A

C

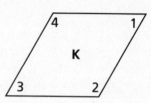

J

K

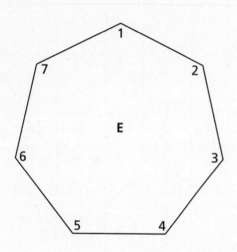

E

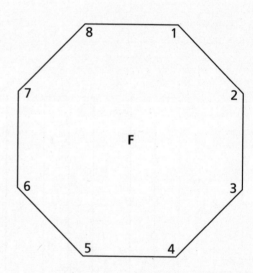

F

H

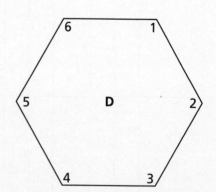

D

Shapes Set

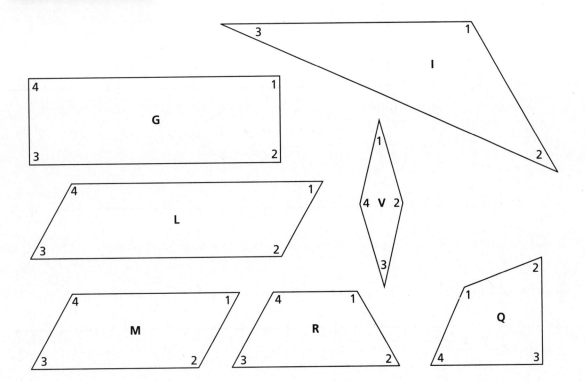

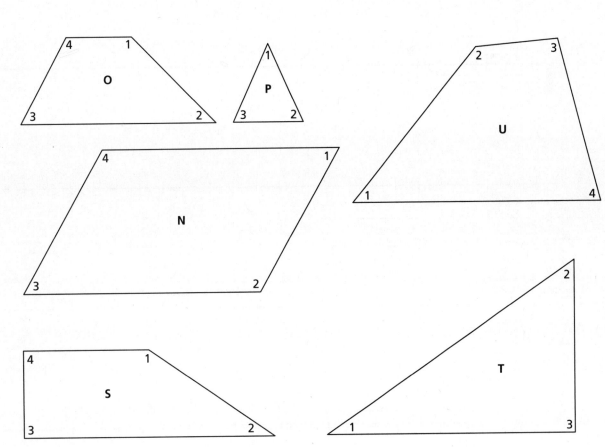

Number Lines

Chip Board

Chip Board

Small Chip Boards

Chip Board

Chip Board

Chip Board

Chip Board

Chip Board

Chip Board

Grid Area Models

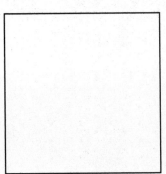

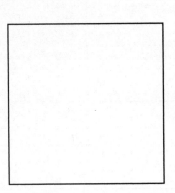
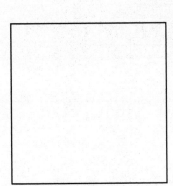

439

Isometric Dot Paper

Centimeter Grid Paper

Generic Grid Paper

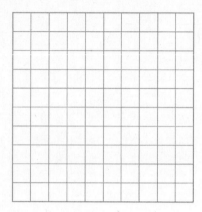
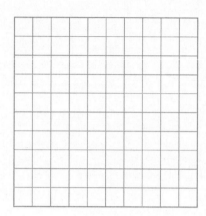

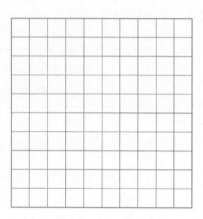
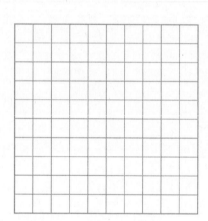

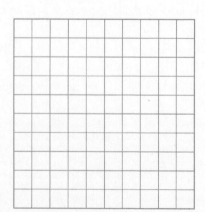
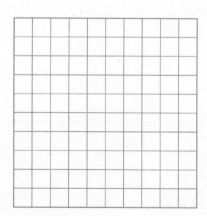

Half-Centimeter Grid Paper

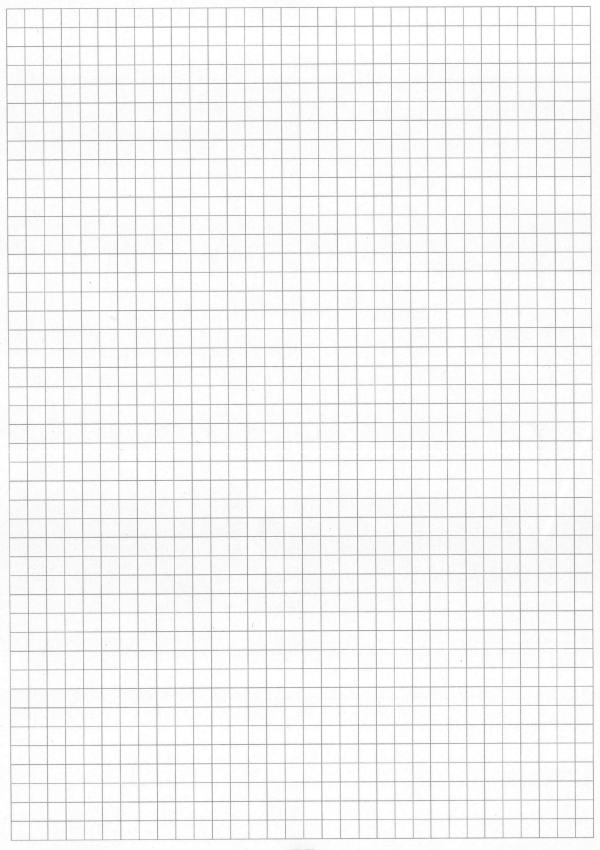

Inch Grid Paper

Quarter-Inch Grid Paper

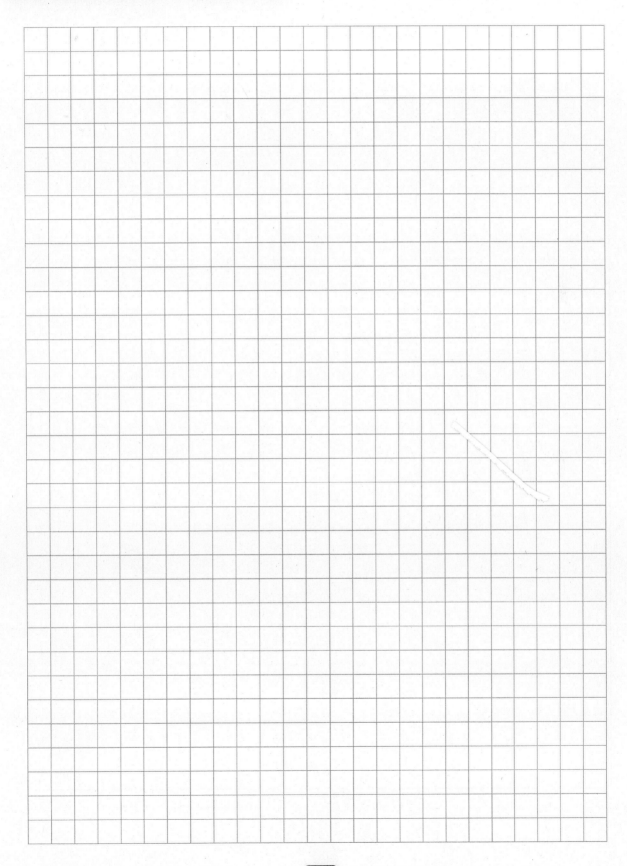

445

Blank Table and Graph

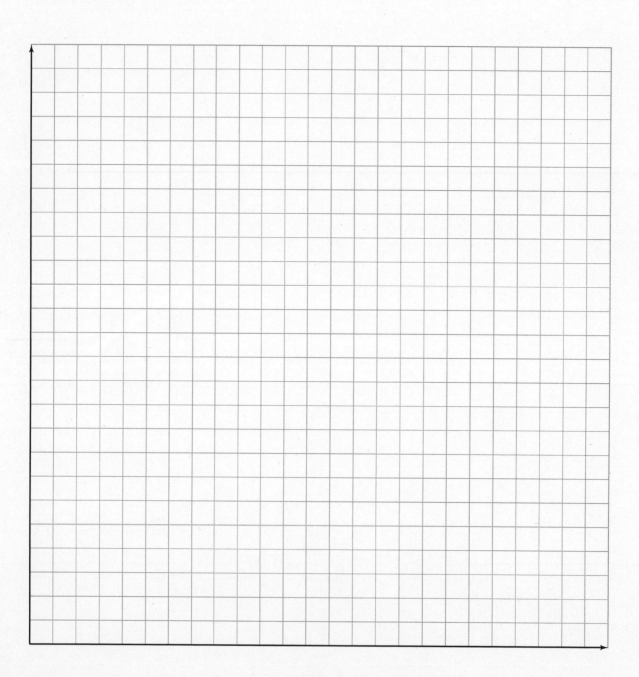

Coordinate Grid

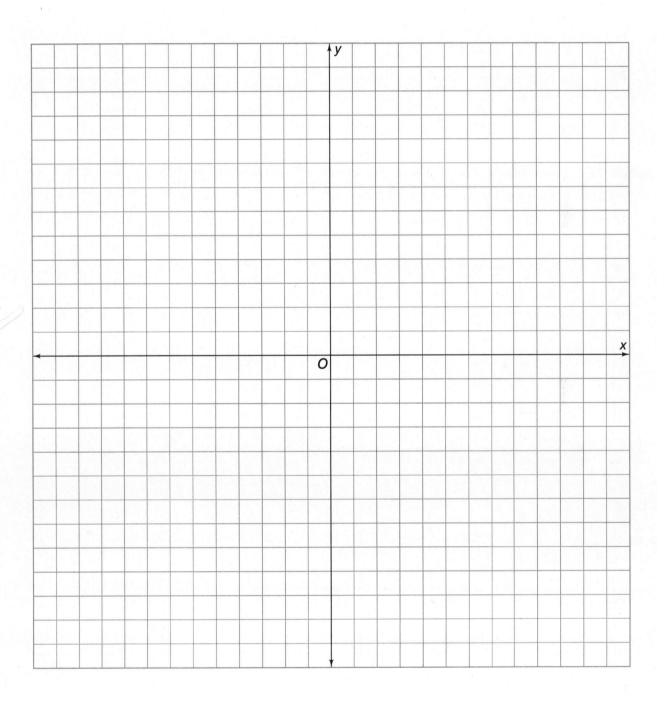

First-Quadrant Grid

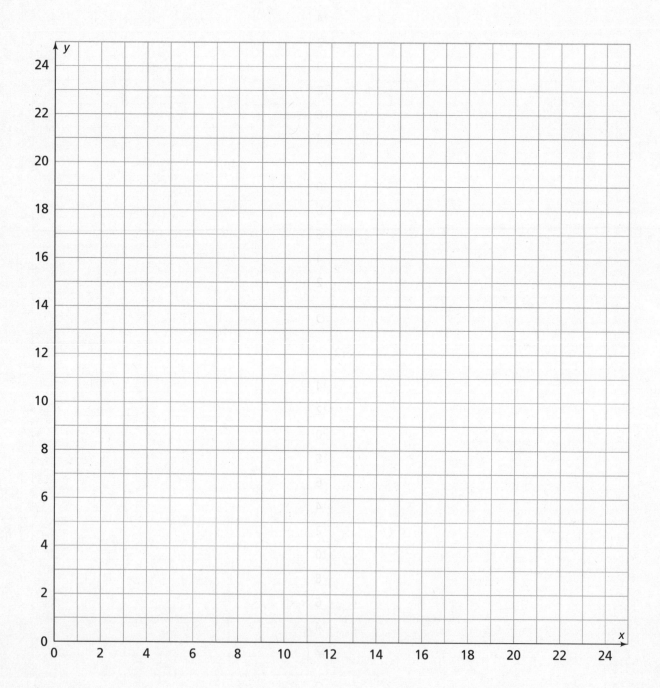

Four First-Quadrant Grids

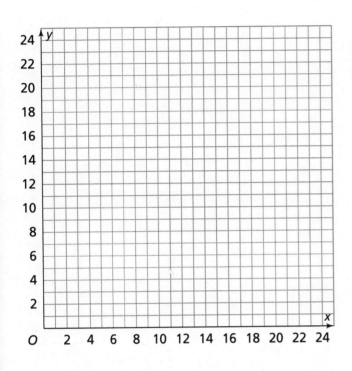

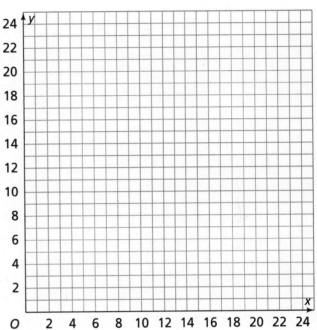

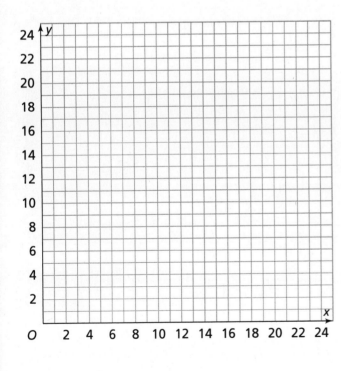

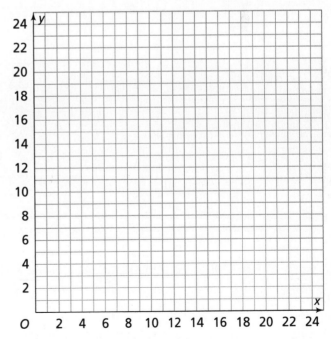

Graph Paper

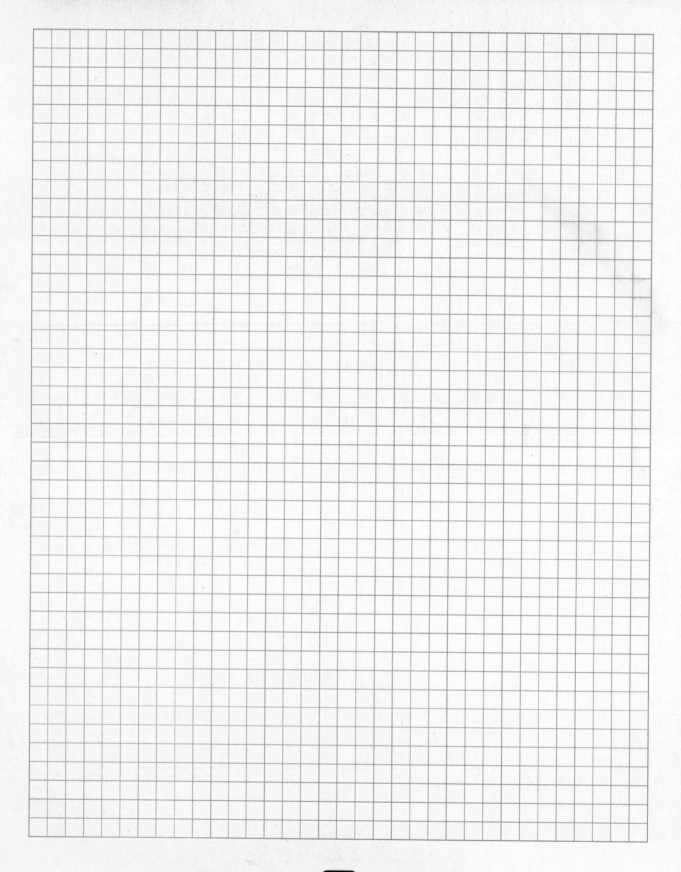